PROGRESS IN STEM CELL RESEARCH

PROGRESS IN STEM CELL RESEARCH

PRASAD S. KOKA
EDITOR

Nova Science Publishers, Inc.
New York

LIBRARY OF CONGRESS CATALOGING-IN-PUBLICATION DATA

Progress in stem cell research / Prasad S. Koka (editor).
     p. ; cm.
  Includes bibliographical references and index.
  ISBN 978-1-60456-065-7
  1. Stem cells. I. Koka, Prasad S.
  [DNLM: 1. Stem Cells. 2. Research--trends. 3. Stem Cell Transplantation. QU 325 P964 2007]
QH588.S83P757 2007
616'.02774--dc22
                              2007039923

Published by Nova Science Publishers, Inc. ✦ *New York*

CONTENTS

PREFACE

Among the many applications of stem cell research are nervous system diseases, diabetes, heart disease, autoimmune diseases as well as Parkinson's disease, end-stage kidney disease, liver failure, cancer, spinal cord injury, multiple sclerosis, Parkinson's disease, and Alzheimer's disease. Stem cells are self-renewing, unspecialized cells that can give rise to multiple types all of specialized cells of the body. Stem cell research also involves complex ethical and legal considerations since they involve adult, fetal tissue and embryonic sources. This new book presents the latest research from around the globe.

FOREWORD: STEM CELLS

The launching of any journal is always a momentous event. This is of even greater significance when the journal is dedicated to stem cell biology and regenerative medicine, particularly at a time when hopes for cures for many serious ailments are being bestowed in stem cell research.

We have introduced the *Journal of Stem Cells (JOSC)* to foster the diverse areas of stem cell biology and medicine into dissemination of information to scientific investigators with aspirations for successful and yet safe and ethical manipulations and therapies using stem cells. This is also reflected in this first issue of the journal consisting of articles that address the importance of stem cells in regenerative medicine. Stem cell dominance in regeneration is conferred by their innate potential for self-renewal and multi-lineage differentiation. It is difficult not to note from these articles that there is ample potential for benefits from stem cell research and for the development of therapeutic strategies using stem cells.

The utilization of stem cells to fight and prevail over various diseases such as different cytopenias arising from congenital defects, viral infections, cancer chemotherapy, heart disease and stroke; autoimmune diseases including multiple sclerosis and diabetes; Parkinson's; retinal and optic-nerve cell degeneration / glaucoma, aging including Alzheimer's, can lead to revolutionary therapies through stem cell reconstitution strategies following repair and regulation of defective intra- or inter-cellular genes and their expression. Such approaches, including gene therapy, may also obviate additional drug or cytokine treatments.

Supporters of stem cell research include famous individuals like Nancy Reagan for her husband Ronald Reagan and Christopher Reeves who suffered from debilitating degenerative ailments or for conditions which might otherwise have found hopes and solutions in stem cell regenerative medicine. Indeed, stem cell regenerative medicine could become more than a solace to current and future patients with cellular degenerative and loss inflicting conditions. It is now a generally well-accepted concept that stem cells hold the promise of recovery from degenerative diseases wherein the existing normal cells of a patient are depleted, a process that may be gradual or sudden but held to be irreversible in nature. The objective in regenerative medicine should be a controlled repopulation of irreversibly depleted cells through engraftment and differentiation of engineered stem cells anew, in the affected areas of the human body. Controlled regeneration of tissue *in vivo* should necessarily exclude any deleterious side effects of the tissue engineering approaches, be it pre- or post-engraftment of the stem cells engineered *ex vivo*.

JOSC accepts both original and review articles with the frequency of publication intended to be increased to each month. A unique feature of this journal is a publication of color figures and illustrations not chargeable to the contributors. This will enable clear depictions of changes in molecular and cellular events discussed in the published articles to the readers and alleviation of publication costs as well to the contributing authors.

The journal also accepts news articles, letters, mini-reviews, meeting / conference announcements and their schedules, and ethical and legal issues, of stem cell research and medicine.

Support from both Nova Science Publishers and the *JOSC* Editorial Board, consisting of investigators from around the globe, ensures a sound beginning for maintaining this journal at the highest quality.

Prasad S. Koka
Editor

In: Progress in Stem Cell Research
Editor: Prasad S. Koka, pp. 1-30

ISBN: 978-1-60456-065-7
© 2008 Nova Science Publishers, Inc.

Chapter 1

MEGAKARYOCYTOPOIESIS: FROM MARROW STEM CELLS TO CIRCULATING PLATELETS

Aaron Tomer[1] and Varda Deutsch[2]

[1]Faculty of Health Sciences
Ben Gurion University of the Negev,
Blood Bank and Transfusion Medicine, Soroka Medical Center
Beer-Sheva 84101, Israel
[2]The Hematology Institute, Tel Aviv Sourasky Medical Center
Tel Aviv University Faculty of Medicine
6 Weizman St .,Tel Aviv 64239

ABSTRACT

Megakaryocytopoiesis involves the commitment of hematopoietic stem cells, proliferation and differentiation of the megakaryocytic progenitors, and cell maturation including endoreduplication and cytoplasmic acquisition of structural and functional properties of platelets. Megakaryocytopoiesis is primarily controlled by thrombopoietin (TPO), which induces the expansion of early progenitors, as well as, the proliferation, endoreduplication and differentiation of megakaryocytes (MKs). Thrombopoietin avidly binds to the c-Mpl receptors on platelets and MKs, and the circulating levels of unbound TPO induce concentration-dependent proliferation and maturation of MK progenitors. Accordingly, decrease in platelet turnover rate results in increased concentration of unbound TPO, enabling the compensatory response of marrow MKs to increased demand for peripheral blood platelets. The process of megakaryocytopoiesis is also mediated by multiple pleiotropic hematopoietic growth factors which include the stem cell factor - c-kit ligand, interleukin-3 (IL-3), IL-6, IL-11, granulocyte-macrophage colony-stimulating factor (GM-CSF) and FGF, as well as chemokines such as SDF-1 with its receptor CXCR-4. The stimulatory effect of the regulating factors is mediated by a concerted action of specific transcription factors such as GATA-1 and FOG, Runx1, Ets and Nuclear Factor-Erythroid-2, while C-myb plays a central negative regulatory role. The demise of

[1] Correspondence: Aaron Tomer, M.D. Director, Blood Bank and Transfusion Medicine, Soroka University Medical Center, Beer-Sheva, P.O.Box 151, 84101 Israel. Phone: 972-8- 6400-301 Fax : 972-8-6400-689. E-mail: atomer@bgu.ac.il

senescent MKs involves a specialized form of apoptosis during the processes of proplatelet formation and platelet release. In this review, the regulation of megakaryocytopoiesis with the quantitative alterations in the megakaryocytic cells and platelet production, in both humans and animal models, is discussed.

DEVELOPMENT OF MEGAKARYOCYTES

Normal Megakaryocytopoiesis

The hematopoietic stem cell which evolves from the multipotential hemangioblast gives rise to the common myeloid progenitor (CMP) that can be cloned as the multi-lineage colony-forming unit GEMM (granulocyte, erythrocyte, MK and monocytes). The CMP can differentiate through molecular signals controlled by regulatory transcription factors (TF) in two directions. One is driven by the PU.1 gives rise to granulocyte-monocyte precursors, which can be cloned as colony-forming unit granulocyte-monocyte (CFU-GM), and the other by GATA-1 giving rise to MK- erythroid progenitors (MK/E-prog). These bipotential progenitors develop into early MK burst-forming unit (BFU-MK), or the more mature smaller colony-forming unit MK (CFU-MK). Similarly, they can progress to early and late erythroid progenitors, the BFU-E and CFU-E [1, 2]. The diploid MK progenitors (megakaryoblasts), at some point lose their capacity for cell division, but retain their ability for DNA replication (endoreduplication). In their terminal maturation, MKs give rise to circulating platelets by the acquisition of the cytoplasmic structural and functional characteristics necessary for platelet action [3, 4]. Mature MKs are large, granular, and polyploid cells. Their size may reach 48μm, and their ploidy ranges up to 128N with modal ploidy of 16N [5-8]. The large cytoplasmic mass is converted into proplatelet projections which give rise to de novo circulating platelets [3, 9-11].

Regulation of Megakaryocytopoiesis

The process of megakaryocytopoiesis occurs within a complex bone marrow microenvironment where chemokines, cytokines as well as adhesive interactions within the extracellular niche, play a major role [12]. Mechanisms regulating mega-karyocytopoiesis operate at the levels of proliferation, differentiation, and platelet release [13-16]. In addition to the steady state megakaryocytopoiesis, which supplies a new turnover of platelets every 8-9 days, MKs also respond to changes in requirements for peripheral blood platelets [17-19].

Megakaryocyte Growth Factors

The primary physiological growth factor for the MK lineage is thrombopoietin (TPO) also known as c-Mpl ligand. After thirty years of searching for the factor regulating megakaryocytopoietic activities, four different groups reported simultaneously in 1994 its isolation, cloning, molecular and physiologic characterization [20-24]. The c-DNA for human and murine TPO belongs to the cytokine family of genes encoding for a glycoprotein homologous with erythropoietin. Binding with its receptor (c-Mpl) on MKs selectively initiates proliferation, maturation and cytoplasmic delivery of platelets into the circulation.

Both the MK colony-stimulating activity and platelet-elevating activity in thrombocytopenic plasma are neutralized by the addition of c-Mpl receptor in excess [23]. Thrombopoietin is a heavily glycosylated protein composed of 332 amino acids that share homology in the amino terminal region (21% sequence identity) with erythropoietin. The gene for TPO is located in chromosome 3 (bands 26 to 28). Interestingly, abnormalities in chromosome 3 (inversion or deletion) are found in megakaryocytic leukemia and other myeloproliferative disorders associated with thrombocytosis [25]. Thrombopoietin-specific messenger RNA is found in the liver, kidney and marrow stroma [20, 22, 24]. Mega-karyocytopoiesis is regulated by plasma levels of unbound TPO. Human plasma thrombopoietin levels are regulated by binding to platelet or megakaryocyte TPO receptors in vivo [26]. The plasma levels of TPO in normal state (95 ± 6 pg/L) increase several orders of magnitude in patients with thrombocytopenia secondary to marrow suppression, and fall after platelet transfusions or recovery of hematopoiesis [27, 28]. Thrombopoietin production is thought to be constitutive, but can be increased during acute inflammation [28, 29].

Thrombopoietin seems to control hematopoietic stem cell development through the regulation of multiple members of the Hox family of transcription factors, which include Hox B4 [30] and Hox A9 [31], through multiple mechanisms. Mice, in which either TPO or its ligand c-mpl genes have been knocked out, have profound thrombocytopenia with residual thrombocytopoiesis and small numbers of functionally normal MKs and platelets. The primary role of TPO therefore appears to be the maintenance of MK numbers, while the final differentiation of MKs to proplatelets and release of mature platelets depends on other signaling systems. The responsiveness of MK progenitors to TPO reflects their number of doublings [32]. Thrombopoietin activates extra-cellular signal-related kinase 1/2 (ERK1/2) phosphorylation in MK, and the classic mitogen-activated protein kinase (MAP) (Raf/mito-gen-induced extracellular kinase (MEK/ERK) pathway directly and indirectly play a critical role in megakaryocytopoiesis. However, Raf-1 is dispensable for megakaryocytopoiesis, and for TPO-induced ERK1/2 activation in primary MK-lineage cells [33].

Thrombopoietin avidly binds to the c-Mpl receptors on platelets (about 200 receptors/platelet). Thrombo-poietin signaling through its c-Mpl receptor, activates several pathways including signal transducers and activators of transcription (STAT)3, STAT5, phosphoinositide 3-kinase-Akt, and p42/44 mitogen-activated protein kinase (MAPK) [15]. Because plasma TPO level is not primarily dependent on gene transcription, it is conceivable that negative feedback regulation is produced by the circulating concentration of platelets through binding of TPO and shedding of soluble c-Mpl-receptor in plasma. Thus, circulating levels of unbound TPO induce concentration-dependent receptor-mediated proliferation and differentiation of early MK progenitors, thereby modulating platelet production rate.

Several pleiotropic hematopoietic growth factors have been shown to exert stimulatory activity on MKs both in vivo and in vitro, including interleukin-3 (IL-3) (multi colony-stimulating factor (CSF), IL-6, IL-11, granulocyte-macrophage colony-stimulating factor (GM-CSF) and fibroblast growth factor (FGF) [5, 34-38]. A schematic outline of the regulation of megakaryocytopoiesis appears in Figure 1. Interleukin-1 may stimulate MKs indirectly [34, 39], and erythropoietin exhibits colony-stimulating activity in animal studies [40, 41]. The stem cell factor, the c-kit ligand, has been shown to promote the early progenitor burst forming unit, BFU-MK, with IL-3, and the later progenitor colony forming unit CFU-MK in synergy with both IL-3 and GM-CSF [42]. GM-CSF may induce megakaryocytic maturation in vivo, as shown in humans [43] and non-human primates [36], although there is no corresponding increase in the circulating platelet counts [44]. The direct stimulatory effect of GM-CSF on MKs is also evident in cultures of MKs purified directly from human marrow aspirates [5]. IL-6 primarily affects MK maturation [34, 45], although the combination of IL-6 and IL-3 promotes MK proliferation [46, 47]. The administration of IL-6 to primates markedly increases platelet counts and the size and ploidy of MK [48]. IL-11 also affect both size and ploidy of MKs [39]. In addition, combined effects have been demonstrated for IL-3 and GM-CSF [34] and IL-3 and IL-11 [39]. Thus, different stages of MKs may be modulated by dose and by additive or synergistic effects among growth factors. In addition, MKs appear to be capable of synthesizing and secreting hematopoietic growth factors, including IL-1, IL-6, and GM-CSF [45].

In animal models, the administration of recombinant human (rHu) GM-CSF to rhesus monkeys resulted in prompt increase in MK ploidy and average volume [44]. Treatment with IL-6 resulted in similar response [48]. However, unlike IL-6, administration of rHuGM-CSF was not associated with notable increase in platelet count [44]. In baboons, administration of rHuTPO or polyethylene glycol derivative MK-growth-and-development-factor (PEG-rHuMGDF), produced a log-linear increase in marrow MK mass (cell number multiplied by volume) up to 6.5 fold associated with marked increase in cell ploidy. Concordantly, there was increase in platelet count up to 5-fold, reaching peak value after 2 to 4 weeks of subcutaneous injections. Because MK volume and ploidy attained predictable maximum values simultaneously, MK ploidy is an accurate measure of the Mpl-ligand stimulation of megakaryocytopoiesis [49-51].

It was hoped that the physiologically powerful stimulators of thrombocytopoiesis, rHuTPO or the truncated cloned rHuMGDF, would be useful in patients with thrombocytopenia responsive to exogenous stimulation of platelet production. However, the development of cross-reacting neutralizing antibody to endogenous TPO led to withdrawal of PEG-rHuMDGF from trials. In addition, although rHuTPO facilitated collection of platelets in normal donors and patients for purpose of transfusion, there was no enhanced platelet recovery in patients following aggressive chemotherapy [52]. In the clinical trials, the administration of TPO before or after stem cell transplantation and myeloablative therapy had no impact on the duration of severe thrombocytopenia nor did it reduce the requirement for platelet transfusions either post transplant or in AML patients [53-55]. This failure is probably due to the paucity of MK progenitors in the grafts despite the escalated TPO levels in these patients [26]. In practice, the clinical promise of TPO in improving thrombocytopoiesis in severely thrombocytopenic cancer patients has not yet come to fruition and TPO is not yet clinically available [56]. Thus, the promise of TPO may be found in thrombocytopenic patients that are not myelosuppressed [57].

A new growth peptide has recently been described, which stimulated robust proliferation of CD34+ hematopoietic progenitor cells and MK in vitro and MK progenitors in transgenic mice via protein kinase C (PKC) signaling pathways. This unique peptide is derived from the cleavable C-terminus of the stress associated form of acetylcholinesterase (AChE), a molecule known for many years to be involved in the regulation of megakaryocytopoiesis [58-61]. This readthrough form (AChE-R), is physiologically functional during stress thrombopoiesis and its c-terminal peptide ARP is currently in preclinical development as a novel thrombopoietic factor [62-64].

A   Regulation of megakaryocytopoiesis

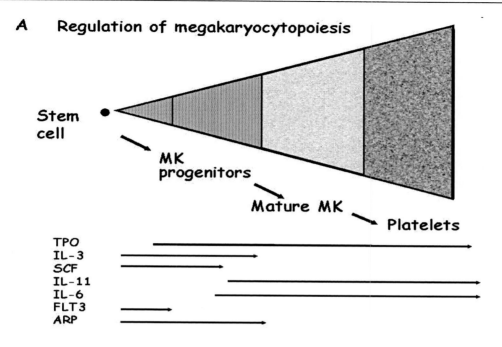

B   Megakaryocyte differentiation and maturation

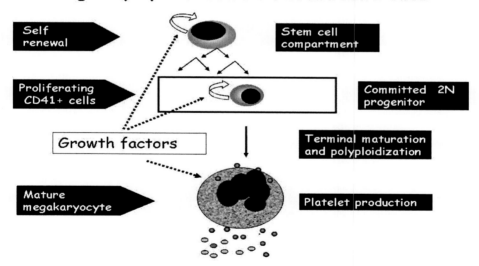

Figure 1. The Development of Megakaryocytes. Megakaryocytopoiesis involves the commitment of hematopoietic stem cells, proliferation and differentiation of the MK progenitors, endoreduplication, cytoplasmic acquisition of structural and functional properties of platelets and platelet release (up to 3 x 10^3 per megakaryocyte)
(A) Regulation of megakaryocytopoiesis by stimulating hematopoietic growth factors
(B) Differentiation and maturation of megakaryocytic cell lineage

Cellular Interactions and Chemokines

Megakaryocytopoiesis and thrombocytopoiesis require the interactions between hematopoietic progenitor cells, and marrow stromal cells derived from mesenchymal stem cells (MSCs). The MSCs residing within the megakaryocytic microenvironment in bone marrow provide key signals for MK stimulation from CD34+ hematopoietic cells [65]. The interaction of MK progenitors with their microenvironment is mediated by chemokines. The chemokines are a family of proinflammatory mediators that promote immune cell adhesion and migration in bone marrow, blood vessels and extramedullary sites [12, 66]. The chemokines can be divided into two subfamilies of CXC and CC chemokines, based on the spacing of the first two cysteine residues near the carboxy terminus of the molecule.

Local chemokines, which include SDF-1 and FGF-4, promote the contact of immature MK with a permissive, endothelial-enriched microenvironment. The interaction of SDF-1 is TPO independent [12]. SDF-1, of the CXC family, is a key chemokine involved in the retention of hematopoietic precursor cells in the bone marrow. The SDF-1 receptor CXCR4, is expressed along the entire differentiation pathway from MK progenitors to platelets [67, 68]. It was shown, that platelet production in vitro, is enhanced during transendothelial migration of CXCR4+ MK in response to SDF-1 [69]. The Rafii group elegantly demonstrated that SDF-1 and FGF-4 support platelet production in TPO-/- or mpl-/- mice through interactions of MK progenitors with the bone marrow vascular niche. FGF-4 fortifies the adhesion of MK progenitors to bone marrow endothelial cells, supporting survival and maturation, and SDF-1 enhanced the movement of MK to the junctions between sinusoidal endothelial cells via VE cadherin, thus driving thrombopoiesis [12]. CXCR4 signaling in MK (but not in platelets) involves both of the serine/threonine mitogen-activated protein kinases (MAPKs) MAPK and AKT MAPK pathways include extracellular signal–related kinase (MEK) and extracellular signal–regulated protein kinase 1 (ERK1)/ERK2; which mainly responds to mitogens and growth factors to regulate cell proliferation and differentiation. Surprisingly, MK development is accompanied by reduced Erk activation by CXCR4 signaling which involves negative regulators of G-protein signaling RGS [70].

A CC family chemokine involved in MK maturation is the platelet basic protein derived connective tissue-activating peptide IIII, CTAP III, which can be further processed to b-thromboglobulin (β-TG) and to neutrophil activating peptide (NAP-2). The molecular upregulation of the CTAP III in MKs is associated with maturation and, as with other chemokines, may be involved in proliferation arrest and cellular interactions with extracellular matrix and platelet production [71].

The engagement of transmembrane integrins, which are heterodimeric receptors, mediates cell membrane–extracellular matrix interaction and have significant effects on cell survival, division and differentiation [72]. Treatment of MK with fibrinogen, a ligand of the prominent platelet integrin receptor, GPIIb/IIIa, promotes megakaryocytopoiesis by increasing the number of CD41+/PI+ cells [73]. Integrins mediate the attachment of cells to extracellular matrix in the bone marrow and elicit a variety of signals into the cell, including strong activation MAPK [74]. The enhanced platelet formation observed, suggests a cross-talk between the integrin engagement pathway, PKC activation, and the Ras/MEK/MAPK cascade [75]. The roles of integrins in MK proliferation, maturation and subsequent platelet formation warrants further study.

Negative Regulators of Megakaryocytopoiesis

A number of cytokines, including transforming growth factor-β1 [76, 77], platelet factor 4 and interleukin-4 (IL-4), have been reported to be able to inhibit MK development [78-81]. Recent studies demonstrate that Src kinase may negatively regulate thrombopoiesis. The Src kinase inhibitor SU6656, was shown to promote megakaryocytic differentiation and functional platelet-like fragment formation from megakaryocytic cell lines and human progenitor cells thrombopoiesis in vitro [82, 83].

Transcription Factors

MK lineage commitment, progenitor proliferation, terminal differentiation and subsequent thrombocytopoiesis are controlled by the concerted action of specific combinations of transcription factors. The interaction of these factors, specifically stimulate the MK lineage precursors and/or concurrently repress activities that support other cell types. Many MK-specific genes are co-regulated by GATA, FOG, and Ets proteins. A key transcription factor that controls proplatelet formation and platelet release is nuclear factor-erythroid 2 (NF-E2)[2] while the proto-oncogene c-myb inhibits thrombopoiesis [84].

GATA-1 and FOG

Megakaryocytic and erythroid lineages are derived from a common bipotential progenitor and share many early lineage-restricted transcription factors [85, 86]. The zinc-finger protein GATA-1, is the most prominent transcription factor directing MK and erythrocyte MK/E commitment and development. GATA-1 is also required for normal proliferation and terminal maturation of MKs. GATA-1 which forms complexes with other transcription factors (Runx-1 and FOG, friend of GATA), depends in part on the histone acetyltransferase CREB-binding protein (CBP)[2].

Many MK-specific genes have functional GATA-1 binding sites implicating its involvement in a broad lineage-specific genetic program. In addition to binding DNA, GATA-1 recruits a cofactor Friend of GATA-1 (FOG-) [87]. The FOG-1/GATA-1 complex is essential for the hematopoietic differentiation of MKs and erythroid cells. The C-terminal and the N-terminal zinc-fingers of GATA-1 (CF and NF, respectively) which are essential for the recognition of GATA motifs and DNA binding, also interact with other transcription factors. The NF is highly conserved and required for interaction with the GATA-1 co-activator FOG and CBP, and it augments the specificity and stability of binding of the DNA binding domains to palindromic GATA recognition sequences [85, 88]. The NF is indispensable for definitive but not for primitive erythropoiesis, while the CF is indispensable for GATA-1 function [89].

Knock-out of either the GATA-1 or the FOG-1 gene in mice results in midgestation embryonic lethality due to severe anemia associated with abnormal or absent megakaryocytopoiesis [90]. The inherited absence of GATA-1 expression in human and murine MKs, that blocks the interaction between GATA-1 and its cofactor FOG-1, causes dyserythro-poietic anemia and severe thrombocytopenia [91]. These MKs have reduced cytoplasm, abnormal demarcation membranes and arrested differentiation [92]. GATA-1-deficient platelets are abnormal, harboring few α-granules and an excess of rER [91]. In humans, GATA-1 mutations leads to severe diseases involving both erythroid cells and MKs [91, 93]. Human mutations in the NF of GATA-1, which also disrupt FOG-1 binding, cause a syndrome of X-linked thrombocytopenia with or without associated anemia [2]. Compound

GATA-1 and GATA-2 mutations knock-in mice, with resulting functional loss of FOG-1 binding, are a phenotypic copy of FOG-1 null mice displaying a complete absence of megakaryocytopoiesis. MK lineage development, therefore, requires FOG-1 association with either GATA-1 or GATA-2, which are interchangeable [94].

Several different GATA mutations have enabled understanding the function of the different domains [2]. The loss of GATA-1 leads to differentiation arrest and apoptosis of erythroid progenitors and accumulation of immature MKs indicating that GATA-1 is absolutely necessary for MK maturation [95]. GATA-1 mutations expressing a shorter isoform named GATA-1s are likely to be an early step in leukemogenesis of Down syndrome (trisomy 21), [91]. Truncated GATA-1s expressing cells can mature and form proplatelets but display aberrant proliferation. Megakaryocytes with a mutation that eliminates FOG binding, V205G GATA-1, exhibited reduced proliferation, but failed to undergo maturation. Several key MK specific genes have reduced expression in GATA-1 compromised mice, including NF-E2, GPIbα, platelet factor 4, and c-mpl [96], well as TGF-β, platelet derived growth factor (PDGF), and vascular endothelial growth factor (VEGF) [2]. GATA-1 is thus required for the regulation of proliferation and terminal maturation of MKs, and these functions can be uncoupled by mutations in GATA-1 [91]. Recent studies raised the possibility that there are two classes of GATA-1 target genes: one that is absolutely dependent on GATA-1, and another with a less stringent requirement, also able to bind GATA-2. A different set of transcription factors may control the latter in the absence of GATA-1 [91].

Runx1

The transcription factor Runx1(previously known as AML1), is the evolutionarily conserved DNA-binding subunit of the transcription complex core-binding factor (CBFA1) and is required for generation of all definitive hematopoietic lineages [97]. GATA-1 binds to Runx1/AML-1, which functions in the transcription complex with the CBFβ. The RUNX1 gene is the frequent target of chromosomal translocations in leukemia, for example, t(8;21) in acute myeloid leukemia resulting in a dominant-negative RUNX1-ETO fusion protein. Human germ line mutations of RUNX1 are associated with autosomal dominant familial platelet disorder FDP with multiple platelet defects and predisposition to acute myelogenous leukemia [98]. Monoallelic loss of RUNX1 complexes reduces both the number and size of MK progenitor colonies [99].

There is high expression of RUNX1 and CBF in MKs and minimal expression in erythroblasts [97]. Runx1 and CBFβ levels increase preceding MK differentiation and decrease prior to erythroid differentiation. RUNX1 participates in the programming of MK lineage commitment through functional and physical interactions with GATA transcription factors. RUNX1-ETO inhibition of GATA function may explain the inhibition of erythroid and MK differentiation seen in leukemias with t(8;21). The amino terminal transcription activation domain of GATA-1, is required for physical and functional interactions with RUNX1 [97]. RUNX1, through its interaction with GATA-1, may participate in programming the branching of the MK from the erythroid lineages and the leukemogenic mechanisms of RUNX1-ETO may involve inhibition of the GATA-1 function.

PU.1

Pu.1 is an Ets-family oncoprotein that is axial throughout myeloid development. Inhibitory interactions with GATA factors, within the Ets DNA-binding domain is mediated through a small C-terminal motif. Pu.1-dependent induction of myeloid genes in early hematopoietic progenitors may be inhibited by GATA-2 binding to Pu.1. The binding of GATA-1 to Pu.1 blocks c-Jun-mediated co-activation of Pu.1-regulated genes. This occurs during erythroid/MK development while activation of myeloid Pu.1/c-Jun target genes in developing myelocytes proceeds under lower concentration of GATA proteins [100]. Reciprocal antagonism Pu.1 and GATA factors thus appear to balance lineage commitment decisions by setting the framework for differentiated states in early uncommitted hematopoietic progenitors [2, 101].

C-Myb

The early hematopoietic transcription factor c-Myb protein plays a crucial role in MK development and platelet production, and has recently been identified as a powerful negative regulator of thrombopoiesis. Hematopoietic development requires c-myb, and null mice die at day E15 lacking transition from fetal to adult hematopoiesis. These mice are anemic with MKs present in the bone marrow and spleen [102]. C-myb is most abundantly expressed in immature hematopoietic cells, with declining expression as the cells differentiate [103] and together with p300 is necessary for erythropoiesis and the limitation of MK development. Germ line loss of c-Myb results in failure of differentiation of most blood lineages except MKs and macrophages [102].

Mice with subnormal levels of the wild-type c-Myb protein, due to a knockdown allele of c-Myb, have elevated MK and macrophage differentiation at the expense of lymphoid and erythroid development, suggesting that distinct thresholds of c-Myb expression regulate different phases of hematopoiesis [104]. Increased numbers of MKs and platelets are also observed in mice carrying a mutation that prevents association of the transcriptional co-activator CBP with c-Myb [105]. In mutated mice harboring a point mutation in the transactivation (TA) domain of c-Myb (M303V) reducing its interaction with the transcriptional co-activator p300, the number of CD41+ MKs increased 5-fold in the bone marrow, with a remarkable 10-fold increase in hematopoietic stem cells found in the spleen [106]. Mice expressing 10% of the normal c-Myb level have good progenitor cell proliferation, with little granulocytic expansion and arrested erythroid differentiation, and excess of MKs as well as elevated platelet counts [107]. Mpl$^{-/-}$ mice harboring mutations in the DNA-binding domain (called plt3) or within the leucine zipper domain (called plt4) of the c-Myb gene, exhibit TPO independent excessive megakaryocytopoiesis, highly enhanced thrombopoiesis and defective erythroid and lymphoid cell production [108]. Elevated numbers of MKs and MK progenitors were found in the bone marrow and spleen, while these mice were B lymphocyte deficient and mildly anemic. These manifestations are strikingly similar to those seen in mice bearing a germ-line mutation in the c-Myb–binding domain of the p300 transcriptional co-activator. It is possible that GATA-1 and c-Myb compete for CBP binding, which could serve to link the functions of diverse transcription factors that instruct or influence MK development. The spleens of irradiated mice, transplanted with Plt3 or Plt4 mutant bone marrow, contained elevated MK progenitors suggesting altered differentiation commitment of the spleen colony-forming units (CFU-S) toward megakaryocytopoiesis in the mutant mice [84].

Ets Factors

A role for Ets factors in MK gene expression is strongly implicated by the close proximity of Ets-binding sites, to GATA sequences in MK specific promoters [109]. Fli-1 is an Ets factor expressed in primary MKs and hemangioblasts. The human Fli-1 locus is located on chromosome 11q24, where its loss is associated with the thrombocytopenic Paris-Trousseau and Jacobsen syndromes [110]. Fli-1 null mice have defective megakaryocytopoiesis, hemato-poietic anomalies, and impaired vascular development dying at embryonic day 11.5 [111]. Megakaryocytes from the fetal liver of these mice display reduced α-granule numbers and disorganized internal membranes [112]. The down-regulation of MK-specific genes in Fli-1 null mice, highly resemble the differentiation arrest in GATA-1-deficient mice. Activation of several MK-specific genes by the physical interaction of Fli-1 with GATA-1, and their cooperative DNA binding in vitro, strongly implicates a regulatory role for a GATA-1: Fli-1 complex [113]. Moreover, FOG-1 co-activation of GATA-dependent genes is enhanced when Fli-1 occupies Ets sites [114]. It is therefore understood that coordinated action of GATA, Ets, and FOG proteins orchestrates the regulation of MK genes.

Nuclear Factor-Erythroid 2

Nuclear Factor-Erythroid 2 (NF-E2) regulates terminal MK maturation and platelet formation [86, 115]. NF-E2 is a heterodimeric leucine zipper transcription factor, comprised of two polypeptide chains, a MK-erythroid specific 45-kDa subunit and a p18 Maf family subunit that is expressed in many cell types [116]. In primary murine MKs, MafG, associates with the p45 subunit [115] and impaired megakaryocytopoiesis and behavioral defects are found in MafG-null mutant mice, with lethality and hematopoietic defects found in compound mafG:mafK mutant mice [117]. Megakaryocyte maturation arrest in P45 NF-E2 deficient mice causes profound thrombocytopenia, with <5% of the normal number of blood platelets [86]. While MK progenitor proliferation is not seriously effected in NF-E2-deficient mice [118], late MK differentiation is blocked with the prominent presence of disorganized internal membranes, reduced granule numbers, and severe platelet deficit [86, 115, 117].

NF-E2-dependent MK-specific genes include β1 tubulin and 3-β hydroxysteroid dehydrogenase (*3β-HSD*) [119, 120]. Hematopoietic-specific β1-tubulin, necessary for microtubule formation, is absent in NF-E2 null MK, debilitating platelet development. NF-E2 deficient mice share similarities with β1-tubulin knockout mice, displaying similar thrombocytopenia resulting from a defect in the generation of proplatelets. Partial restoration of proplatelet production in NF-E2 null cells can be obtained by forced co-expression of β1 tubulin and 3β-HSD, implicating NF-E2 to be upstream of the regulation of these genes [121]. In addition to the developmental arrest of MK in NF-E2 deficient mice, large number of immature MK accumulate and the mice have high bone mass at the bony sites of hematopoiesis, similar to GATA-1 deficient mice. NF-E2-deficient MKs also have defective inside-out signaling by the $\alpha_{IIb}\beta_3$ integrin [122]and absence of the Rab27b protein [123].

Expression of Rab27b, which depends on NF-E2 is greatly increased with terminal MK differentiation. In maturing MKs, NF-E2 is recruited to the Rab27b promoter. Inhibition of endogenous Rab27 function in MKs causes severe defects in proplatelet formation similar to the *gunmetal* phenotype. In these *gunmetal* mutated mice, inherited abnormalities in platelet formation, platelet number and cytoplasmic organelles are associated with altered expression of low molecular weight guanosine triphosphate binding proteins in [124] implying that efficient thrombopoiesis and granule biosynthesis rely on the degree of prenylation and membrane association of the Rab protein. Rab27b, is therefore a key NF-E2 dependent target gene product, which directs proplatelet formation with granule transport [123]. NF-E2 thus coordinates terminal MK differentiation by regulating a panoply of MK genes, which are key elements in the process of platelet production.

MEGAKARYOCYTE DIFFERENTIATION AND MATURATION

Morphological Changes

The morphological hallmarks of MK maturation are endoreduplication (polyploidy) and increasing cytoplasmic mass. These changes are accompanied by the formation of intracellular organelles manifest as increased cytoplasmic granularity at the light microscope level. MK maturation is classically divided into four morphologically recognizable stages [125-127]. Stage I MKs, or megakaryoblasts, have the highest nuclear/cytoplasmic ratio. These immature cells have a high RNA content, prominent ribosomes and rough endoplasmic reticulum, and express platelet peroxidase. These cells already contain α-granules and dense bodies, and the beginning of the demarcation membrane system [126]. Stage II MKs have an indented to horseshoe-shaped nucleus. The cytoplasm is more abundant and less basophilic. The content of platelet organelles and the demarcation membrane system are increased [126]. At this stage of development, DNA synthesis and endomitosis appear to cease, resulting in fixed ploidy levels [127]. Stage III MKs are relatively large (40 to 50μm), with abundant granular polychromatophilic cytoplasm, well-developed demarcation membranes and organelles. Stage IV MK nuclei show signs of involution, being more compact and dense than the nuclei of stage III cells. MKs in this stage are capable of releasing platelets.

The endomitotic cell cycle in MKs consists of a DNA replication S-phase, an M-phase with multiple pole spindles, aborted anaphase B, aborted cytokinesis and a Gap-phase that allows re-entry into the next round of S-phase. The G_1-phase cyclin D3, is a key inducer of MK polyploidization and is overexpressed in maturing cells [128, 129]. Aurora-B/AIM-1, a fundamental regulator of mitosis, is absent or mislocalized at late anaphase [130]. This factor however, appears to have normal expression and localization during prophase and early anaphase in endoreplicating bone marrow MKs [131]. The segregation of chromosomes in polyploidy MK is asymmetrical with a normal metaphase/anaphase checkpoints [132].

Molecular Markers

Megakaryocyte differentiation markers may be characterized by the expression of functional receptors and proteins that necessary for platelet function (Figure 2). These markers may be identified by monoclonal antibodies directed against the major platelet membrane glycoproteins, such as the integrin $α_{IIb}β_3$ (CD41a or gpIIb/IIIa complex), CD41b (gpIIb), CD61(gpIIIa), CD42a(gpIX), CD42b (gpIb) and CD51(αV), as well as against the platelet α-granule proteins, such as von Willebrand factor (vWF), platelet factor 4 (PF4), β-thromboglobulin (β-TG), fibrinogen, coagulation factor VIII, and factor V. Thus, monoclonal antibodies may facilitate the identification and study of relatively immature, morphologically unidentifiable MKs [133].

Platelet anti-GPIIb or anti-GP-IIIa antibodies stain small "lymphoid" marrow cells, as well as small cells present in colonies derived from CFU-MK (promegakaryoblasts) [134, 135]. These cells are detected in culture by day 4 or 5 [135]. Ploidy measurements of these cells show that they are 2N or 4N. At the ultrastructural level, they do not exhibit platelet organelles such as demarcation membranes or platelet α-granules, but they do express the cytochemical marker, platelet peroxidase [126].

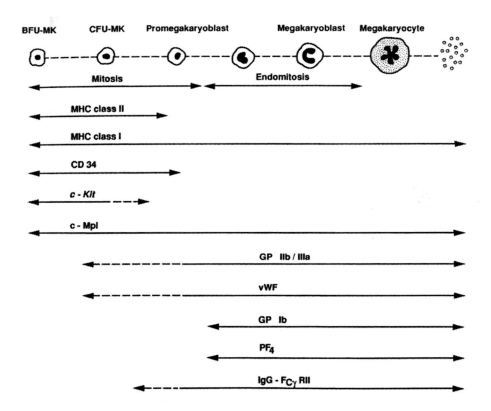

Figure 2. Differentiation markers of the megakaryocytic lineage. BFU-MK, megakaryocytic burst-forming units; CFU-MK, megakaryocytic colony-forming units; HLA, histocompatibility antigens; CD, cluster designation; c-*Kit*, cellular *Kit* gene encodes for the receptor to stem cell factor; c-Mpl, cellular *Mpl* gene encodes for the receptor to thrombopoietin

Recent flow cytometric studies have demonstrated that vWF is robustly expressed by early (2N and 4N) marrow MKs [133], enabling their complete resolution from the other marrow cells at a level superior to that achieved with GPIIb/IIIa as a lineage-specific marker (Figure 3). The high level of resolution permits the reliable identification of the less mature megakaryocytic marrow cells for further studies of their cellular and molecular characteristics throughout the differentiation and maturation process. Compared with the rapid acquisition of vWF, the acquisition of its receptor GPIb (CD42b) was relatively slow, in a rate that is approximately half that of GPIIb/IIIa [133]. Glycoprotein IX, which exists as a heterodimer complex with GPIb and GPV in the platelet membrane, is concomitantly expressed with GPIb during MK differentiation. In contrast, platelet glycoprotein GPIV and the thrombospondin (TSP) receptor (CD36) appears at a later stage of differentiation [136]. Following activation, the platelet GPIIb/IIIa complex functions as a receptor for four adhesive proteins - fibrinogen, fibronectin, vitronectin, and vWF; However, GPIb is the major receptor for vWF. The expression of myeloid IgG-FcγRII (CDw32) increased with MK maturation and contrasted with the declining expression of HLA-DR (negative in platelets). Interleukin-6 receptor expression in MKs is higher than in other marrow cells [133].

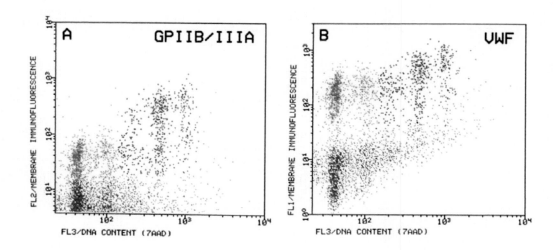

Figure 3. Co-expression of von Willebrand factor (vWF) and of GPIIb/IIIa by human marrow MKs. The MKs were simultaneously labeled with fluoresceinated-MoAb to vWF and PE-labeled MoAb to the lineage specific GPIIb/IIIa complex (CD41a), and stained with 7-amino actinomycin-D for measurement of cell DNA content. The megakaryocytic cells are highly resolved from the general marrow cell population by virtue of their distinct expression level. . (A) Resolution of marrow MKs by expression of GPIIb/IIIa. (B) Resolution of MKs by the expression of vWF. Small (2N/4N) MKs express high level of vWF relative to that of the more mature 16N MKs (ratio=0.5), as compared to the relative expression of GPIIb/IIIa in the same cell populations (ratio=0.2). Thus, the expression of vWF is a sensitive marker for identification of young marrow MKs.

Among the platelet proteins present in the α-granules, PF4, β-TG, and TSP have also been detected in small MK cells. However, only a fraction of GPIIb/IIIa positive precursor cells may contain the platelet proteins [135]. Fibrinogen appears to be acquired by a process of endocytosis from plasma, rather than by neosynthesis and is only detected at late stages of differentiation immediately prior to platelet shedding [137]. Topographical organization is found in the α-granule and vWF being localized at a pole near the α-granule membrane [138].

Cytometric Changes

Quantitative analysis of MK cellular differentiation markers may be useful for the study of mechanisms regulating platelet production. However, the study of the cellular differentiation of MKs has proven difficult, in part, because of their rarity (constituting about

0.05% of all nucleated bone marrow cells), fragility, and tendency to aggregate [139]. Thus, a large number of marrow cells and a highly selective method for megakaryocytic identification are needed for their isolation and analysis.

To overcome some of the technical limitations associated with methodology based on physical separation, flow cytometry has been developed for the analysis of animal MKs [140, 141]. This method has been shown to be sensitive and rapid for the analysis of infrequent cell population, even in complex cell mixtures such as bone marrow. With the use of fluorescence-activating cell sorting on human marrow aspirates, it has been possible to prepare on a routine basis highly pure (>98%) viable MKs isolated on the basis of a lineage marker identified by specific monoclonal antibodies [5]. The cultured cells were capable of responding to hematopoietic growth factor and synthesizing both protein and DNA. This technique has also been adapted to the direct analysis of human MKs in routine bone marrow aspirates [7, 8]. The method has proved useful for studying of megakaryocytopoiesis in disease state [8] and monitoring of drug effect in humans [142], and of the effect of hematopoietic growth factors on megakaryocytopoiesis in humans and nonhuman primates [49,51].

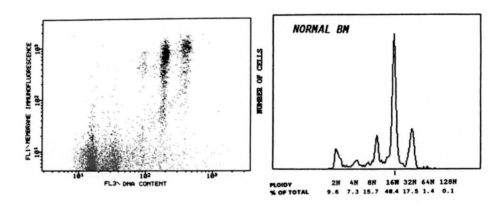

Figure 4. Analysis of normal human MKs in unfractionated marrow by flow cytometry. The left panel shows the distribution of marrow cells according to membrane-GPIIb/IIIa immunofluorescence and the DNA content. Cells with background fluorescence represent the major marrow cell population with ploidy classes of 2N and 4N (red). The highly fluorescent cells represent the MK population with polyploid subclasses (blue). The DNA histogram of the MK population is shown in the right panel. The modal ploidy is 16N comprising about half of the MK population with approximately equal proportions of cells being 8N or lower and 32N or higher.

In all animals studied, ploidy classes are identified as geometric progressions of 2N (diploid), i.e., 4N, 8N, 16N, etc. In normal guinea pigs and rats, the 16N class is most frequent [143, 144]. Earlier data of the distribution of ploidy levels have been confirmed with the use of flow cytometric analysis of bone marrow [140, 141]. With primarily cytophotometric techniques, the ploidy distribution of normal human MKs has been shown to have a modal ploidy of 16N [7, 145]. The ploidy distribution obtained by flow cytometry on a large number (1,200-3,000) of cells in fractionated and unfractionated normal marrow demonstrates 16N for approximately half of the MK population, 23% of cells being 8N or lower and 22% 32N or higher (Figure 4) [5, 7, 49, 133, 142]. Using multi-parameter correlative analysis these studies also showed that the expression of GPIIb/IIIa, GPIIIa, GPIb and CD36 correlated directly with cell size and ploidy [133]. Using slit-scan technique (time-of-flight), the diameter of the MK population was $37\pm4\mu m$ (mean$\pm$1SD) compared to $14\pm2\mu m$ for the total marrow cells, ranging from $21\pm4\mu m$ for 2N cells to $56\pm8\mu m$ for 64N cells. Cell size directly correlated with cell DNA. Receptor density of GPIIb/IIIa and GPIb decreased with the transition from 2N to 4N cells, then reached maximum at 32N-cells [133].

Quantitation of Megakaryocytes

Because platelets are derived from MK cytoplasm, it follows that the MK cytoplasmic mass represents the substrate available for platelet production. The MK cytoplasmic mass may be calculated as the product of the mean MK cytoplasmic volume and the total number of MKs [49, 142, 146-148]. By determining the ratio of MKs to nucleated erythroid precursors in marrow preparations by flow cytometric means, it was possible to estimate MK mass in patients with primary thrombocytosis [49, 142]. Measurements were performed prior to and after treatment with the platelet reductive agent anagrelide. Pre-treatment MK frequency and the average volume were approximately two-fold greater than normal, yielding calculated MK masses 3.4 fold greater than normal values. Interestingly, this result correlated with the 3.6 fold increase in platelet counts. Following treatment, both cell frequency and volume decreased towards normal, resulting in decreased MK mass by about half, similar to the decrease in platelet count.

Compensatory Responses of Megakaryocytes

Compensatory responses of marrow MKs increase platelet production through an increase in cell proliferation, maturation and release of platelets, as early as 24-48 hours after inducing thrombocytopenia. Increased number and size of MKs are noted following thrombocytopheresis and in thrombocytopenias of immune etiology [149, 150]. Reciprocal changes occur with experimentally induced thrombocytosis, i.e., decreases in MK size, ploidy, and volume [140, 151].

Increase in MK ploidy in response to accelerated platelet consumption has been observed in humans in agreement with the observations in experimental animals [8, 146, 152]. An increased proportion of high-ploidy cells in idiopathic thrombocytopenic purpura (ITP) patients has been found with flow cytometric techniques for analysis of relatively large numbers of MKs [7]. In all patients, MK ploidy was significantly shifted toward high ploidy classes associated with increase in cell size. These changes found in both experimental animals and human subjects are primarily mediated by TPO, which may have considerable application in thrombocytopenic states secondary to impaired platelet production.

Megakaryocytopoiesis and platelet production can increase without an apparent thrombocytopenic stimulus. For example, secondary thrombocytosis can occur in patients with iron deficiency, most often due to blood loss. Inflammatory disorders and malignant diseases are occasionally associated with elevated platelet counts. In the inflammatory disorders serum IL-6 levels are significantly greater than those of controls. In contrast, serum IL-6 levels of patients with primary thrombocytosis were not significantly different from those of normal controls [153].

THROMBOCYTOPOIESIS

Platelet Production and Release

Platelet production by cytoplasmic fragmentation requires highly structured intricate changes in the MK cytoskeleton and concomitant assembly of anucleate platelets. High ploidy MKs form extensive internal demarcation membranes and a surface-connected canalicular system, which are essential for platelet formation. Platelet release in the bone marrow occurs when the MK cytoplasm is transformed into long pseudopodia known as proplatelets, which give rise to about 2000-3000 new platelets [154-156]. Because megakaryocytopoiesis occurs in the extravascular marrow space, platelets must gain access to the marrow sinusoids for release into the circulation. Quantitative electron microscopic analysis has shown that MKs are located less than 1 µm away from a marrow sinus wall [157]. Mature MKs extend filaments of cytoplasm into sinusoidal spaces, where they detach and fragment into individual platelets [158-160]. Because entire MK may pass through transendothelial apertures of 6-µm diameter, some MKs reach the lungs through the circulation [161] which may provide an alternative site for platelet production [162-164]. The nascent platelets do not contain nuclear material but rather contain mitochondria and ribosomal RNA (reticulated platelets), and all the components necessary for platelet function in hemostasis. The energy that is normally used for cytokinesis is saved and efficiently utilized in cytoskeletal reorganization and proplatelet packaging necessary for platelet production [129].

Currently there are two models of thrombo-poiesis. One model proposes pre-formed platelet territories within the MK with internal membranes demarcating prepackaged platelet and subsequent fragmentation of the cytoplasm releases platelets. This theory is based on electron microscopy analysis of the internal membranes of MKs [160, 165, 166]. Mature MK, when cultured in contact with subendothelial extracellular matrix, are stimulated to produce platelets by a highly efficient explosive fragmentation of the entire cytoplasm [167]. In vivo and ex vivo observations of platelet release from MKs with phase-contrast microscopy strongly support the explosive-fragmentation theory [47, 168].

The other model conceives platelet assembly through cytoplasmic extensions, called proplatelets, which consist of multiple platelet-size beads along their length. Platelet release from bone marrow MKs occurs when the MK cytoplasm has been transformed into long proplatelet pseudopodia which give rise to new platelets [11, 155, 169]. Megakaryocytes with proplatelet-like processes protruding into the bone marrow sinusoids have been observed in vivo [157]. In vitro, cultured MKs develop various degrees of the demarcation membrane system in addition to proplatelet extensions [170]. The proplatelet segments are delineated by constricted areas with bundles of microtubules running parallel to the axis of the proplatelet. Transversal microtubules form a net on both sides of the constriction zones.

Proplatelet formation, may not be a prerequisite for platelet release from MKs under physiological conditions [168]. It seems that both models of platelet release from the MK, the proplatelet model and the explosive fragmentation model, are not mutually exclusive [168].

Platelet Formation and Apoptosis of Megakaryocytes

Several biological processes associated with platelet fragmentation are similar to those in cells undergoing programmed cell death [171]. These include, ruffling, blebbing and condensation of the plasma and nuclear membranes; reorganization and disruption of the cytoskeletal architecture; DNA fragmentation, and, finally, cell shrinkage and packaging of cellular components into vesicles called apoptotic bodies [172]. Membrane and cytoskeletal changes which involve cytoskeletal filaments, actin filaments and microtubule reorganization are characteristic of both platelet formation and programmed cell death [86, 119]. Microtubule-disrupting agents such as nocodazole, vincristine and colchicines [173] , microfilament disruption by cytochalasine B [11] and interference with F-actin aggregation or blocking integrin signaling or PKC all inhibit platelet production by MKs [174].

In cultures of MKs derived from CD34+ cells, a clear correlation between MK maturation and apoptosis was found. Moreover, the kinetics of platelet release in the culture supernatants also corresponded to apoptosis in these cells, supporting the notion that maximal platelet production and MK apoptosis are closely related [175]. Unlike apoptosis in diploid cells, the senescent MK nucleus must undergo apoptosis and phagocytosis after the viable platelets have been released. It is therefore clear that the demise of the mature MK involves a specialized form of apoptosis during the processes of proplatelet formation and release of mature platelets.

Regulation of Apoptotic Processes

Bcl-2 and Bcl-x

Cellular regulation of the apoptotic death signals resides within the *bcl-2/bax* gene family [176]. The key pro-apoptotic proteins include Bax, Bad, and Bid, and the main anti-apoptotic proteins include Bcl-2 and Bcl-xL. Interaction between pro- and anti-apoptotic Bcl-2 family members and the life/death decision depend on the ratio of pro- vs. anti- apoptotic proteins and the reaction of the Bcl-2 family to those signals. The anti-apoptotic Bcl-2 family members associate with the inner and outer mitochondrial membranes, where they control ion transport and protect against leaks in the membrane. These proteins can inhibit the translocation and homodimerization of pro-apoptotic Bcl-2 family members. Bcl-2 members seem to be differentially regulated during megakaryocytopoiesis and may be targeted to different populations of mitochondria, as Bcl-2 is known to be absent from mature blood platelets [177].

The anti-apoptotic Bcl-xL is highly expressed in normal bone marrow MK, but absent from senescent/apoptotic MK. Bcl-x is also highly expressed in cell lines with megakaryocytic and erythroid properties (K562, HEL, CMK, and Mo7E) [177, 178], and MK differentiation induction with phorbol ester induced overexpression of Bcl-x [171]. In contrast, it appears that the final stages of platelet production requires the down regulation of BCL-x, as evidenced by slow recovery of platelets in transgenic mice overexpressing Bcl-xL following the induction of immune thrombocytopenia. Proplatelet formation in vitro, by transgenic MKs was also hampered [179]. Combined, these finding demonstrate that a regulated balance of Bcl-xL expression in MK, is crucial for the development of cells with a high capacity for platelet production.

TPO, NO and MK Apoptosis

Thrombopoietin-induced terminal differentiation of MK is closely associated with apoptosis [180]. Following TPO treatment of MKs, many of the genes differentially expressed in MKs are involved in coding apoptosis related proteins such as TGFβ-1, calpain, programmed cell death interacting protein and APAF. Many of the downstream proteins of TGFβ1- induced apoptosis, including SMAD-interacting proteins, JNK-related proteins, such as c-jun and c-fos, calcium- dependent protease and calpain-1 and -4. These are all highly expressed in mature MK cells, suggesting that TGF-β1 and SMAD pathways may play a key regulatory role in apoptosis of MKs [171].

Nitrous oxide (NO) is another factor involved in both platelet production and apoptotic pathways. MK apoptosis is promoted by NO, whether exogenously supplied or endogenously produced following induction by inflammatory cytokines [181]. NO, when combined with TPO, markedly enhanced the production of platelet-sized particles. Marked decrease in platelet count was found in nitric oxide synthase (iNOS) knockout mice [181]. Thus, NO may have a dual function in enhancing maturation and platelet release via cyclic GMP-independent and driving MK apoptosis via a cyclic GMP-dependent mechanism [182].

Caspases in MK and Platelets

Caspase-mediated cleavage of specific cyto-skeletal regulatory and cell adhesion proteins, which include gelsolin, fodrin, focal adhesion kinase (FAK) and b-catenin [171] regulates the final stages of programmed cell. This induces irreversible physical and biochemical changes triggered within the cells. In MKs, caspase activation is required for both proplatelet formation and production of functional platelets, as both processes are inhibited by caspase blockers in vitro. During the terminal stages of MK maturation, prior to proplatelet formation, activated caspases-3 and -9 are exhibited [183]. However, unlike apoptotic cells which display diffuse caspase staining, the staining the of cytoplasmic caspase in mature MK is punctuate [183, 184] with no detectable DNA fragmentation. Forced induction of apoptosis in MK results in diffuse caspase activation and DNA fragmentation, with no proplatelet formation. As MKs mature to the proplatelet-forming stage, they exhibit clear caspase activation in the main cell body and some nuclear changes. Platelet production is also driven by pro-apoptotic stimulus of Fas ligation. However, functional platelets, which retain inner mitochondrial membrane potential, and membrane phosphatidylserine asymmetry do not have caspase-9 that is present in MKs, but do express high levels of caspase-3. Freshly released platelets are not recognized for clearance by macrophages and differ entirely from the nonfunctional, thrombogenic and short-lived apoptotic bodies produced by the conventional apoptotic process [184].

The unique compartmentalization of apoptotic events in MK undergoing fragmentation into platelets is necessary for retaining functional mitochondria and maintaining the integrity of the nascent platelets. The importance of caspase activation and apoptotic changes in MKs is limited by the stage of MK differentiation and its intracellular distribution. Characterization of the mechanisms that regulate the spatiotemporal discrimination of apoptotic components and proplatelet formation are not yet resolved.

Other Factors

Recently, prostacyclin (PGI2)-mediated cyclic AMP accumulation has been implicated in the modulation of compartmentalized apoptosis, which is characteristic of terminal MK differentiation stages, following localization of mature MK in to the vascular niche [182]. PGI2 was recently demonstrated to completely block NO-mediated generation and the increased activity of the cleaved form of caspase-3. This inhibition could be fully prevented by suppression of adenylyl or guanylyl cyclase activities. Apparently, PGI2 and NO regulate opposite MK survival responses via balanced cyclic nucleotide levels and caspase-3 activity [185]. Glutamate signaling, independent of TPO mediated effects, may also be involved in platelet production, as selective blocking of the N-methyl-d-aspartate acid (NMDA) receptor diminished the expression of the MK markers CD61, CD41a, and CD42a, and severely damaged the formation of alpha-granules, demarcated membranes, and proplatelet formation [186].

SUMMARY

Megakaryocytopoiesis involves the commitment, proliferation, and differentiation of the megakaryo-cytic cell lineage together with the cytoplasmic acquisition of functional and structural properties of platelets. Marrow megakaryocytes respond to increased demand for peripheral blood platelets by modifying the progenitor cell compartment, cellular replication, endoreduplication, cytoplasmic dif-ferentiation, and platelet shedding. The regulation of megakaryocytopoiesis is mediated through multiple hematopoietic growth factors, primarily thrombo-poietin, via signal transduction pathways and integrated transcription factors. Thrombopoietin may be useful in the future in supporting platelet production in thrombocytopenic states with adequate numbers of cytokine responsive precursors. Stimulated megakaryocytopoiesis typically manifests increased megakaryocytic number, size, ploidy, and a shortened cytoplasmic maturation time. Studies of megakaryocytic cells in culture are essential for determination of the molecular mechanisms regulating megakaryocytopoiesis. Flow cytometric analysis of aspirated marrow is a powerful technique for quantitative characterization of megakaryocytic number, size, ploidy, and cytoplasmic differentiation. In general, platelet turnover correlates directly with the megakaryocytic cytoplasmic mass, and a discrepancy between the available megakaryocytic cytoplasmic substrate and platelet turnover reflects ineffective thrombocytopoiesis. Senescent megakaryocytes undergo a specialized form of apoptosis throughout the processes of proplatelet formation and platelet release.

ACKNOWLEDGEMENTS

This review is dedicated in the memory of Prof. Amiram Eldor, colleague, friend and collaborator whose life was devoted to patients, students and research.

AT acknowledges support from Lyonel G Israels fund, Winnipeg, Manitoba, Canada.

VRD acknowledges research funding from the Israel Ministry of Science and the BMBF-Germany, The Israel Cancer Association – donation of Don and Donna Sherman and The Israel Ministry of Health.

REFERENCES

[1] Vainchenker W, Kieffer N. Human megakaryo-cytopoiesis: in vitro regulation and characterization of megakaryocytic precursor cells by differentiation markers. *Blood Rev* 1988;2(2):102-7.

[2] Schulze H, Shivdasani RA. Molecular mechanisms of megakaryocyte differentiation. *Semin Thromb Hemost* 2004;30(4):389-98.

[3] Gewirtz AM. Human megakaryocytopoiesis. *Semin Hematol* 1986;23(1):27-42.

[4] Schick PK, Schick BP. Megakaryocyte biochemistry. *Prog Clin Biol Res* 1986;215:265-79.

[5] Tomer A, Harker LA, Burstein SA. Purification of human megakaryocytes by fluorescence-activated cell sorting. *Blood* 1987;70(6):1735-42.

[6] Levine RF, Hazzard KC, Lamberg JD. The significance of megakaryocyte size. *Blood* 1982;60(5):1122-31.

[7] Tomer A, Harker LA, Burstein SA. Flow cytometric analysis of normal human megakaryocytes. *Blood* 1988;71(5):1244-52.

[8] Tomer A, Friese P, Conklin R, Bales W, Archer L, Harker LA, et al. Flow cytometric analysis of megakaryocytes from patients with abnormal platelet counts. *Blood* 1989;74(2):594-601.

[9] Breton-Gorius J, Vainchenker W. Expression of platelet proteins during the in vitro and in vivo differentiation of megakaryocytes and morphological aspects of their maturation. *Semin Hematol* 1986;23(1):43-67.

[10] Radley JM, Scurfield G. The mechanism of platelet release. *Blood* 1980;56(6):996-9.

[11] Italiano JE, Jr., Lecine P, Shivdasani RA, Hartwig JH. Blood platelets are assembled principally at the ends of proplatelet processes produced by differentiated megakaryocytes. *J Cell Biol* 1999;147(6):1299-312.

[12] Avecilla ST, Hattori K, Heissig B, Tejada R, Liao F, Shido K, et al. Chemokine-mediated interaction of hematopoietic progenitors with the bone marrow vascular niche is required for thrombopoiesis. *Nat Med* 2004;10(1):64-71.

[13] Williams N, McDonald TP, Rabellino EM. Maturation and regulation of megakaryocytopoiesis. *Blood Cells* 1979;5(1):43-55.

[14] Avraham H. Regulation of megakaryocytopoiesis. Stem *Cells* 1993;11(6):499-510.

[15] Kaushansky K. Thrombopoietin: a tool for under-standing thrombopoiesis. *J Thromb Haemost* 2003;1(7): 1587-92.

[16] Gewirtz AM. Megakaryocytopoiesis: the state of the art. *Thromb Haemost* 1995;74(1):204-9.

[17] Corash L, Chen HY, Levin J, Baker G, Lu H, Mok Y. Regulation of thrombopoiesis: effects of the degree of thrombocytopenia on megakaryocyte ploidy and platelet volume. *Blood* 1987;70(1):177-85.

[18] Burstein SA, Adamson JW, Erb SK, Harker LA. Megakaryocytopoiesis in the mouse: response to varying platelet demand. *J Cell Physiol* 1981;109(2): 333-41.

[19] Tomer A, Hanson SR, Harker LA. Autologous platelet kinetics in patients with severe thrombocytopenia: discrimination between disorders of production and destruction. *J Lab Clin Med* 1991;118(6):546-54.

[20] de Sauvage FJ, Hass PE, Spencer SD, Malloy BE, Gurney AL, Spencer SA, et al. Stimulation of mega-karyocytopoiesis and thrombopoiesis by the c-Mpl ligand. *Nature* 1994;369(6481):533-8.

[21] Kaushansky K. The mpl ligand: molecular and cellular biology of the critical regulator of megakaryocyte development. *Stem Cells* 1994;12 Suppl 1:91-6; discussion 96-7.

[22] Lok S, Foster DC. The structure, biology and potential therapeutic applications of recombinant thrombopoietin. *Stem Cells* 1994;12(6):586-98.

[23] Wendling F, Maraskovsky E, Debili N, Florindo C, Teepe M, Titeux M, et al. cMpl ligand is a humoral regulator of megakaryocytopoiesis. *Nature* 1994;369 (6481):571-4.

[24] Bartley TD, Bogenberger J, Hunt P, Li YS, Lu HS, Martin F, et al. Identification and cloning of a mega-karyocyte growth and development factor that is a ligand for the cytokine receptor *Mpl. Cell* 1994;77(7): 1117-24.

[25] Yamamoto K, Nagata K, Tsurukubo Y, Morishita K, Hamaguchi H. A novel translocation t(3;22)(q21;q11) involving 3q21 in myelodysplastic syndrome-derived overt leukemia with thrombocytosis. *Leuk Res* 2000;24(5):453-7.

[26] Scheding S, Bergmann M, Shimosaka A, Wolff P, Driessen C, Rathke G, et al. Human plasma thrombo-poietin levels are regulated by binding to platelet thrombopoietin receptors in vivo. *Transfusion* 2002;42(3):321-7.

[27] Kuter DJ, Rosenberg RD. The reciprocal relationship of thrombopoietin (c-Mpl ligand) to changes in the platelet mass during busulfan-induced thrombocytopenia in the rabbit. *Blood* 1995;85(10):2720-30.

[28] Kaushansky K. Thrombopoietin: basic biology and clinical promise. Leukemia 1997;11 *Suppl* 3:426-7.

[29] Burmester H, Wolber EM, Freitag P, Fandrey J, Jelkmann W. Thrombopoietin production in wild-type and inter-leukin-6 knockout mice with acute inflammation. *J Interferon Cytokine Res* 2005;25(7): 407-13.

[30] Kirito K, Fox N, Kaushansky K. Thrombopoietin stimulates Hoxb4 expression: an explanation for the favorable effects of TPO on hematopoietic stem cells. *Blood* 2003;102(9):3172-8.

[31] Kirito K, Fox N, Kaushansky K. Thrombopoietin induces HOXA9 nuclear transport in immature hematopoietic cells: potential mechanism by which the hormone favorably affects hematopoietic stem cells. *Mol Cell Biol* 2004;24(15):6751-62.

[32] Paulus JM, Debili N, Larbret F, Levin J, Vainchenker W. Thrombopoietin responsiveness reflects the number of doublings undergone by megakaryocyte progenitors. *Blood* 2004;104(8):2291-8.

[33] Kamata T, Pritchard CA, Leavitt AD. Raf-1 is not required for megakaryocytopoiesis or TPO-induced ERK phosphorylation. *Blood* 2004;103(7):2568-70.

[34] Hoffman R. Regulation of megakaryocytopoiesis. *Blood* 1989;74(4):1196-212.

[35] Hoffman R, Briddell R, Bruno E. Numerous growth factors can influence in vitro megakaryocytopoiesis. *Yale J Biol Med* 1990;63(5):411-8.

[36] Stahl CP, Winton EF, Monroe MC, Holman RC, Zelasky M, Liehl E, et al. Recombinant human granulocyte-macrophage colony-stimulating factor promotes megakaryocyte maturation in nonhuman primates. *Exp Hematol* 1991;19(8):810-6.

[37] Quesenberry PJ, McGrath HE, Williams ME, Robinson BE, Deacon DH, Clark S, et al. Multifactor stimulation of megakaryocytopoiesis: effects of interleukin 6. *Exp Hematol* 1991;19(1):35-41.

[38] Han ZC, Bikfalvi A, Shen ZX, Bodevin E. Recombinant acidic human fibroblast growth factor (aFGF) stimulates murine megakaryocyte colony formation in vitro. *Int J Hematol* 1992;55(3):281-6.

[39] Bruno E, Briddell RA, Cooper RJ, Hoffman R. Effects of recombinant interleukin 11 on human megakaryocyte progenitor cells. *Exp Hematol* 1991;19(5):378-81.

[40] Vainchenker W, Bouguet J, Guichard J, Breton-Gorius J. Megakaryocyte colony formation from human bone marrow precursors. *Blood* 1979;54(4):940-5.

[41] Dessypris EN, Gleaton JH, Armstrong OL. Effect of human recombinant erythropoietin on human marrow megakaryocyte colony formation in vitro. *Br J Haematol* 1987;65(3):265-9.

[42] Briddell RA, Bruno E, Cooper RJ, Brandt JE, Hoffman R. Effect of c-kit ligand on in vitro human megakaryo-cytopoiesis. *Blood* 1991;78(11):2854-9.

[43] Aglietta M, Monzeglio C, Sanavio F, Apra F, Morelli S, Stacchini A, et al. In vivo effect of human granulocyte-macrophage colony-stimulating factor on megakaryo-cytopoiesis. *Blood* 1991;77(6):1191-4.

[44] Tomer A, Stahl CP, McClure HM, Anderson DC, Myers LA, Liehl E, et al. Effects of recombinant human granulocyte-macrophage colony-stimulating factor on platelet survival and activation using a nonhuman primate model. *Exp Hematol* 1993;21(12):1577-82.

[45] Navarro S, Debili N, Le Couedic JP, Klein B, Breton-Gorius J, Doly J, et al. Interleukin-6 and its receptor are expressed by human megakaryocytes: in vitro effects on proliferation and endoreplication. *Blood* 1991;77(3): 461-71.

[46] Bruno E, Cooper RJ, Briddell RA, Hoffman R. Further examination of the effects of recombinant cytokines on the proliferation of human megakaryocyte progenitor cells. *Blood* 1991;77(11):2339-46.

[47] Deutsch VR, Olson TA, Nagler A, Slavin S, Levine RF, Eldor A. The response of cord blood megakaryocyte progenitors to IL-3, IL-6 and aplastic canine serum varies with gestational age. *Br J Haematol* 1995;89(1): 8-16.

[48] Stahl CP, Zucker-Franklin D, Evatt BL, Winton EF. Effects of human interleukin-6 on megakaryocyte development and thrombocytopoiesis in primates. *Blood* 1991;78(6):1467-75.

[49] Tomer A, Harker LA. Measurements of in vivo megakaryocytopoiesis: studies in nonhuman primates and patients. *Stem Cells 1996;14 Suppl* 1:18-30.

[50] Harker LA, Hunt P, Marzec UM, Kelly AB, Tomer A, Hanson SR, et al. Regulation of platelet production and function by megakaryocyte growth and development factor in nonhuman primates. *Blood* 1996;87(5):1833-44.

[51] Harker LA, Marzec UM, Kelly AB, Cheung E, Tomer A, Nichol JL, et al. Prevention of thrombocytopenia and neutropenia in a nonhuman primate model of marrow suppressive chemotherapy by combining pegylated recombinant human megakaryocyte growth and development factor and recombinant human granulocyte colony-stimulating factor. *Blood* 1997;89(1):155-65.

[52] Kaushansky K. Thrombopoietin: the primary regulator of platelet production. *Blood* 1995;86(2):419-31.

[53] Schuster MW, Beveridge R, Frei-Lahr D, Abboud CN, Cruickshank S, Macri M, et al. The effects of pegylated recombinant human megakaryocyte growth and development

factor (PEG-rHuMGDF) on platelet recovery in breast cancer patients undergoing autologous bone marrow transplantation. *Exp Hematol* 2002;30(9):1044-50.

[54] Bernstein SH, Jusko WJ, Krzyzanski W, Nichol J, Wetzler M. Pharmacodynamic modeling of thrombo-poietin, platelet, and megakaryocyte dynamics in patients with acute myeloid leukemia undergoing dose intensive chemotherapy. *J Clin Pharmacol* 2002;42(5):501-11.

[55] Nash RA, Takatu A, Feng Z, Slichter S, Abrams K, Espino G, et al. Effect of c-mpl ligands after total body irradiation (TBI) with and without allogeneic hematopoietic stem cell transplantation: low-dose TBI does not prevent sensitization. *Biol Blood Marrow Transplant* 2002;8(7):360-7.

[56] Kuter DJ. Whatever happened to thrombopoietin? *Transfusion* 2002;42(3):279-83.

[57] Kuter DJ, Begley CG. Recombinant human thrombo-poietin: basic biology and evaluation of clinical studies. *Blood* 2002;100(10):3457-69.

[58] Jackson CW. Cholinesterase as a possible marker for early cells of the megakaryocytic series. *Blood* 1973;42 (3):413-21.

[59] Long MW, Williams N, McDonald TP. Immature megakaryocytes in the mouse: in vitro relationship to megakaryocyte progenitor cells and mature mega-karyocytes. *J Cell Physiol* 1982;112(3):339-44.

[60] Lev-Lehman E, Ginzberg D, Hornreich G, Ehrlich G, Meshorer A, Eckstein F, et al. Antisense inhibition of acetylcholinesterase gene expression causes transient hematopoietic alterations in vivo. *Gene Ther* 1994;1(2):127-35.

[61] Lev-Lehman E, Deutsch V, Eldor A, Soreq H. Immature human megakaryocytes produce nuclear-associated acetylcholinesterase. *Blood* 1997;89(10): 3644-53.

[62] Deutsch VR, Pick M, Perry C, Grisaru D, Hemo Y, Golan-Hadari D, et al. The stress-associated acetyl-cholinesterase variant AChE-R is expressed in human CD34(+) hematopoietic progenitors and its C-terminal peptide ARP promotes their proliferation. *Exp Hematol* 2002;30(10):1153-61.

[63] Grisaru D, Deutsch V, Shapira M, Pick M, Sternfeld M, Melamed-Book N, et al. ARP, a peptide derived from the stress-associated acetylcholinesterase variant, has hemato-poietic growth promoting activities. *Mol Med* 2001;7(2):93-105.

[64] Pick M, Flores-Flores C, Grisaru D, Shochat S, Deutsch V, Soreq H. Blood-cell-specific acetylcholinesterase splice variations under changing stimuli. *Int J Dev Neurosci* 2004;22(7):523-31.

[65] Cheng L, Qasba P, Vanguri P, Thiede MA. Human mesenchymal stem cells support megakaryocyte and pro-platelet formation from CD34(+) hematopoietic progenitor cells. *J Cell Physiol* 2000;184(1):58-69.

[66] Broxmeyer HE, Youn BS, Kim C, Hangoc G, Cooper S, Mantel C. Chemokine regulation of hematopoiesis and the involvement of pertussis toxin-sensitive G alpha i proteins. *Ann N Y Acad Sci* 2001;938:117-27; discussion 127-8.

[67] Wang JF, Liu ZY, Groopman JE. The alpha-chemokine receptor CXCR4 is expressed on the megakaryocytic lineage from progenitor to platelets and modulates migration and adhesion. *Blood* 1998;92(3):756-64.

[68] Hamada T, Mohle R, Hesselgesser J, Hoxie J, Nachman RL, Moore MA, et al. Transendothelial migration of megakaryocytes in response to stromal cell-derived factor 1 (SDF-1) enhances platelet formation. *J Exp Med* 1998;188(3):539-48.

[69] Lane WJ, Dias S, Hattori K, Heissig B, Choy M, Rabbany SY, et al. Stromal-derived factor 1-induced megakaryocyte migration and platelet production is dependent on matrix metalloproteinases. *Blood* 2000;96(13):4152-9.

[70] Berthebaud M, Riviere C, Jarrier P, Foudi A, Zhang Y, Compagno D, et al. RGS16 is a negative regulator of SDF1-CXCR4 signaling in megakaryocytes. *Blood* 2005.

[71] Deutsch V, Bitan M, Friedmann Y, Eldor A, Vlodavsky I. Megakaryocyte maturation is associated with expression of the CXC chemokine connective tissue-activating peptide CTAP III. *Br J Haematol* 2000;111(4):1180-9.

[72] Hynes RO. Integrins: versatility, modulation, and signaling in cell adhesion. *Cell* 1992;69(1):11-25.

[73] Fuse A, Kakuda H, Shima Y, Van Damme J, Billiau A, Sato T. Interleukin 6, a possible autocrine growth and differentiation factor for the human megakaryocytic cell line, CMK. *Br J Haematol* 1991;77(1):32-6.

[74] Lin K, Abraham KM. Targets of p56(lck) activity in immature thymoblasts: stimulation of the Ras/Raf/MAPK pathway. *Int Immunol* 1997;9(2):291-306.

[75] Jiang F, Jia Y, Cohen I. Fibronectin- and protein kinase C-mediated activation of ERK/MAPK are essential for proplateletlike formation. *Blood* 2002;99(10):3579-84.

[76] Kuter DJ, Gminski DM, Rosenberg RD. Transforming growth factor beta inhibits megakaryocyte growth and endomitosis. *Blood* 1992;79(3):619-26.

[77] Fortunel N, Hatzfeld J, Kisselev S, Monier MN, Ducos K, Cardoso A, et al. Release from quiescence of primitive human hematopoietic stem/progenitor cells by blocking their cell-surface TGF-beta type II receptor in a short-term in vitro assay. *Stem Cells* 2000;18(2):102-11.

[78] Griffin CG, Grant BW. Effects of recombinant interferons on human megakaryocyte growth. *Exp Hematol* 1990;18(9):1013-8.

[79] Han ZC, Bellucci S, Caen JP. Megakaryocytopoiesis: characterization and regulation in normal and pathologic states. *Int J Hematol* 1991;54(1):3-14.

[80] Zauli G, Catani L. Human megakaryocyte biology and pathophysiology. *Crit Rev Oncol Hematol* 1995;21(1-3):135-57.

[81] Baatout S. Megakaryocytopoiesis: growth factors, cell cycle and gene expression. *Anticancer Res* 1998;18(3B):1871-82.

[82] Gandhi MJ, Drachman JG, Reems JA, Thorning D, Lannutti BJ. A novel strategy for generating platelet-like fragments from megakaryocytic cell lines and human progenitor cells. *Blood Cells Mol Dis* 2005;35(1):70-3.

[83] Lannutti BJ, Blake N, Gandhi MJ, Reems JA, Drachman JG. Induction of polyploidization in leukemic cell lines and primary bone marrow by Src kinase inhibitor SU6656. *Blood* 2005;105(10):3875-8.

[84] Metcalf D, Carpinelli MR, Hyland C, Mifsud S, Dirago L, Nicola NA, et al. Anomalous megakaryocytopoiesis in mice with mutations in the c-Myb gene. *Blood* 2005;105(9):3480-7.

[85] Shivdasani RA, Fujiwara Y, McDevitt MA, Orkin SH. A lineage-selective knockout establishes the critical role of transcription factor GATA-1 in megakaryocyte growth and platelet development. *Embo J* 1997;16(13):3965-73.

[86] Shivdasani RA, Rosenblatt MF, Zucker-Franklin D, Jackson CW, Hunt P, Saris CJ, et al. Transcription factor NF-E2 is required for platelet formation independent of the

actions of thrombopoietin/MGDF in megakaryocyte development. *Cell* 1995;81(5):695-704.

[87] Tsang AP, Visvader JE, Turner CA, Fujiwara Y, Yu C, Weiss MJ, et al. FOG, a multitype zinc finger protein, acts as a cofactor for transcription factor GATA-1 in erythroid and megakaryocytic differentiation. *Cell* 1997;90(1):109-19.

[88] Crispino JD, Lodish MB, MacKay JP, Orkin SH. Use of altered specificity mutants to probe a specific protein-protein interaction in differentiation: the GATA-1:FOG complex. *Mol Cell* 1999;3(2):219-28.

[89] Perry C, Soreq H. Transcriptional regulation of erythropoiesis. Fine tuning of combinatorial multi-domain elements. *Eur J Biochem* 2002;269(15):3607-18.

[90] Crawford SE, Qi C, Misra P, Stellmach V, Rao MS, Engel JD, et al. Defects of the heart, eye, and megakaryocytes in peroxisome proliferator activator receptor-binding protein (PBP) null embryos implicate GATA family of transcription factors. *J Biol Chem* 2002;277(5):3585-92.

[91] Muntean AG, Crispino JD. Differential requirements for the activation domain and FOG-interaction surface of GATA-1 in megakaryocyte gene expression and development. *Blood* 2005;106(4):1223-31.

[92] Freson K, Devriendt K, Matthijs G, Van Hoof A, De Vos R, Thys C, et al. Platelet characteristics in patients with X-linked macrothrombocytopenia because of a novel GATA1 mutation. *Blood* 2001;98(1):85-92.

[93] Schulze H, Korpal M, Bergmeier W, Italiano JE, Jr., Wahl SM, Shivdasani RA. Interactions between the megakaryocyte/platelet-specific beta1 tubulin and the secretory leukocyte protease inhibitor SLPI suggest a role for regulated proteolysis in platelet functions. *Blood* 2004;104(13):3949-57.

[94] Chang AN, Cantor AB, Fujiwara Y, Lodish MB, Droho S, Crispino JD, et al. GATA-factor dependence of the multitype zinc-finger protein FOG-1 for its essential role in megakaryopoiesis. *Proc Natl Acad Sci U S A* 2002;99(14):9237-42.

[95] Gurbuxani S, Vyas P, Crispino JD. Recent insights into the mechanisms of myeloid leukemogenesis in Down syndrome. *Blood* 2004;103(2):399-406.

[96] Vyas P, Ault K, Jackson CW, Orkin SH, Shivdasani RA. Consequences of GATA-1 deficiency in mega-karyocytes and platelets. *Blood* 1999;93(9):2867-75.

[97] Elagib KE, Racke FK, Mogass M, Khetawat R, Delehanty LL, Goldfarb AN. RUNX1 and GATA-1 coexpression and cooperation in megakaryocytic differentiation. *Blood* 2003;101(11):4333-41.

[98] Downing JR. The AML1-ETO chimaeric transcription factor in acute myeloid leukaemia: biology and clinical significance. *Br J Haematol* 1999;106(2):296-308.

[99] Song WJ, Sullivan MG, Legare RD, Hutchings S, Tan X, Kufrin D, et al. Haploinsufficiency of CBFA2 causes familial thrombocytopenia with propensity to develop acute myelogenous leukaemia. *Nat Genet* 1999;23(2): 166-75.

[100] Behre G, Whitmarsh AJ, Coghlan MP, Hoang T, Carpenter CL, Zhang DE, et al. c-Jun is a JNK-independent coactivator of the PU.1 transcription factor. *J Biol Chem* 1999;274(8):4939-46.

[101] Rekhtman N, Choe KS, Matushansky I, Murray S, Stopka T, Skoultchi AI. PU.1 and pRB interact and cooperate to repress GATA-1 and block erythroid differentiation. *Mol Cell Biol* 2003;23(21):7460-74.

[102] Mucenski ML, McLain K, Kier AB, Swerdlow SH, Schreiner CM, Miller TA, et al. A functional c-myb gene is required for normal murine fetal hepatic hematopoiesis. *Cell* 1991;65(4):677-89.

[103] Oh IH, Reddy EP. The myb gene family in cell growth, differentiation and apoptosis. *Oncogene* 1999;18(19): 3017-33.

[104] Clarke D, Vegiopoulos A, Crawford A, Mucenski M, Bonifer C, Frampton J. In vitro differentiation of c-myb(-/-) ES cells reveals that the colony forming capacity of unilineage macrophage precursors and myeloid progenitor commitment are c-Myb independent. *Oncogene* 2000;19(30):3343-51.

[105] Kasper LH, Boussouar F, Ney PA, Jackson CW, Rehg J, van Deursen JM, et al. A transcription-factor-binding surface of coactivator p300 is required for haemato-poiesis. *Nature* 2002;419(6908):738-43.

[106] Sandberg ML, Sutton SE, Pletcher MT, Wiltshire T, Tarantino LM, Hogenesch JB, et al. c-Myb and p300 regulate hematopoietic stem cell proliferation and differentiation. *Dev Cell* 2005;8(2):153-66.

[107] Emambokus N, Vegiopoulos A, Harman B, Jenkinson E, Anderson G, Frampton J. Progression through key stages of haemopoiesis is dependent on distinct threshold levels of c-Myb. *Embo J* 2003;22(17):4478-88.

[108] Carpinelli MR, Hilton DJ, Metcalf D, Antonchuk JL, Hyland CD, Mifsud SL, et al. Suppressor screen in Mpl-/- mice: c-Myb mutation causes supraphysiological production of platelets in the absence of thrombopoietin signaling. *Proc Natl Acad Sci USA* 2004;101(17):6553-8.

[109] Lemarchandel V, Ghysdael J, Mignotte V, Rahuel C, Romeo PH. GATA and Ets cis-acting sequences mediate megakaryocyte-specific expression. *Mol Cell* Biol 1993;13(1):668-76.

[110] Krishnamurti L, Neglia JP, Nagarajan R, Berry SA, Lohr J, Hirsch B, et al. Paris-Trousseau syndrome platelets in a child with Jacobsen's syndrome. *Am J Hematol* 2001;66(4):295-9.

[111] Kawada H, Ito T, Pharr PN, Spyropoulos DD, Watson DK, Ogawa M. Defective megakaryopoiesis and abnormal erythroid development in Fli-1 gene-targeted mice. *Int J Hematol* 2001;73(4):463-8.

[112] Hart A, Melet F, Grossfeld P, Chien K, Jones C, Tunnacliffe A, et al. Fli-1 is required for murine vascular and megakaryocytic development and is hemizygously deleted in patients with thrombo-cytopenia. *Immunity* 2000;13(2):167-77.

[113] Eisbacher M, Holmes ML, Newton A, Hogg PJ, Khachigian LM, Crossley M, et al. Protein-protein interaction between Fli-1 and GATA-1 mediates synergistic expression of megakaryocyte-specific genes through cooperative DNA binding. *Mol Cell Biol* 2003;23(10):3427-41.

[114] Wang X, Crispino JD, Letting DL, Nakazawa M, Poncz M, Blobel GA. Control of megakaryocyte-specific gene expression by GATA-*1 and FOG-1: role of Ets transcription factors.* Embo J 2002;21(19):5225-34.

[115] Lecine P, Shivdasani RA. Cellular and molecular biology of megakaryocyte differentiation in the absence of lineage-restricted transcription factors. *Stem Cells* 1998;16 Suppl 2:91-5.

[116] Blank V, Kim MJ, Andrews NC. Human MafG is a functional partner for p45 NF-E2 in activating globin gene expression. *Blood* 1997;89(11):3925-35.

[117] Onodera K, Shavit JA, Motohashi H, Yamamoto M, Engel JD. Perinatal synthetic lethality and hemato-poietic defects in compound mafG::mafK mutant mice. *Embo J* 2000;19(6):1335-45.

[118] Levin J, Peng JP, Baker GR, Villeval JL, Lecine P, Burstein SA, et al. Pathophysiology of thrombo-cytopenia and anemia in mice lacking transcription factor NF-E2. *Blood* 1999;94(9):3037-47.

[119] Lecine P, Italiano JE, Jr., Kim SW, Villeval JL, Shivdasani RA. Hematopoietic-specific beta 1 tubulin participates in a pathway of platelet biogenesis dependent on the transcription factor NF-E2. *Blood* 2000;96(4):1366-73.

[120] Nagata Y, Yoshikawa J, Hashimoto A, Yamamoto M, Payne AH, Todokoro K. Proplatelet formation of megakaryocytes is triggered by autocrine-synthesized estradiol. *Genes Dev* 2003;17(23):2864-9.

[121] Italiano JE, Jr., Bergmeier W, Tiwari S, Falet H, Hartwig JH, Hoffmeister KM, et al. Mechanisms and implications of platelet discoid shape. *Blood* 2003; 101(12):4789-96.

[122] Shiraga M, Ritchie A, Aidoudi S, Baron V, Wilcox D, White G, et al. Primary megakaryocytes reveal a role for transcription factor NF-E2 in integrin alpha IIb beta 3 signaling. *J Cell Biol* 1999;147(7):1419-30.

[123] Tiwari S, Italiano JE, Jr., Barral DC, Mules EH, Novak EK, Swank RT, et al. A role for Rab27b in NF-E2-dependent pathways of platelet formation. *Blood* 2003;102(12):3970-9.

[124] Novak EK, Reddington M, Zhen L, Stenberg PE, Jackson CW, McGarry MP, et al. Inherited thrombo-cytopenia caused by reduced platelet production in mice with the gunmetal pigment gene mutation. *Blood* 1995;85(7):1781-9.

[125] Williams N, Levine RF. The origin, development and regulation of megakaryocytes. *Br J Haematol* 1982;52 (2):173-80.

[126] Breton-Gorius J, Reyes F. Ultrastructure of human bone marrow cell maturation. *Int Rev Cytol* 1976;46:251-321.

[127] Ebbe S. Experimental and clinical megakaryocyto-poiesis. *Clin Haematol* 1979;8(2):371-94.

[128] Zimmet J, Ravid K. Polyploidy: occurrence in nature, mechanisms, and significance for the megakaryocyte-platelet system. *Exp Hematol* 2000;28(1):3-16.

[129] Ravid K, Lu J, Zimmet JM, Jones MR. Roads to polyploidy: the megakaryocyte example. *J Cell Physiol* 2002;190(1):7-20.

[130] Zhang Y, Nagata Y, Yu G, Nguyen HG, Jones MR, Toselli P, et al. Aberrant quantity and localization of Aurora-B/AIM-1 and survivin during megakaryocyte polyploidization and the consequences of Aurora-B/AIM-1-deregulated expression. *Blood* 2004;103 (10):3717-26.

[131] Geddis AE, Kaushansky K. Megakaryocytes express functional Aurora-B kinase in endomitosis. *Blood* 2004;104(4):1017-24.

[132] Roy L, Coullin P, Vitrat N, Hellio R, Debili N, Weinstein J, et al. Asymmetrical segregation of chromosomes with a normal metaphase/anaphase checkpoint in polyploid megakaryocytes. *Blood* 2001;97(8):2238-47.

[133] Tomer A. Human marrow megakaryocyte differentiation: multiparameter correlative analysis identifies von Willebrand factor as a sensitive and distinctive marker for early (2N and 4N) megakaryocytes. *Blood* 2004;104(9):2722-7.

[134] Mazur EM, Hoffman R, Chasis J, Marchesi S, Bruno E. Immunofluorescent identification of human megakaryocyte colonies using an antiplatelet glycoprotein antiserum. *Blood* 1981;57(2):277-86.

[135] Vinci G, Tabilio A, Deschamps JF, Van Haeke D, Henri A, Guichard J, et al. Immunological study of in vitro maturation of human megakaryocytes. *Br J Haematol* 1984;56(4):589-605.

[136] Asch AS, Barnwell J, Silverstein RL, Nachman RL. Isolation of the thrombospondin membrane receptor. *J Clin Invest* 1987;79(4):1054-61.

[137] Cramer EM, Debili N, Martin JF, Gladwin AM, Breton-Gorius J, Harrison P, et al. Uncoordinated expression of fibrinogen compared with thrombospondin and von Willebrand factor in maturing human megakaryocytes. *Blood* 1989;73(5):1123-9.

[138] Cramer EM, Vainchenker W, Vinci G, Guichard J, Breton-Gorius J. Gray platelet syndrome: immuno-electron microscopic localization of fibrinogen and von Willebrand factor in platelets and megakaryo-cytes. *Blood* 1985;66(6):1309-16.

[139] Rabellino EM. Biology of human megakaryocytes: recent developments. *Prog Hemost Thromb* 1984;7:151-66.

[140] Jackson CW, Brown LK, Somerville BC, Lyles SA, Look AT. Two-color flow cytometric measurement of DNA distributions of rat megakaryocytes in unfixed, unfractionated marrow cell suspensions. *Blood* 1984;63(4):768-78.

[141] Worthington RE, Nakeff A, Micko S. Flow cytometric analysis of megakaryocyte differentiation. *Cytometry* 1984;5(5):501-8.

[142] Tomer A. Effects of anagrelide on in vivo megakaryocyte proliferation and maturation in essential thrombocythemia. *Blood* 2002;99(5):1602-9.

[143] Odell TT, Jr., Jackson CW. Polyploidy and maturation of rat megakaryocytes. *Blood* 1968;32(1):102-10.

[144] Paulus JM. DNA metabolism and development of organelles in guinea-pig megakaryocytes: a combined ultrastructural, autoradiographic and cytophotometric study. *Blood* 1970;35(3):298-311.

[145] Rabellino EM, Bussel JB. Human megakaryocytes. VII. Analysis of megakaryocytes for nuclear DNA content distribution in whole marrow cell suspensions by flow cytometry. *Exp Hematol* 1990;18(3):167-73.

[146] Harker LA, Finch CA. Thrombokinetics in man. *J Clin Invest* 1969;48(6):963-74.

[147] Traynor JE, Ingram M. A membrane filter technique for enumerating megakaryocytes. *J Lab Clin Med* 1965;66(4):705-8.

[148] Harker LA. Magakaryocyte quantitation. *J Clin Invest* 1968;47(3):452-7.

[149] Odell TT, Jr., Jackson CW, Friday TJ, Charsha DE. Effects of thrombocytopenia on megakaryocytopoiesis. *Br J Haematol* 1969;17(1):91-101.

[150] Sullivan LW, Adams WH, Liu YK. Induction of thrombocytopenia by thrombopheresis in man: patterns of recovery in normal subjects during ethanol ingestion and abstinence. *Blood* 1977;49(2):197-207.

[151] Burstein SA, Adamson JW, Thorning D, Harker LA. Characteristics of murine megakaryocytic colonies in vitro. *Blood* 1979;54(1):169-79.

[152] Mazur EM, Lindquist DL, de Alarcon PA, Cohen JL. Evaluation of bone marrow megakaryocyte ploidy distributions in persons with normal and abnormal platelet counts. *J Lab Clin Med* 1988;111(2):194-202.

[153] Hollen CW, Henthorn J, Koziol JA, Burstein SA. Elevated serum interleukin-6 levels in patients with reactive thrombocytosis. *Br J Haematol* 1991;79(2): 286-90.

[154] Scurfield G, Radley JM. Aspects of platelet formation and release. *Am J Hematol* 1981;10(3):285-96.

[155] Choi ES, Nichol JL, Hokom MM, Hornkohl AC, Hunt P. Platelets generated in vitro from proplatelet-displaying human megakaryocytes are functional. *Blood* 1995;85(2):402-13.

[156] Zucker-Franklin D. The submembranous fibrils of human blood platelets. *J Cell Biol* 1970;47(1):293-9.

[157] Lichtman MA, Chamberlain JK, Simon W, Santillo PA. Parasinusoidal location of megakaryocytes in marrow: a determinant of platelet release. *Am J Hematol* 1978;4(4):303-12.

[158] Wright JJ. The histogenesis of the blood platelets. J.Morphol. 1910; 21:203-209.

[159] Theiry JPaB, M. . Mecanisme de la plaquettogenese: Etude in vivo par la microcinematographie. *Rev.Hematol.* 1956;11(162.-5).

[160] Behnke O. An electron microscopic study of the rat megakaryocyte. II. Some aspects of platelet release and microtubules. *J.Ultrastruct.Res.* 1969; 26. (111-115).

[161] Tavassoli MaA, M. Migration of entire megakaryocytes through the marrow blood barrier. . *Br.J.Haematol* 1981;48::35- 39.

[162] Martin JF, Slater DN, Trowbridge EA. Platelet production in the lungs. *Agents Actions Suppl* 1987;21:37-57.

[163] Eldor A, Vlodavsky I, Deutsch V, Levine RF. Megakaryocyte function and dysfunction. *Baillieres Clin Haematol* 1989;2(3):543-68.

[164] Zucker-Franklin D, Philipp CS. Platelet production in the pulmonary capillary bed: new ultrastructural evidence for an old concept. *Am J Pathol* 2000;157(1):69-74.

[165] Zucker-Franklin D, Petursson S. Thrombocytopoiesis--analysis by membrane tracer and freeze-fracture studies on fresh human and cultured mouse megakaryocytes. *J Cell Biol* 1984;99(2):390-402.

[166] Mori M, Tsuchiyama J, Okada S. Proliferation, migration and platelet release by megakaryocytes in long-term bone marrow culture in collagen gel. *Cell Struct Funct* 1993;18(6):409-17.

[167] Caine YG, Vlodavsky I, Hersh M, Polliack A, Gurfel D, Or R, et al. Adhesion, spreading and fragmentation of human megakaryocytes exposed to subendothelial extracellular matrix: a scanning electron microscopy study. *Scan Electron Microsc* 1986(Pt 3):1087-94.

[168] Kosaki G. In vivo platelet production from mature megakaryocytes: does platelet release occur via proplatelets? *Int J Hematol* 2005;81(3):208-19.

[169] Scurfield G RJ. Aspects of platelet formation and release. *Am J Hematol* 1981;10:285-296.

[170] Cramer EM, Norol F, Guichard J, Breton-Gorius J, Vainchenker W, Masse JM, et al. Ultrastructure of platelet formation by human megakaryocytes cultured with the Mpl ligand. *Blood* 1997;89 (7):2336-46.

[171] Kaluzhny Y, Ravid K. Role of apoptotic processes in platelet biogenesis. *Acta Haematol* 2004;111 (1-2):67-77.

[172] Newmeyer DD, Ferguson-Miller S. Mitochondria: releasing power for life and unleashing the machineries of death. *Cell* 2003;112(4):481-90.

[173] Tablin F, Castro M, Leven RM. Blood platelet formation in vitro. The role of the cytoskeleton in megakaryocyte fragmentation. *J Cell Sci* 1990;97 (Pt 1):59-70.

[174] Rojnuckarin P, Kaushansky K. Actin reorganization and proplatelet formation in murine megakaryocytes: the role of protein kinase calpha. *Blood* 2001;97(1):154-61.

[175] Falcieri E, Bassini A, Pierpaoli S, Luchetti F, Zamai L, Vitale M, et al. Ultrastructural characterization of maturation, platelet release, and senescence of human cultured megakaryocytes. *Anat Rec* 2000;258(1):90-9.

[176] Hengartner MO. The biochemistry of apoptosis. *Nature* 2000;407(6805):770-6.

[177] Sanz C, Benet I, Richard C, Badia B, Andreu EJ, Prosper F, et al. Antiapoptotic protein Bcl-x(L) is up-regulated during megakaryocytic differentiation of CD34(+) progenitors but is absent from senescent megakaryocytes. *Exp Hematol* 2001;29(6):728-35.

[178] Terui Y, Furukawa Y, Kikuchi J, Iwase S, Hatake K, Miura Y. Bcl-x is a regulatory factor of apoptosis and differentiation in megakaryocytic lineage cells. *Exp Hematol* 1998;26(3):236-44.

[179] Broxmeyer HE, Cooper S, Kohli L, Hangoc G, Lee Y, Mantel C, et al. Transgenic expression of stromal cell-derived factor-1/CXC chemokine ligand 12 enhances myeloid progenitor cell survival/antiapoptosis in vitro in response to growth factor withdrawal and enhances myelopoiesis in vivo. *J Immunol* 2003;170(1):421-9.

[180] Ryu KH, Chun S, Carbonierre S, Im SA, Kim HL, Shin MH, et al. Apoptosis and megakaryocytic differentiation during ex vivo expansion of human cord blood CD34+ cells using thrombopoietin. *Br J Haematol* 2001;113(2):470-8.

[181] Battinelli E, Loscalzo J. Nitric oxide induces apoptosis in megakaryocytic cell lines. *Blood* 2000;95(11):3451-9.

[182] Gordge MP. Megakaryocyte apoptosis: sorting out the signals. *Br J Pharmacol* 2005;145(3):271-3.

[183] De Botton S, Sabri S, Daugas E, Zermati Y, Guidotti JE, Hermine O, et al. Platelet formation is the consequence of caspase activation within megakaryocytes. *Blood* 2002;100(4):1310-7.

[184] Clarke MC, Savill J, Jones DB, Noble BS, Brown SB. Compartmentalized megakaryocyte death generates functional platelets committed to caspase-independent death. *J Cell Biol* 2003;160(4):577-87.

[185] Pozner RG, Negrotto S, D'Atri LP, Kotler ML, Lazzari MA, Gomez RM, et al. Prostacyclin prevents nitric oxide-induced megakaryocyte apoptosis. *Br J Pharmacol* 2005;145(3):283-92.

[186] Hitchcock IS, Skerry TM, Howard MR, Genever PG. NMDA receptor-mediated regulation of human megakaryocytopoiesis. *Blood* 2003;102(4):1254-9.

In: Progress in Stem Cell Research
Editor: Prasad S. Koka, pp. 31-46

ISBN: 978-1-60456-065-7
© 2008 Nova Science Publishers, Inc.

Chapter 2

A Novel Serum-Free Culture System for the Analysis of Human Hematopoietic Progenitor Cells

Mary Beth Hanley,[a] Elizabeth Sinclair,[b] Willis H. Navarro,[b] Mary E. Keir,[a] and Joseph M. McCune[a,b]*

[a]Gladstone Institute of Virology and Immunology, San Francisco, CA
[b]Department of Medicine, University of California, San Francisco, CA

Abstract

Objective

We sought to develop a culture system in which the interactions between human hematopoietic progenitor cells (HPCs) and bone marrow stromal cells could be studied in vitro in the absence of exogenously added serum and/or hematopoietic cytokines.

Methods

Human bone marrow (BM) hematopoietic and stromal cells were cultured in vitro in a serum-free, cytokine-free system. Flow cytometric and hematopoietic assays were employed to assess the maintenance of human HPCs as a function of time and culture conditions.

---

* Corresponding author: Joseph M. McCune. Gladstone Institute of Virology and Immunology 1650 Owens St. San Francisco, CA 94158 (415) 734-5060. mmccune@gladstone.ucsf.edu

Results

In the absence of serum, HPCs and stromal cells were observed to form clusters (microaggregates, or MAGs). These MAGs appear to promote interactions important for the maintenance and maturation of CD34+ as well as more primitive CD34+CD38- multilineage HPCs, possibly upon provision of hematopoietic cytokines by stromal cells and/or by cell-cell interactions between BM stroma and hematopoietic cells. Additionally, the behavior of HPCs in the MAGs mirrors that observed in more traditional (e.g., serum replete) cultures. Thus, predictable hematosuppressive effects were seen in response to treatment of MAG cultures with IFNα and azidothymidine. Reciprocally, the cytokines thrombopoietin and erythropoietin enhanced the survival of CD34+CD38- HPCs and erythroid cells, respectively.

Conclusions

The MAG culture system provides an *in vitro* system in which human HPCs and their progeny can be evaluated in the absence of exogenously added serum and/or hematopoietic cytokines.

INTRODUCTION

Multilineage and lineage-restricted HPCs are maintained and stimulated to differentiate within specialized hematopoietic microenvironments. In the BM microenvironment, by example, stromal and accessory cells express soluble and membrane-bound cytokines, secrete an extracellular matrix, and bind to adjacent cells through adhesion molecules.[1-4] Should one or more of these components be removed or altered, hematopoiesis may not occur efficiently, if at all.

A variety of *in vitro* culture models have been used to study the cell-cell interactions that occur in the BM hematopoietic microenvironment. Amongst these, long-term BM cultures (LTBMC) have been used most frequently.[5, 6] Since such cultures require the exogenous addition of high (e.g. 20%) concentrations of serum and of hematopoietic cytokines, their use is less attractive for the examination of certain hypotheses, e.g. testing the possibility that viral infection of the BM might perturb hematopoiesis by altering the production of positive and negative regulatory factors in the environment. To address such a possibility, it would instead be preferable to use a BM culture system that was self-supporting, i.e. one that maintained human HPCs and facilitated their differentiation in the absence of exogenously added serum and/or cytokines.

Serum-free or –deficient cultures of whole human BM have been described.[7, 8] In such cultures, however, full development of the stromal component does not occur and an adherent layer, seen in serum-replete cultures, is usually not present. Myeloid and erythroid progenitors are maintained in these cultures at somewhat lower levels than those observed in serum-containing cultures; maintenance of primitive progenitor cells, however, has not been examined. Serum-free culture systems have also been described for the maintenance and expansion of both primitive and committed HPCs.[7-9] Typically, these systems comprise cytokine-supplemented liquid cultures of purified populations, such as CD34+ cells, in the absence of stroma.[8] Much has been learned about the individual and combined effects of hematopoietic cytokines in these studies. The potential impact of interactions that occur between stromal cells and hematopoietic progenitors, however, cannot be assessed.

Here, we describe a BM culture system that sustains human multilineage hematopoiesis in the absence of exogenously added serum and/or cytokines. Apparently, the formation of micro-aggregates between bone marrow HPCs and stromal cells nurture hematopoiesis. We hypothesize that this MAG culture system fosters BM progenitor cell survival and maintenance in a manner that is physiologically more appropriate than *in vitro* BM culture systems that have been previously described.

MATERIALS AND METHOD

Bone Marrow Cells

Human fetal bones (18-24 weeks gestation) in RPMI media (Mediatech Inc., Herndon, VA) were obtained from Advanced Biosciences Resources (Alameda, CA). After extraction of marrow cells, low-density mononuclear cells were isolated by centrifugation on a density (Histopaque-1077, Sigma Chemical Co, St. Louis, Mo.) gradient. The mononuclear cell layer was collected, washed, resuspended in serum-free BIT medium (IMDM with 20% BIT supplement, Stem Cell Technologies, Vancouver) containing penicillin-streptomycin (Gibco, Carlsbad, Ca.), L-glutamine (Gibco), and 10^{-4} M 2-mercaptoethanol (Sigma), and counted on a hemacytometer using trypan blue (Sigma) exclusion.

Stromal Cells

Mononuclear cells from fetal BM were plated in stromal medium containing IMDM with 15% FBS (Gibco), 15% horse serum (Gibco), 10^{-4} M 2-mercaptoethanol (Sigma), 10^{-6} M hydrocortisone (Sigma), 50 U/ml penicillin, 50 µg/ml streptomycin, and 2 mM L-glutamine (all from Gibco) at a concentration of 1×10^6 cells/ml. Subconfluent layers of primary stromal cells were split by trypsinization (trypsin-EDTA, Gibco).

MAG Cultures

Early passage fetal BM stromal cells were seeded in BIT medium at a density of $3-5 \times 10^5$ cells/well in 6-well tissue culture plates (BD Biosciences, San Jose, CA). Within 2-4 hours, an adherent layer would form. 2.5×10^6 freshly isolated fetal BM cells were then added and the cultures were incubated at 37°C in 5% CO_2 for 5-7 days, with supplementation with 1 ml of fresh BIT media at day 3-4. In some experiments, transwell tissue culture plates (Corning Costar, Corning, NY) were used to separate stroma from BM cells. In the experiments where bone marrow only (no stroma) cultures were included, the same number of freshly isolated BM cells was added per well (2.5×10^6) without the inclusion of the preformed adherent stromal layer. In the case of experiments evaluating the effects of exogenously added agents, azidothymidine (AZT, Sigma), interferon-alpha (IFNα, BioSource International, Camarillo,

CA), erythropoietin (EPO, R&D Systems, Minneapolis, MN), or thrombopoietin (TPO, R&D Systems) were added at the start of the MAG cultures, at specified concentrations.

Flow Cytometry

Single cell suspensions from the MAG cultures were pre-incubated with 1 mg/ml human gamma globulin (Gemini Bio-Products, Woodland, CA) to block Fc receptor binding. Cell surface antigens were detected using fluorochrome-conjugated monoclonal antibodies against CD34 (BD Biosciences) and CD38 (from BD Pharmingen, San Diego, CA). After incubation with antibodies for 30 minutes at 4°C in the dark, the cells were washed in PBS containing 2% fetal bovine serum (Gemini Bioproducts), resuspended, and fixed in 1% paraformaldehyde (Sigma). Samples were analyzed within 48 hours by flow cytometry (FACSCalibur, BD Biosciences) using either Cellquest (BD Biosciences) or FlowJo (Treestar Inc., San Carlos, CA). A live cell gate using forward and side scatter criteria was used to enumerate live cells positive for a specific antibody, and appropriate isotype controls were used to determine the levels of background fluorescence. In experiments where CD34+ purified cells were used the mononuclear BM fraction was incubated with an anti-CD34 antibody (BD Biosciences) for 30 minutes at 4°C in the dark. CD34+ cells were then sorted using a FACSVantage (BD Biosciences).

Immunohistochemistry

Immunohistochemistry was used to visualize the cellular components of the microaggregates. Fibroblasts, hematopoietic cells, and macrophages were detected using mouse anti-human vimentin, CD45, and CD68 (all from Dako, Glostrup, Denmark), respectively. Microaggregates were fixed in 4% paraformaldehyde for 30 minutes at room temperature. Paraformaldehyde was then removed and replaced by PBS. Microaggregates were gently resuspended, allowed to settle, and washed one more time in PBS. The supernatant was aspirated leaving the microaggregates in a total volume of 200 ul, which was then transferred to a cytoblock cassette (Shandon, Pittsburg, PA) so that excess PBS could be drained. The cassette was then filled with low gelling temperature agarose (1%, Sigma) and cooled to 45°C. Once the agarose was set, the cassettes were transferred to 4% paraformaldehyde and processed for paraffin sectioning. 6-micron sections were cut for immunohistochemical staining. Slides were dewaxed in xylene (Fisher Scientific, Pittsburgh, PA) and then rehydrated through subsequent washes in 100% ethanol, 70% ethanol, and distilled water. Non-specific staining was blocked by a 30-minute incubation in 2% fetal bovine serum/tris-buffered saline (FBS/TBS). The primary antibody, diluted in 2% FBS/TBS, was added to the slides for 1 hour. Slides were washed in TBS and then incubated for 30 minutes with biotinylated goat anti-mouse IgG (Vector Laboratories Burlingame, CA) diluted in PBS with 4% normal human serum. After washing in TBS, slides were incubated in phosphatase-conjugated avidin-biotin complex (Vectastain kit, Vector Laboratories) for 20 minutes. The slides were washed in TBS and then incubated in New Fuschsin substrate solution (Dako) with 0.5 mg of levamisole (Sigma) for 20 minutes. Slides were washed in

TBS, rinsed in water and counterstained in Mayer's hematoxylin (Sigma) for 2 minutes. Sections were mounted in Gel Mount (Fisher Scientific).

CFU-C assay

Hematopoietic colony forming cells (CFU-C) were enumerated in semi-solid methylcellulose cultures. BM cells were added to methylcellulose medium (Stem Cell Technologies, Vancouver, British Columbia, Canada) supplemented with 2 U/ml EPO, 100 ng/ml granulocyte-macrophage colony-stimulating factor (GM-CSF), 100 ng/ml stem cell factor, 10 ng/ml Interleukin-3, and 10 ng/ml Interleukin-6 (all from R&D Systems). After 14 days at 37°C, triplicate plates were scored for colony-forming units-granulocyte-macrophage (CFU-GM), burst-forming units-erythroid (BFU-E), and colony-forming units-granulocyte, erythroid, monocyte, megakaryocyte (CFU-GEMM), using standard criteria for their detection with an inverted microscope (Nikon, Tokyo, Japan). [10]

Data Analysis

Statistical analysis was performed using StatView 5.0 (SAS Institute Inc., Cary, N.C.). P values were determined using the unpaired student's t-test. Error bars in graphs represent the standard error for the replicate samples of each donor.

RESULTS

Effects of Serum in Co-Cultures

We investigated the effects of serum on the maintenance of HPCs in co-cultures of fetal BM and BM stromal cells. As expected, serum-supplemented cultures developed an adherent stromal monolayer (Fig. 1A) that persisted for the length of the cultures (5-7 days). Adherent cells were also observed in serum-free cultures; interestingly, however, these cultures also contained large, non-adherent clusters (microaggregates or MAGs) of fibroblast-like cells admixed with smaller, BM-derived mononuclear cells. Within 4 hours of adding bone marrow mononuclear cells to an adherent stromal layer, stromal cells were observed to round up in areas where bone marrow cells had attached. Over the course of several days stromal and bone marrow cells gradually formed adherent clumps, which completely detached from the plates to form MAGS by day 4 or 5 (Fig 1B).

We hypothesized that interactions between BM cells and stromal fibroblasts were facilitated by the absence of serum, permitting multiple cell-cell contacts that resulted in the formation of the MAGs. To test this possibility, stromal cells were plated in serum-free medium alone or in the presence of fetal BM mononuclear cells. Stromal cells that were plated alone formed an adherent layer that detached after a week or so in culture; no MAGs formed during this time. By contrast, when freshly isolated BM cells were added to the adherent stromal layer, the adherent layer detached more quickly and MAGs developed. This observation suggests that BM mononuclear cells were actively involved in the formation of the MAGs.

To determine the composition of individual MAGs, seven day-old cultures were fixed in 4% paraformaldehyde, embedded in agarose, and processed for paraffin sectioning. Serial sections were stained for vimentin, CD45, and CD68. Large fibroblast-like, vimentin-positive cells were found clustered in the center of each MAG (Fig. 1C). These cells were negative for CD45 (not shown) and were surrounded by a ring of smaller CD45-positive cells (hematopoietic lineage, Fig. 1D), many of these smaller cells were positive for CD68 (monocyte/macrophage lineage, Fig. 1E).

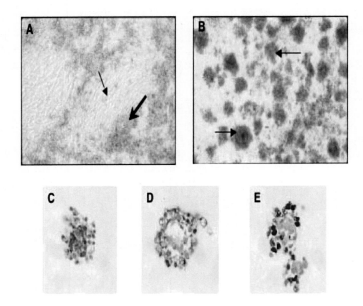

Figure 1. BM microaggregate (MAG) formation in serum-free culture. Human fetal BM cells were plated onto an adherent layer of BM stroma in the presence (A) or the absence (B) of serum. In the cultures with serum (A), BM cells (*thick black* arrow) were observed to attach to a monolayer of attached adherent cells (*thin* black arrow). In the absence of serum (B), BM cells attached to adherent cells, which subsequently detached from the plate to form admixed microaggregates, or MAGs (arrows). The MAGs were fixed and paraffin-processed for immunohistochemistry (C-E). Red staining identifies vimentin+ stromal cells (C), CD45+ hematopoietic cells (D), and CD68+ monocytic cells (E)

Effects of Stroma in Serum-Free Cultures

To determine whether the stromal compartment in the MAG cultures could support HPC proliferation and differentiation, MAG cultures were compared to cultures lacking stroma (no stroma, NS) after 5-8 days in serum-free culture. Cell counts were obtained after the cultures were dissociated, and the expression of CD34 and CD38 cell surface antigens was measured by flow cytometry. A typical staining profile for CD34 and CD38 is shown in Fig. 2A. CD34-positive cells were defined by the upper two quadrants (Fig. 2A) and multilineage HPCs were defined as CD34 high and CD38-, as shown in Region 1 (R1) of Fig. 2A. The number of total cells recovered was higher in the MAG cultures compared with the no stroma cultures;

significantly so in 6/11 donors (donors B4, E4, K2, Q2, T2, and U1 in Fig. 2B). The number of CD34+ HPCs recovered from MAG cultures was significantly higher (p<0.05) than that recovered from cultures without stroma in 8/11 experiments (all but donors A4, E4, and T4 in Fig. 2C). In 6/11 experiments, the recovery of CD34+CD38- HPCs was also increased in MAG cultures (p<0.05, Fig. 2D).

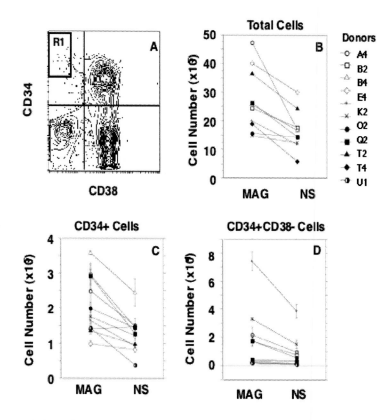

Figure 2. Hematopoietic cell survival is enhanced by the presence of stroma in serum-free culture. After 5 to 8 days of culture, cells were harvested from MAG cultures and cultures of BM cells only (no stroma, NS). Multiparameter flow cytometry was used (A) to enumerate CD34+ (upper quadrants) and CD34+CD38- (R1) HPCs. The number of total cells recovered in the MAG cultures was The number of total cells recovered was significantly higher in 6/11 donors (donors B4, E4, K2, Q2, T2, and U1, 2B). The number of CD34+ cells recovered in the MAG cultures was significantly higher (p<0.05) in 8/11 donors (all but donors A4, E4, and T4 2C). The number of CD34+CD38- cells was higher (p<0.05) in MAG culture for 6/11 donors (D). Each line represents results from a separate donor.

The functional capacity of the HPCs maintained in MAG cultures was assessed with the CFU-C assay. The yield of CFU-GM colonies was significantly higher (p<0.05) in MAG cultures compared to cultures without stroma (Fig. 3A). The yield of BFU-E was more variable: in 3/5 experiments an increase was seen but, in the other 2 experiments, a decrease was noted (Fig. 3B). The yield of CFU-GEMM was increased in 3/3 experiments (Fig. 3C), with a difference that was significant for one donor (A4, p<0.05). These data suggest that MAG cultures foster the survival of lineage-restricted progenitor cells with myeloid potential and also perhaps multilineage progenitor cells.

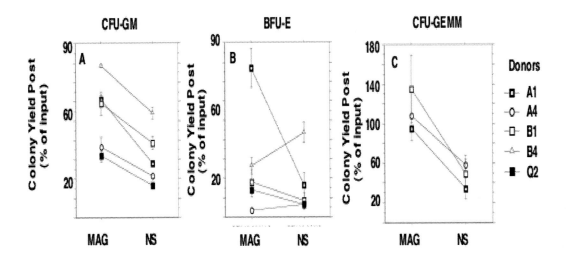

Figure 3. CFU-C yields after MAG culture. BM cells obtained after MAG or BM only (no stroma, NS) cultures were plated in CFU-C assay. CFU-GM (A), BFU-E (B), and CFU-GEMM (C) yields were calculated after 14 days in culture by comparing the number of colonies observed after culture to that observed in the input cells prior to culture. Each line represents results from a separate donor.

Contact Versus Non-Contact Co-Cultures

To determine whether the survival of HPCs in MAG cultures was dependent upon their contact with stromal cells, BM cells were separated from the stromal layer by a semi-permeable transwell membrane. In such transwell cultures, MAGs did not form even though cytokines could diffuse across the semi-permeable membrane (not shown). The number of total cells recovered was higher in the MAG cultures compared with the transwell cultures for most donors; significantly so in 2/6 donors (donors B4 and Q2 in Fig. 4A). The number of CD34+ HPCs recovered was higher in MAG cultures (Fig. 4B), a difference that was significant in 4/6 experiments (all but donors E4 and T6) compared with transwell cultures. The recovery of CD34+CD38- HPCs was also increased in 5/6 MAG cultures (Fig. 4C), significantly so ($p<0.05$) for 3/6 donors. These results suggest that cell-cell contact is important for the maintenance of HPCs in MAG cultures and that the release of soluble cytokines by stromal cells alone cannot account for the improved survival observed in the presence of stroma in these serum-free cultures.

CD34+ MAG Co-Cultures

To investigate the ability of stroma to support purified CD34+ fetal BM progenitors in serum-free MAG cultures, CD34+ cells were enriched (to >85% purity) from fetal BM by fluorescent activated cell sorting (FACS). The sorted cells were grown in serum-free media, either alone or in MAG culture with fetal BM stromal cells. In two donors, total cell recovery was increased in MAG cultures ($p<0.05$, Fig. 5A) when compared with NS cultures. There were also significant increases in the recovery of CD34+ cells ($p<0.005$, Fig. 5B) and of

CD34+CD38- cells (p<0.005, Fig. 5C) in MAG cultures compared to NS cultures. In fact, in MAG cultures, an average of 28% (37 and 19%) of recovered cells were CD34+ after 7 days in serum-free MAG culture, compared to an average of 5.7% (1.3 and 10%) in cultures plated without stroma (data not shown).

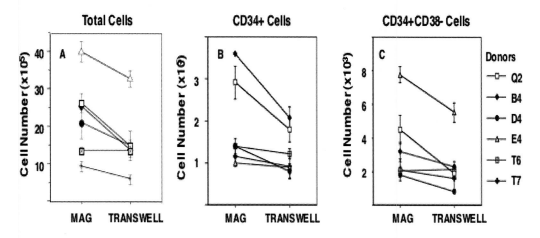

Figure 4. Contact with stroma increases HPC recovery. BM hematopoietic cells and stromal cells were cultured together (forming MAGs) or separated by a semi-permeable membrane (Transwell). The number of total cells recovered (A) was higher in the MAG cultures, significantly so in 2/6 donors (donors B4 and Q2, 4A) as was the CD34+ cell recovery (B) (p<0.05 for all but donors E4 and T6) and CD34+CD38- cell recovery (C) (p<0.05 for all donors but T6).

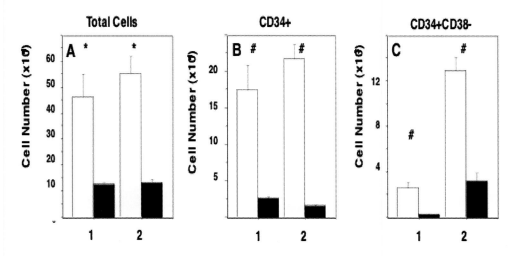

Figure 5. Survival of purified CD34+ HPCs is enhanced by the presence of stroma in MAGs. FACS-purified CD34+ progenitor cells from two separate donors (1 and 2) were cultured in the absence (black bars) or presence of stromal cells (white bars). After 7 days in culture, harvested cells were counted for total cells (A), CD34+ progenitors (B), and CD34+CD38- progenitors (C). A significant increase was seen (*p<0.05, #p<0.005) for each population (A-C) when stroma was included in the culture to form MAGs

The Effect of Hematosuppressive Agents on HPCs in MAG Cultures

To determine whether HPC in MAG cultures were affected by exogenous agents in an expected manner, cultures were treated with two different known hematosuppressive agents: IFNα and AZT. IFNα was added to MAG cultures at doses ranging from 0 to 2000 ug/ml. As would be observed in serum-replete cultures [11-13], there was a dose-dependent reduction in the recovery of CD34+ and CD34+CD38- HPCs as well as a decrease in CFU-GMs and BFU-Es (Fig. 6A). MAG cultures prepared from 3 additional donors were treated with 1000 ug/ml of IFNα. All 3 showed significant (p<0.05) reductions in the recovery of total cells (Fig. 6B, left panel). Although the CD34+ HPC recovery was less for all three donors treated with IFNα, only one (Fig. 6B, middle panel, donor L4) demonstrated a decrease in CD34+ HPCs that was significant (p<0.05). In this donor and in donor M4, there was also a significant decrease (p<0.05) in CD34+CD38- HPCs after treatment with IFNα (Fig. 6B, right panel, donor M4).

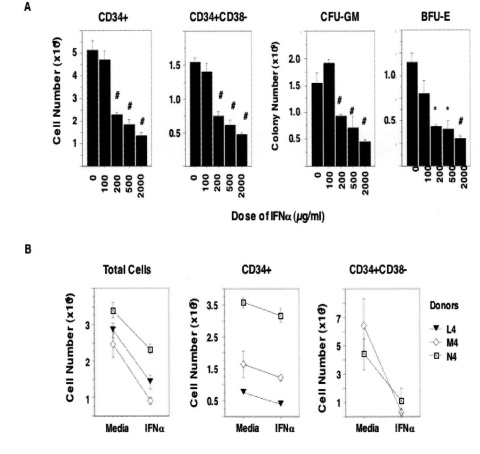

Figure 6. IFNα causes a dose-dependent reduction in the number of HPCs recovered in MAG cultures. MAG cultures treated with increasing amounts of IFNα for 7 days were harvested for quantitation of progenitor cells by multiparameter flow cytometry and by methylcellulose culture for CFU-C (A). A significant, dose-dependent decrease was seen (*p<0.05, #p<0.005). MAG cultures from 3 additional donors were maintained for 7 days in the absence or presence of IFNα (1000 μg/ml) and then harvested for the quantitation of progenitor cells by multiparameter flow cytometry (B)

The addition of AZT to MAG cultures also resulted in a marked dose-dependent decreases in the number of total cells as well as the number of cells that were glycophorin-A+, CD34+, or CD34+CD38- (Fig. 7A). Similar dose-dependent decreases were also observed in 3 other donor tissues (not shown, p<0.05). AZT treatment resulted in a marked drop in the number of CFU-GMs, BFU-Es, and CFU-GEMMs for all 3 donors (Fig. 7B).

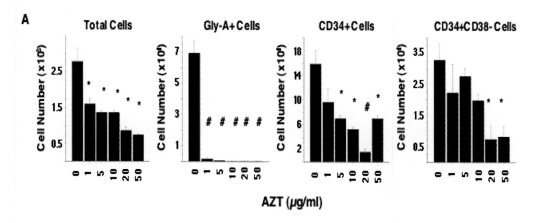

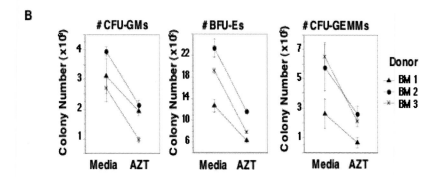

Figure 7. AZT causes a dose-dependent reduction in the number of HPCs and erythroid cells in MAG cultures. MAG cultures treated with increasing doses of AZT were harvested after 7 days in culture. There was a dose-dependent decrease in the recovery of total cells, glycophorin-A+ (erythroid) cells, CD34+ cells, and CD34+CD38- cells (A, *p<0.05, #p<0.005). In 3 different experiments, the number of CFU-GM, BFU-E, and CFU-GEMM colonies also decreased after AZT treatment of MAG cultures (B)

The Effect of Hematopoietic Cytokines on HPCs in MAG Cultures

The cytokines erythropoietin (EPO) and thrombopoietin (TPO) were added to MAG cultures to determine if the expected positive effects on hematopoiesis might occur. The addition of EPO (2 U/ml) significantly increased the number of total BM cells (p<0.05) and of glycophorin A+ cells (p<0.0005) (Fig. 8). TPO (10 ng/ml) resulted in a significant increase (p<0.005) of CD34+CD38- HPCs in MAG cultures, with no change in total BM cell numbers (Fig. 8).

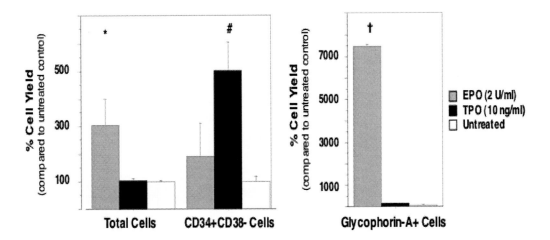

Figure 8. EPO and TPO stimulation of BM cells in MAG culture. MAG cultures treated with EPO (2 U/ml) or TPO (10 ng/ml) were harvested after 7 days in culture. As a percentage of untreated controls, the yield of total cells and of glycophorin-A+ (erythroid) cells increased significantly (*p<0.05, †p<0.0005) after EPO treatment. TPO addition to MAG cultures increased the CD34+CD38- cell yield (as a percent of untreated controls, #p<0.005)

DISCUSSION

The aim of this study was to develop a culture system in which the interactions between human HPCs and BM stromal cells could be studied in the absence of exogenously added serum and/or hematopoietic cytokines. Previously-reported serum-free BM cultures have been proven to be useful in the analysis of intra- and inter-cellular interactions required for hematopoiesis.[14-16] However, in such cultures, the development of BM stromal cells occurs only minimally, if at all.[7, 8] An alternative method has been to add exogenous serum to allow for stromal cell formation *in vitro*.[17, 18] However, some interactions between hematopoietic cells and stromal cells may be obscured in an unpredictable manner by known and unknown factors contained in serum. We investigated the effect of removing serum and cytokines from *in vitro* BM cultures while including preformed BM stroma. Interestingly, under such conditions, microaggregates of BM stromal cells and HPCs formed. We reasoned that the MAGs observed in serum-free cultures might facilitate cell-cell contact between stromal and hematopoietic cells. If so, they might provide a more relevant model for the analysis of interactions between HPCs and their stromal support cells.

The CD34+ cell fraction contains lineage-restricted progenitors at various stages of differentiation, including a subpopulation of CD34+CD38- cells enriched for primitive progenitors with long-term, multilineage repopulating capability.[19, 20] We studied the CD34+ and CD34+CD38- subpopulations in these experiments as a reflection of HPC maintenance. Addition of preformed stroma to serum-free BM cultures, resulting in the generation of MAGs, maintained HPC survival more efficiently than cultures without stroma. This effect was evident for at least one week. The number of both CD34+ and CD34+CD38- cells was higher in the MAG cultures. This increase in HPC number was accompanied by an increase in the number of recovered CFU-GM and CFU-GEMM colonies, suggesting that the

HPCs, formed in MAG cultures, were functional and multilineage in potential. The effect of adding stroma to serum-free culture was most pronounced when sort-purified CD34+ HPCs were cultured.

Though secreted factors from the stromal cells most likely contributed to HPC maintenance, we found that cell-cell contact between the HPCs and the stromal cells was also beneficial for HPC maintenance. When a transwell membrane separated stromal cells and BM cells, for instance, the recovery of CD34+ and CD34+CD38- progenitor cells was decreased. It has been previously shown that direct contact with stromal cells regulates hematopoiesis and increases LTBMC cell output.[21-23] Additionally, freshly-isolated BM has been shown to contain clusters of cells (hematons) that are able to support human HPCs.[24] These hematons contain cells known to belong to the BM microenvironment, aggregating with progenitor cells. We surmise that the MAGs described here formed as a consequence of cell adhesion mechanisms that normally promote cell-cell interactions *in vivo,* ones that might be inhibited by the high serum levels found in LTBMC. In many ways, the MAG cultures would appear to be more closely related to the hematons described above than are serum-free culture systems that exclude the stromal compartment.

To validate the use of the MAG culture system as a means by which to study the effect of exogenous agents on hematopoiesis, hematosuppressive (IFNα and AZT) and stimulatory (EPO and TPO) agents were evaluated. IFNα has been shown to suppress colony growth of both myeloid and erythroid lineages, to increase negative regulatory cytokine release from stromal cells, and to decrease stimulatory cytokine expression from stromal cells.[25] AZT has been shown to suppress proliferation of HPCs, in particular those of the erythroid lineage.[26] EPO and TPO are cytokines that are produced in extramedullary sites (the kidney and liver, respectively) and that regulate hematopoiesis through stimulation of either erythropoiesis or megakaryopoiesis.[27-30] Additionally, TPO has been shown to synergize with stem cell factor and/or interleukin-3 to stimulate primitive CD34+CD38-/low HPCs.[28, 31-33] EPO promotes progenitor cell survival, particularly in cells of the erythroid lineage.[29, 30, 34] The addition of IFNα or AZT to MAG cultures resulted in the expected loss of progenitor cells and of colony-forming cells. Reciprocally, the addition of TPO or EPO to MAG cultures resulted in an increased yield of CD34+CD38- HPCs and erythroid cells respectively.

Collectively, these observations demonstrate that the MAG culture system can support short-term (1 week) proliferation and differentiation of human HPC in the absence of exogenously added serum and/or cytokines. Such maintenance of hematopoiesis is dependent upon cell-cell contact between BM mononuclear cells and stromal cells. Possibly, such cell-cell contact permits, *in vitro*, the appropriate balance of signals normally required for hematopoiesis in the BM microenvironment *in vivo*. As demonstrated by the effect of agents such as IFNα, AZT, TPO, and EPO, HPCs in the MAG cultures respond to exogenously added agents in an expected manner. This observation suggests that the MAG culture system might enable the evaluation of other agents (e.g., viruses and antibodies against selected functions) and their impact on human hematopoiesis.

ACKNOWLEDGEMENTS

This work was supported by a grant (to JMM) from the NIAID (R37 AI40312). J.M.M. is a recipient of the Burroughs Wellcome Fund Clinical Scientist Award in Translational Research and the NIH Director's Pioneer Award Program, part of the NIH Roadmap for Medical Research, through grant number DPI OD00329.

REFERENCES

[1] Dexter TM. Haemopoiesis in long-term bone marrow cultures. A review. *Acta Haematol* 1979;62:299-305

[2] Allen TD, Dexter TM. Long term bone marrow cultures: an ultrastructural review. *Scan Electron Microsc* 1983:1851-66

[3] Clark BR, Keating A. Biology of bone marrow stroma. *Ann N Y Acad Sci* 1995;770:70-8

[4] Dexter TM, Heyworth CM, Spooncer E and Ponting IL. The role of growth factors in self-renewal and differentiation of haemopoietic stem cells. *Philos Trans R Soc Lond B Biol Sci* 1990;327:85-98

[5] Haas R, Kiesel S, Ogniben E, et al. The effect of human recombinant GM-CSF on the myelopoiesis in a long-term bone marrow culture (LTBMC). *Behring Inst Mitt* 1988:278-83

[6] Eaves AC, Eaves CJ. Maintenance and proliferation control of primitive hemopoietic progenitors in long-term cultures of human marrow cells. *Blood Cells* 1988;14:355-68

[7] Drouet X, Douay L, Giarratana MC, et al. Human liquid bone marrow culture in serum-free medium. *Br J Haematol* 1989;73:143-7

[8] Douay L, Giarratana MC, Drouet X, Bardinet D and Gorin NC. The role of recombinant haematopoietic growth factors in human long-term bone marrow culture in serum-free medium. *Br J Haematol* 1991;79:27-32

[9] Lebkowski JS, Schain LR and Okarma TB. Serum-free culture of hematopoietic stem cells: a review. *Stem Cells* (Dayt) 1995;13:607-12

[10] Eaves C, Lambie K. Atlas of Human Hematopoietic Cells. *StemCell Technologies Inc.*, 1995

[11] Mazur EM, Richtsmeier WJ and South K. Alpha-interferon: differential suppression of colony growth from human erythroid, myeloid, and megakaryocytic hematopoietic progenitor cells. *J Interferon Res* 1986;6:199-206

[12] Tarumi T, Sawada K, Sato N, et al. Interferon-alpha-induced apoptosis in human erythroid progenitors. *Exp Hematol* 1995;23:1310-8

[13] Geissler RG, Ottmann OG, Kojouharoff G, et al. Influence of human recombinant interferon-alpha and interferon-gamma on bone marrow progenitor cells of HIV-positive individuals. *AIDS Res Hum Retroviruses* 1992;8:521-5

[14] Dexter TM, Heyworth CM and Whetton AD. The role of haemopoietic cell growth factor (interleukin 3) in the development of haemopoietic cells. *Ciba Found Symp* 1985;116:129-47

[15] Ieki R, Kudoh S, Kimura H, Ozawa K, Asano S and Takaku F. Human granulocyte colony formation in serum-free cultures stimulated with purified recombinant granulocyte colony-stimulating factor. *Exp Hematol* 1990;18:883-7

[16] Sonoda Y, Yang YC, Wong GG, Clark SC and Ogawa M. Analysis in serum-free culture of the targets of recombinant human hemopoietic growth factors: interleukin 3 and granulocyte/macrophage-colony-stimulating factor are specific for early developmental stages. *Proc Natl Acad Sci USA* 1988;85:4360-4

[17] Dexter TM, Wright EG, Krizsa F and Lajtha LG. Regulation of haemopoietic stem cell proliferation in long term bone marrow cultures. *Biomedicine* 1977;27:344-9

[18] Gartner S, Kaplan HS. Long-term culture of human bone marrow cells. *Proc Natl Acad Sci USA* 1980;77:4756-9

[19] Terstappen LW, Huang S, Safford M, Lansdorp PM and Loken MR. Sequential generations of hematopoietic colonies derived from single nonlineage-committed CD34+CD38- progenitor cells. *Blood* 1991;77:1218-27

[20] Rusten LS, Jacobsen SE, Kaalhus O, Veiby OP, Funderud S and Smeland EB. Functional differences between CD38- and DR- subfractions of CD34+ bone marrow cells. *Blood* 1994;84:1473-81

[21] Koller MR, Oxender M, Jensen TC, Goltry KL and Smith AK. Direct contact between CD34+lin- cells and stroma induces a soluble activity that specifically increases primitive hematopoietic cell production. *Exp Hematol* 1999;27:734-41

[22] Prosper F, Verfaillie CM. Regulation of hematopoiesis through adhesion receptors. *J Leukoc Biol* 2001;69:307-16

[23] Coombe DR. The role of stromal cell heparan sulphate in regulating haemopoiesis. *Leuk Lymphoma* 1996;21:399-406

[24] Blazsek I, Misset JL, Comisso M and Mathe G. Hematon: a multicellular functional unit in primary hematopoiesis. *Biomed Pharmacother* 1988;42:661-8

[25] Rosenthal GJ, Stranahan RP, 3rd, Thompson M, et al. Organ-specific hematopoietic changes induced by a recombinant human interferon-alpha in mice. *Fundam Appl Toxicol* 1990;14:666-75

[26] Dainiak N, Worthington M, Riordan MA, Kreczko S and Goldman L. 3'-Azido-3'-deoxythymidine (AZT) inhibits proliferation in vitro of human haematopoietic progenitor cells. Br *J Haematol* 1988;69:299-304

[27] Odell TT, Jr., Mc DT and Detwiler TC. Stimulation of platelet production by serum of platelet-depleted rats. *Proc Soc Exp Biol Med* 1961;108:428-31

[28] Young JC, Bruno E, Luens KM, Wu S, Backer M and Murray LJ. Thrombopoietin stimulates megakaryoc-ytopoiesis, myelopoiesis, and expansion of CD34+ progenitor cells from single CD34+Thy-1+Lin- primitive progenitor cells. *Blood* 1996;88:1619-31

[29] Silva M, Grillot D, Benito A, Richard C, Nunez G and Fernandez-Luna JL. Erythropoietin can promote erythroid progenitor survival by repressing apoptosis through Bcl-XL and Bcl-2. *Blood* 1996;88:1576-82

[30] Muta K, Krantz SB, Bondurant MC and Wickrema A. Distinct roles of erythropoietin, insulin-like growth factor I, and stem cell factor in the development of erythroid progenitor cells. *J Clin Invest* 1994;94:34-43

[31] Luens KM, Travis MA, Chen BP, Hill BL, Scollay R and Murray LJ. Thrombopoietin, kit ligand, and flk2/flt3 ligand together induce increased numbers of primitive

hematopoietic progenitors from human CD34+Thy-1+Lin- cells with preserved ability to engraft SCID-hu bone. *Blood* 1998;91:1206-15

[32] Murray LJ, Young JC, Osborne LJ, Luens KM, Scollay R and Hill BL. Thrombopoietin, flt3, and kit ligands together suppress apoptosis of human mobilized CD34+ cells and recruit primitive CD34+ Thy-1+ cells into rapid division. *Exp Hematol* 1999;27:1019-28

[33] Yoshida M, Tsuji K, Ebihara Y, et al. Thrombopoietin alone stimulates the early proliferation and survival of human erythroid, myeloid and multipotential progenitors in serum-free culture. *Br J Haematol* 1997;98:254-64

[34] Muta K, Krantz SB. Apoptosis of human erythroid colony-forming cells is decreased by stem cell factor and insulin-like growth factor I as well as erythropoietin. *J Cell Physiol* 1993;156:264-71

In: Progress in Stem Cell Research
Editor: Prasad S. Koka, pp. 47-61

ISBN: 978-1-60456-065-7
© 2008 Nova Science Publishers, Inc.

Chapter 3

POTENTIAL OF BONE MARROW STROMAL STEM CELLS TO REPAIR BONE DEFECTS AND FRACTURES

Stan Gronthos[1,] and Andrew C.W. Zannettino[2]*

[1]Mesenchymal Stem Cell Group, Division of Haematology, Institute of Medical and Veterinary Science/Hanson Institute/University of Adelaide, Adelaide, South Australia, Australia.
[2]Myeloma and Mesenchymal Research Group, Matthew Roberts Foundation Laboratory, Division of Haematology, Institute of Medical and Veterinary Science/Hanson Institute/ University of Adelaide, Adelaide, South Australia, Australia.

ABSTRACT

In the emerging age of cellular therapy, bone marrow stromal stem cells (BMSSC) represent a population of cells with enormous therapeutic potential. Whilst in their relative infancy, numerous studies suggest that BMSSC are capable of restoring cardiac function, neural regeneration, defects of articular cartilage, improving hematopoietic engraftment and most promisingly, the repair of large osseous defects. Segmental defects of bone, or non-union fractures represent a significant and intractable clinical problem, in which the volume of bone loss results in delayed healing or non-union. Currently there are several therapies employed to facilitate osseous repair, ranging from the use of autograft bone, allograft bone and an array of artificial bone substitutes. However, all these approaches are often associated with various limitations making it difficult to predict outcome. Major problems include secondary site morbidity associated with autologous bone, availability and suitability of allogeneic bone, and the variable osteo-conductivity of different biomaterials. The ability to generate osteogenic progenitor cells derived from culture expanded BMSSC has provided, for the first time, the potential to overcome many of these limitations. When used in conjunction with existing osteo-conductive bone void fillers, BMMSC may not only facilitate the repair of large segemental defects following disease or trauma, but may also provide a cellular therapy for spinal fusion and craniofacial reconstructive surgery. The following review outlines

---

* Corresponding author: Stan Gronthos, Mesenchymal Stem Cell Laboratory, Division of Haematology, Institute of Medical and Veterinary Science, Frome Road, Adelaide, 5000, South Australia, Australia, Phone: 61-8-8222 3460, Fax: 61-8-8222 3139, E-mail: stan.gronthos@imvs.sa.gov.au

the possible applications and highlights the potential limitations of BMSSC for developing novel tissue engineering approaches for orthopaedic applications.

INTRODUCTION

The pioneering work of Friedentsien and colleagues led to the discovery of a second, non-hematopoietic stem cell population contained within the bone marrow microenvironment [1]. These cells were characterized as quiescent stromal stem cells with the ability to form clonogenic adherent colonies comprised of fibroblast-like cells (CFU-F: colony forming units-fibroblast). Considerable variations in the morphology, proliferation capacity and developmental potential between individually expanded CFU-F colonies have been reported [2-7], supporting the concept of a stromal hierarchy of cellular differentiation. In this model, the different stromal cell lineages (myelosupportive stroma, adipocytes, smooth muscle cells, chondrocytes and osteoblasts) arise from a common, self-replicating multi-potential stem cell (Figure 1), referred to in contemporary literature as mesenchymal stem cells (MSC) or bone marrow stromal stem cells (BMSSC). As a consequence, there is now a concerted effort by numerous academic research groups and biotechnology companies to exploit BMSSC as a potential novel cellular based therapy for the treatment of a wide range of human diseases and tissue defects.

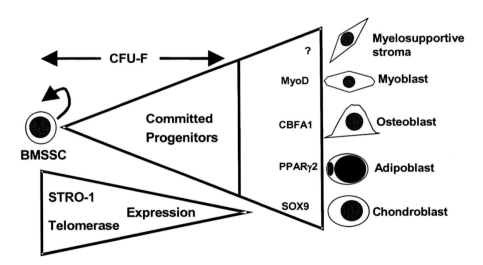

Figure 1. Proposed Hierarchy of BMSSC Cellular Differentiation Modified from Owen and Friedenstein (1988) [1]. Primitive uncommitted BMSSC express high levels of the STRO-1 antigen and telomerase expression which are subsequently down regulated during differentiation into different stromal cell lineages.

Although capable of multi-lineage differentiation, human BMSSC most readily undergo osteogenic differentiation when cultured in defined *in vitro* conditions [7,8]. Following osteogenic induction, the BMSSC express high levels of the osteoblast associated proteins, alkaline phosphatase and osteocalcin, and form adherent cell layers which synthesise a mineralized matrix comprised of collagen fibrils, consistent with physiological hydroxyapatite [7,8]. Clonal analysis of *ex vivo* expanded human BMSSC has revealed that a large portion of clonal BMSSC lines exhibit levels of osteogenic potential above other differentiation pathways [3-5,9]. Similarly, *in vivo* studies of implants containing human BMSSC were shown to develop functional ectopic bone/marrow organ-like structures when transplanted into immunocompromised animals [10-16]. The majority of the calcified tissue in these transplants was found to be comprised of mature lamella bone of donor origin, while the hematopoietic tissue was host-derived. The propensity for osteogenic differentiation was observed in approximately 60% of the clonal BMSSC lines following transplantation into immunocompromised mice, with less than half of these clones exhibiting the capacity for hematopoietic support [3,4]. To date, the heterogeneous growth rates and differential developmental potential exhibited by BMSSC preparations has limited their wide spread use in cellular therapies. Whilst, this technology holds much promise, further characterization of the precise nature and properties of BMSSC is required in order to realize their full clinical potential. Nevertheless, these studies demonstrate that at least a proportion of *ex vivo* expanded BMSSC possess the potential for generating significant bone regeneration *in vivo*.

THERAPEUTIC POTENTIAL OF BMSSC FOR BONE REGENERATION

The hematopoietic system is comprised of a rare population of self-renewing, pluripotent CD34[+] hematopoietic stem cells that give rise to an expanded progenitor cell pool capable of generating the different myeloid and lymphoid lineages. This hierarchy of cellular differentiation is regarded as the archetypal model for defining the characteristics of postnatal stem/progenitor cell populations. These developments have led to the generation of novel stem cell therapies for the treatment of various hematological disorders and malignancies [17,18]. Spurred on by the long-term clinical success of hematopoietic stem cell therapies, various investigators have attempted to determine the potential use of human BMSSC as novel treatments for the repair of non-union fractures, congenital bone defects, bone disorders and bone destruction caused by cancer.

A number of studies have reported the efficacy of using BMSSC to regenerate new bone formation in pre-clinical animal models. In one study, *ex vivo* expanded mouse BMSSC were implanted into surgically created critical-sized craniotomy defects using immunocompromised mice. Significant levels of healing were achieved in recipient mice implanted with BMSSC in comparison with the control group comprised of spleen derived stromal cells [19]. Human BMSSC have also been shown to increase bone formation in critical-sized segmental defects when implanted into the femurs of adult athymic rats [20]. Femurs receiving BMSSC were found to be biomechanically stronger than the control group which did not receive BMSSC. Additional supporting studies using larger animal models provide confirmation of the therapeutic potential of autologous BMSSC-mediated bone regeneration of large osseous defects [21-24].

We have recently examined the bone regeneration potential of BMSSC using an ovine critical sized segmental bone defect model. In these studies, ovine BMSSC were prospectively isolated using immunoselction based on their cell surface expression of VCAM-1/CD106 (Figure 2) [3]. Autologous VCAM-1[+] ovine BMSSC were cultured as multilayered skins and subsequently used to cover a centrally placed titanium pin spanning a surgically created non-union defect (Figure 3). In these studies, animals receiving autologous BMSSC demonstrated a significant regeneration of mineralised bone in the area of segmental defect. In contrast, sham control animals exhibited little recovery at 6 months (Figure 3) and beyond. Collectively, these large animal 'proof of principle' studies provide the foundation for developing human BMSSC based therapies for repairing large bone defects and fractures.

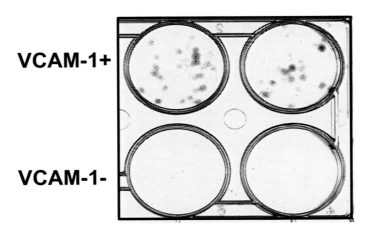

Figure 2. Clonogenic Ovine BMSSC are Almost Exclusively Restricted to the VCAM-1 Positive Fraction of bone marrow. Following density separation of iliac crest-derived ovine bone marrow, the bone marrow mononuclear cells (BMMNC) were sequentially incubated with the mouse anti-sheep VCAM-1, QE469, biotinylated goat anti-mouse IgG γ-chain specific and streptavidin microbeads prior to magnetic activated cell sorting (MACS) [3]. Single cell suspensions of unfractionated BMMNC and MACS isolated VCAM-1+ and VCAM-1- BMMNC were plated into regular growth medium supplemented with 20% FBS to assess the incidence of adherent colony-forming cells in each cell fraction. Following 12 days of culture, colonies (aggregates of 50 cells or more) were stained with 0.1% Toluidine Blue/1% paraformaldehyde. Our data demonstrate that BMSSC are almost exclusively restricted to the VCAM-1 positive fraction of ovine BMMNC.

Consistent with the findings observed in animal models of bone loss, the use of BMSSC to facilitate osseous repair has been examined in human clinical trials of patients with the severe brittle bone disease, osteogenesis imperfecta (OI), show real promise. Studies by Horwitz and colleagues show that subjects with OI receiving autologous bone marrow aspirates (containing BMSSCs) or cultured preparations of BMSSC, exhibited improved healing over conventional treatments [25-27]. Similar improvements in bone formation have also been reported in patients with Hurler Syndrome and metachromatic leukodistrophy, following trans-plantation of allogeneic BMSSC obtained from HLA-compatible siblings [28]. In another study, autologous *ex vivo* expanded BMSSC were co-transplanted with mobilised peripheral blood stem cells into breast cancer patients following myeloablative chemotherapy [29]. The majority of subjects in this trial experienced rapid hematological recovery with no ill effects after transplantation. These pioneering studies have helped develop an increased acceptance of the potential use of BMSSC to treat various connective tissue disorders such as OI, osteoporosis, muscular dystrophy and to help improve hematological reconstitution following ablative therapy.

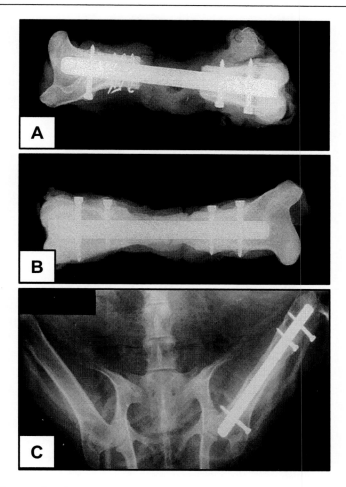

Figure 3. The Efficacy of Ovine BMSSC to Regenerate Bone *In Vivo*. An ovine model of segmental defect was established in which 25-30% of the mid portion of the ovine femur was surgically resected and the structural stability maintained by insertion of an intramedullary "nail" locked proximally and distally by transfixing screws. *Ex vivo* expanded VCAM-1/CD106 selected ovine BMSSC were then transplanted directly into the defect site as a multilayer skin. X-ray assessment of *de novo* bone formation was performed at 6 and 12 months. Representative X-rays are shown of untreated animals (A) and animals receiving BMSSC transplants (B) at six months. A representative X-ray is shown depicting the degree of bone regeneration 12 months post-transplantation of BMSSC (C).

Recently, autologous human BMSSC have been successfully used for the treatment of human segmental bone defects [30]. Following *ex vivo* expansion, autologous BMSSC were transplanted with a macroporous hydroxyapatite scaffold into several patients with non-healing bone defects caused from either unsuccessful surgical bone lengthening attempts, trauma or plurifragmental fractures. The newly regenerated bone appeared to integrate well with the existing host bone tissue and the healing period was reported to have been substantially shortened in comparison to conventional treatments.

A recent case report has been described [31], in which a large part of surgically removed mandible was reconstructed using a tissue engineering approach. A custom-made mandible shape scaffold was designed and filled with bovine bone mineral blocks impregnated with autologous bone marrow cells and BMP-7. In this study, it was presumed that the action of

BMP-7 and the BMSSC present in the marrow aspirate facilitated the bone regeneration. The implant was subsequently used to surgically reconstruct a mandible that demonstrated remodeling to the extent that the patient had regained some masticatory function. These innovative human clinical studies provide strong circumstantial evidence of the efficacy of utilizing BMSSC for cell-based therapies for a range of different orthopaedic applications. However, the fate of the BMSSC and their direct contribution to the new bone formation remains to be determined in the majority of animal and human studies published to date.

While the use of autologous BMSSC represents the most desirable and safest scenario for any tissue engineering application, this approach is somewhat limited due to variations in the quality and quantity of the bone marrow aspirates and the cost effectiveness of generating autologous BMSSC preparations on an individual basis. An alternative to the use of autologous BMSSC comes from studies describing the capacity of *ex vivo* expanded allogeneic BMSSC to inhibit proliferation and activation of host immune T-cells predominantly using *in vitro* based assays [32-36]. This is supported by allogeneic bone marrow transplantation studies that demonstrate the presence of donor derived BMSSC in patients that received co-transplantations of cultured BMSSC and HSC derived either from HLA-identical siblings or from sex mismatched unrelated donors [37]. In accord with these observations, similar findings have been reported in studies using animal models [38,39]. However, the immune tolerance of BMSSC remains a contentious issue due to conflicting data in comparable transplantation studies in both human subjects and in animal models. One study of a rat femoral defect model showed that transplants of allogeneic BMSSC preparations demonstrated similar bone regeneration effects only after a short period of immunosuppression of the recipient animals in comparison to immune competent animals receiving autologous BMSSC [40]. In contrast, another study demonstrated equivalent bone repair in an alveolar bone defect model in animals receiving either allogeneic or autologous cultured BMSSC [41]. Much work is clearly needed to fully address the mechanisms of any BMSSC mediated suppression of immune responses. If substantiated, the notion of BMSSC mediated immune tolerance opens up the possibility of developing generic allogeneic "off the shelf" therapeutics as an alternative to harvesting and propagating large numbers of autologous BMSSC.

THE ROLE OF BIOMATERIALS IN BONE REPAIR

Whilst, many studies have described the *in vivo* osteogenic potential of rodent derived BMSSC in the absence of an osteo-conductive matrix, the interactions between human BMSSC and an appropriate bio-compatible carrier material appears to be critical for actively stimulating new bone formation *in vivo*. Published reports have described the ectopic bone formation potential of rodent BMSSC in association with several kinds of carriers including demineralised bone, coral exoskeleton, gelatin, polyvinyl sponge, collagen gels and synthetic polymers such as polylactic acid and polglycolic acid [15,42,43]. Interestingly, while many of these carriers can support human BMSSC growth and even osteogenic differentiation *in vitro*, human BMSSC implants using these scaffolds often failed to demonstrate new bone formation when transplanted into immunocompromised mice [15,44]. Collectively, these studies indicate that human and animal BMSSC do not always exhibit equivalence in their requirements for factors that mediate osteogenesis. Moreover, great care should be taken in choosing biomaterials that appear suitable for rodent or larger animal models, which may not always be applicable for the treatment of human bone defects.

Human BMSSC can readily form new bone when transplanted into immunocompromised mice in combination with a porous ceramic carrier material comprised of either hydroxyapatite, tricalcium phosphate or, more favorably, a combination of the two. These have been used as either larger fitted blocks of several cm^3 or as small particles of varying sizes of approximately 0.5 to 1.0 mm in diameter [3,4,45]. Other studies have determined that the level of bone induction is related to the HA/TCP ratio, where it was shown that a higher TCP% of approximately 80% tends to produce better outcomes in respect to the amount of new bone formation [44]. Similarly, HA/TCP powder-type I bovine fibrillar collagen strips (Collagraft, Zimmer) also appear to be an effective matrix for stimulating human BMSC bone formation *in vivo*, equivalent to that observed with HA/TCP particles [4,15]. From the literature, there is a clear necessity to develop and test biocompatible scaffold/materials that specifically facilitate human BMSSC osteogenic differentiation *in vivo*. This approach will help develop appropriate strategies for generating significant bone regeneration and integration into the surrounding environment of the bone defects in human subjects.

THERAPEUTIC POTENTIAL OF GENETICALLY MODIFIED BMSSC

The clinical use of primary cultured BMSSC for bone regeneration poses multiple logistical problems due to the limited life-span of human BMSSC *in vitro* and because of their steady decline for osteogenic potential over successive cell passages. Many studies have examined the use of different supplements and factors in regular culture expansion media in an attempt to extend the growth and differentiation potential of human BMSSC beyond their normal limits. Some growth medium supplements that have shown promise in extending the growth and developmental potential of human BMSSC *in vitro*, include FGF-2, BMPs, PDGF and EGF under serum-replete or –deprived conditions [14,46-48]. The addition of dexamethasone and ascorbate at the initiation of culture have been reported to increase the overall capacity of human BMSSC to generate new bone formation *in vivo* [3,4]. Other manipulations including pre-coating the biomaterials with different extracellular matrix components such as fibronectin and laminin or apatite coated polymers (HA-poly lactic-co-glycolic acid) have been shown to be affective in stimulating increased levels of bone formation *in vivo* to varying degrees [49,50]. Continued research into this area is hoped to generate a significant increase in the efficacy of BMSSC based therapies leading to improved clinical outcomes.

The genetic manipulation of *ex vivo* expanded BMSSC populations has been examined as an alternate strategy for generating large numbers of viable cells in order to provide a consistent and renewable source of osteogenic progenitor cells. Some tissue engineering approaches have facilitated lineage restricted differentiation of BMSSC for improved osteochondral tissue repair *in vivo*, by enforced expression of various growth factors such as BMP-2, -7, -9 and IGF-1 [40,51-56]. In several studies, over-expression of BMP-2 and BMP-4 by BMSSC was reported to be an efficient system for delivering both potent osteoinductive proteins and relevant bone cell populations to the defect site, leading to increased healing of large segmental femoral and craniofacial defects in different animal models [57-59].

Other studies have tried to regulate and maintain the growth of multi-potential BMSSC following *ex vivo* expansion. Enforced expression of telomerase by human BMSSC was found to cause an increase in both their normal lifespan and the differentiation capacity of BMSSC, resulting in enhanced osteogenic capacity *in vitro* and *in vivo* [60-62]. Whilst, these cell lines are generally not immortal and respond to normal apoptotic signals, recent evidence suggests that some telomerase expressing human BMSSC lines have the potential to undergo spontaneous transformation following a period of growth arrest and crisis [63]. This development underscores the importance of more rigorous assessment of any genetically modified BMSSC lines prior to their use in pre-clinical trials. Nevertheless, it is anticipated that further improvements in the development of novel inducible or suicide promoters may facilitate the use of telomerase and other gene products to enhance and regulate the stem cell qualities of *ex vivo* expanded BMSSC.

ALTERNATIVE SOURCES OF MSC

Early studies by Friedenstein and colleagues identified rodent MSC-like cells in different tissues that were termed 'inducible osteoprogenitor cells' due their inability to spontaneously form bone *in vivo* when compared to their bone marrow counterparts [64,65]. More recently, many groups have actively pursued alternative tissues sources (adipose, bone, synovium, dermis skeletal muscle, dental pulp and periodontal ligament) as potential reservoirs of mesenchymal stem cells [66-74]. From these studies, adipose tissue has proved to be a reliable and extensive source of multipotent MSC-like cells termed adipose-derived adult stromal (ADAS) cells [69,70,75-77]. In particular, *ex vivo* expanded ADAS cells demonstrated an extensive capacity to undergo osteogensis both *in vitro* and *in vivo* [50,69,75,78,79]. One study demonstrated the effectiveness of murine ADAS cells to repair critical sized calvarial defects created in syngeneic mice [50]. The great potential of ADAS cells for bone regeneration and their relative accessibility and abundance of adipose tissue is an important advantage to utilize ADAS cells for therapies. However, MSC isolated from non-bone marrow sources demonstrate wide variations in their growth and developmental potentials that differ significantly to BMSSC [66,73,80]. More importantly, human ADSC may have the potential to undergo transformation if cultured for extensive periods *in vitro*, which has not been reported for unmanipulated human BMSSC [81]. In light of these data, great care should be taken in designing stem cell-based therapies that utilize the appropriate stem cell populations from the most favorable donor site. This will ensure that the appropriate source of postnatal stem cell population is utilized for particular regenerative medicine applications.

Several studies have reported that peripheral blood may contain circulating MSCs [67,82,83]. These MSC, demonstrated similar properties to BMSSC, in respect to their capacity to form clonogenic adherent cell clusters, and by their ability for osteo/adipogenic differentiation *in vitro* and potential to generate bone when transplanted into immunocompromised mouse [67]. However, conflicting data from other studies suggests that peripheral blood MSC were only found in patients receiving chemotherapy and G/GM-CSF administration, but not from healthy donors [82]. Recently, the existence and multipotency of mesenchymal cells in umbilical cord blood and placenta was also demonstrated [84-86]. These findings suggests that MSC in circulation may have some function during development or in times of stress and disease in postnatal organisms. Further studies are clearly required to elucidate their characteristics and roles in tissue healing or regeneration.

CONCLUSION

Accumulating evidence strongly supports the notion that BMSSC and other MSC populations can be utilized not only for bone regeneration but also for the treatment of other non-bone-related diseases. It is clear that continued research in this field is required to more completely identify the stem cell characteristics, full developmental potential and relationship of different MSC populations. Together with advances in bio-material/scaffold design, these studies will undoubtedly help us develop appropriate methodologies to propagate multi-potential stem cells *in vitro* for their use as effective clinical therapies for osseous defects.

ACKNOWLEDGMENTS

We acknowledge the contribution of Prof. PJ Simmons and SE Graves in the ovine bone defect studies.

REFERENCES

[1]   Owen, M., and Friedenstein, A. J. (1988). Stromal stem cells: marrow-derived osteogenic precursors. *Ciba Found Symp*, 136, 42-60

[2]   Bennett, J. H., Joyner, C. J., Triffitt, J. T., and Owen, M. E. (1991). Adipocytic cells cultured from marrow have osteogenic potential. *J Cell Sci*, 99 (Pt 1), 131-139

[3]   Gronthos, S., Zannettino, A. C., Hay, S. J., Shi, S., Graves, S. E., Kortesidis, A., and Simmons, P. J. (2003). Molecular and cellular characterisation of highly purified stromal stem cells derived from human bone marrow. *J Cell Sci*, 116, 1827-1835.

[4]   Kuznetsov, S. A., Krebsbach, P. H., Satomura, K., Kerr, J., Riminucci, M., Benayahu, D., and Robey, P. G. (1997). Single-colony derived strains of human marrow stromal fibroblasts form bone after transplantation in vivo. *J Bone Miner Res*, 12, 1335-1347.

[5]   Muraglia, A., Cancedda, R., and Quarto, R. (2000). Clonal mesenchymal progenitors from human bone marrow differentiate in vitro according to a hierarchical model. *J Cell Sci*, 113, 1161-1166.

[6]   Owen, M. E., Cave, J., and Joyner, C. J. (1987). Clonal analysis in vitro of osteogenic differentiation of marrow CFU-F. *J Cell Sci*, 87, 731-738.

[7]   Pittenger, M. F., Mackay, A. M., Beck, S. C., Jaiswal, R. K., Douglas, R., Mosca, J. D., Moorman, M. A., Simonetti, D. W., Craig, S., and Marshak, D. R. (1999). Multilineage potential of adult human mesenchymal stem cells. *Science*, 284, 143-147.

[8]   Gronthos, S., Graves, S. E., Ohta, S., and Simmons, P. J. (1994). The STRO-1+ fraction of adult human bone marrow contains the osteogenic precursors. *Blood*, 84, 4164-4173.

[9]   Friedenstein, A. J. (1980). Stromal mechanisms of bone marrow: cloning in vitro and retransplantation in vivo. *Hamatol Bluttransfus*, 25, 19-29

[10] Ashton, B. A., Allen, T. D., Howlett, C. R., Eaglesom, C. C., Hattori, A., and Owen, M. (1980). Formation of bone and cartilage by marrow stromal cells in diffusion chambers in vivo. *Clin Orthop*, 294-307

[11] Friedenstein, A. J., Latzinik, N. W., Grosheva, A. G., and Gorskaya, U. F. (1982). Marrow microenvironment transfer by heterotopic transplantation of freshly isolated and cultured cells in porous sponges. *Exp Hematol*, 10, 217-227.

[12] Bab, I., Ashton, B. A., Gazit, D., Marx, G., Williamson, M. C., and Owen, M. E. (1986). Kinetics and differentiation of marrow stromal cells in diffusion chambers in vivo. *J Cell Sci*, 84, 139-151

[13] Goshima, J., Goldberg, V. M., and Caplan, A. I. (1991). The osteogenic potential of culture-expanded rat marrow mesenchymal cells assayed in vivo in calcium phosphate ceramic blocks. *Clin Orthop*, 298-311

[14] Cassiede, P., Dennis, J. E., Ma, F., and Caplan, A. I. (1996). Osteochondrogenic potential of marrow mesenchymal progenitor cells exposed to TGF-beta 1 or PDGF-BB as assayed in vivo and in vitro. *J Bone Miner Res*, 11, 1264-1273

[15] Krebsbach, P. H., Kuznetsov, S. A., Satomura, K., Emmons, R. V., Rowe, D. W., and Robey, P. G. (1997). Bone formation in vivo: comparison of osteogenesis by transplanted mouse and human marrow stromal fibroblasts. *Transplantation*, 63, 1059-1069.

[16] Mizuno, M., Shindo, M., Kobayashi, D., Tsuruga, E., Amemiya, A., and Kuboki, Y. (1997). Osteogenesis by bone marrow stromal cells maintained on type I collagen matrix gels in vivo. *Bone*, 20, 101-107

[17] Bacigalupo, A., Frassoni, F., and Van Lint, M. T. (2000). Bone marrow or peripheral blood as a source of stem cells for allogeneic transplants. *Curr Opin Hematol*, 7, 343-347.

[18] Buckner, C. D. (1999). Autologous bone marrow transplants to hematopoietic stem cell support with peripheral blood stem cells: a historical perspective. *J Hematother*, 8, 233-236.

[19] Krebsbach, P. H., Mankani, M. H., Satomura, K., Kuznetsov, S. A., and Robey, P. G. (1998). Repair of craniotomy defects using bone marrow stromal cells. *Transplantation*, 66, 1272-1278.

[20] Bruder, S. P., Kurth, A. A., Shea, M., Hayes, W. C., Jaiswal, N., and Kadiyala, S. (1998). Bone regeneration by implantation of purified, culture-expanded human mesenchymal stem cells. *J Orthop Res*, 16, 155-162

[21] Chistolini, P., Ruspantini, I., Bianco, P., Corsi, A., Cancedda, R., and Quarto, R. (1999). Biomechanical evaluation of cell-loaded and cell-free hydroxyapatite implants for the reconstruction of segmental bone defects. *J Mater Sci Mater Med*, 10, 739-742

[22] Petite, H., Viateau, V., Bensaid, W., Meunier, A., de Pollak, C., Bourguignon, M., Oudina, K., Sedel, L., and Guillemin, G. (2000). Tissue-engineered bone regeneration. *Nat Biotechnol*, 18, 959-963

[23] Kon, E., Muraglia, A., Corsi, A., Bianco, P., Marcacci, M., Martin, I., Boyde, A., Ruspantini, I., Chistolini, P., Rocca, M., Giardino, R., Cancedda, R., and Quarto, R.

(2000). Autologous bone marrow stromal cells loaded onto porous hydroxyapatite ceramic accelerate bone repair in critical-size defects of sheep long bones. *J Biomed Mater Res*, 49, 328-337

[24] Shang, Q., Wang, Z., Liu, W., Shi, Y., Cui, L., and Cao, Y. (2001). Tissue-engineered bone repair of sheep cranial defects with autologous bone marrow stromal cells. *J Craniofac Surg*, 12, 586-593; discussion 594-585

[25] Horwitz, E. M., Gordon, P. L., Koo, W. K., Marx, J. C., Neel, M. D., McNall, R. Y., Muul, L., and Hofmann, T. (2002). Isolated allogeneic bone marrow-derived mesenchymal cells engraft and stimulate growth in children with osteogenesis imperfecta: Implications for cell therapy of bone. *Proc Natl Acad Sci U S A*, 99, 8932-8937

[26] Horwitz, E. M., Prockop, D. J., Fitzpatrick, L. A., Koo, W. W., Gordon, P. L., Neel, M., Sussman, M., Orchard, P., Marx, J. C., Pyeritz, R. E., and Brenner, M. K. (1999). Transplantability and therapeutic effects of bone marrow-derived mesenchymal cells in children with osteogenesis imperfecta. *Nat Med*, 5, 309-313

[27] Horwitz, E. M., Prockop, D. J., Gordon, P. L., Koo, W. W., Fitzpatrick, L. A., Neel, M. D., McCarville, M. E., Orchard, P. J., Pyeritz, R. E., and Brenner, M. K. (2001). Clinical responses to bone marrow transplantation in children with severe osteogenesis imperfecta. *Blood*, 97, 1227-1231

[28] Koc, O. N., Day, J., Nieder, M., Gerson, S. L., Lazarus, H. M., and Krivit, W. (2002). Allogeneic mesenchymal stem cell infusion for treatment of metachromatic leukodystrophy (MLD) and Hurler syndrome (MPS-IH). *Bone Marrow Transplant*, 30, 215-222

[29] Koc, O. N., Gerson, S. L., Cooper, B. W., Dyhouse, S. M., Haynesworth, S. E., Caplan, A. I., and Lazarus, H. M. (2000). Rapid hematopoietic recovery after coinfusion of autologous-blood stem cells and culture-expanded marrow mesenchymal stem cells in advanced breast cancer patients receiving high-dose chemotherapy. *J Clin Oncol*, 18, 307-316

[30] Quarto, R., Mastrogiacomo, M., Cancedda, R., Kutepov, S. M., Mukhachev, V., Lavroukov, A., Kon, E., and Marcacci, M. (2001). Repair of large bone defects with the use of autologous bone marrow stromal cells. *N Engl J Med*, 344, 385-386

[31] Warnke, P. H., Springer, I. N., Wiltfang, J., Acil, Y., Eufinger, H., Wehmoller, M., Russo, P. A., Bolte, H., Sherry, E., Behrens, E., and Terheyden, H. (2004). Growth and transplantation of a custom vascularised bone graft in a man. *Lancet*, 364, 766-770

[32] Krampera, M., Glennie, S., Dyson, J., Scott, D., Laylor, R., Simpson, E., and Dazzi, F. (2003). Bone marrow mesenchymal stem cells inhibit the response of naive and memory antigen-specific T cells to their cognate peptide. *Blood*, 101, 3722-3729

[33] Le Blanc, K., Tammik, L., Sundberg, B., Haynesworth, S. E., and Ringden, O. (2003). Mesenchymal stem cells inhibit and stimulate mixed lymphocyte cultures and mitogenic responses independently of the major histocompatibility complex. *Scand J Immunol*, 57, 11-20

[34] Beyth, S., Borovsky, Z., Mevorach, D., Liebergall, M., Gazit, Z., Aslan, H., Galun, E., and Rachmilewitz, J. (2005). Human mesenchymal stem cells alter antigen-presenting cell maturation and induce T-cell unresponsiveness. *Blood*, 105, 2214-2219

[35] Augello, A., Tasso, R., Negrini, S. M., Amateis, A., Indiveri, F., Cancedda, R., and Pennesi, G. (2005). Bone marrow mesenchymal progenitor cells inhibit lymphocyte

proliferation by activation of the programmed death 1 pathway. *Eur J Immunol*, 35, 1482-1490

[36] Plumas, J., Chaperot, L., Richard, M. J., Molens, J. P., Bensa, J. C., and Favrot, M. C. (2005). Mesenchymal stem cells induce apoptosis of activated T cells. *Leukemia*, 19, 1597-1604

[37] Lazarus, H. M., Koc, O. N., Devine, S. M., Curtin, P., Maziarz, R. T., Holland, H. K., Shpall, E. J., McCarthy, P., Atkinson, K., Cooper, B. W., Gerson, S. L., Laughlin, M. J., Loberiza, F. R., Jr., Moseley, A. B., and Bacigalupo, A. (2005). Cotransplantation of HLA-identical sibling culture-expanded mesenchymal stem cells and hematopoietic stem cells in hematologic malignancy patients. *Biol Blood Marrow Transplant*, 11, 389-398

[38] Chung, N. G., Jeong, D. C., Park, S. J., Choi, B. O., Cho, B., Kim, H. K., Chun, C. S., Won, J. H., and Han, C. W. (2004). Cotransplantation of marrow stromal cells may prevent lethal graft-versus-host disease in major histocompatibility complex mismatched murine hematopoietic stem cell transplantation. *Int J Hematol*, 80, 370-376

[39] Maitra, B., Szekely, E., Gjini, K., Laughlin, M. J., Dennis, J., Haynesworth, S. E., and Koc, O. N. (2004). Human mesenchymal stem cells support unrelated donor hematopoietic stem cells and suppress T-cell activation. *Bone Marrow Transplant*, 33, 597-604

[40] Tsuchida, H., Hashimoto, J., Crawford, E., Manske, P., and Lou, J. (2003). Engineered allogeneic mesenchymal stem cells repair femoral segmental defect in rats. *J Orthop Res*, 21, 44-53

[41] De Kok, I. J., Peter, S. J., Archambault, M., van den Bos, C., Kadiyala, S., Aukhil, I., and Cooper, L. F. (2003). Investigation of allogeneic mesenchymal stem cell-based alveolar bone formation: preliminary findings. *Clin Oral Implants Res*, 14, 481-489

[42] Gurevitch, O., Kurkalli, B. G., Prigozhina, T., Kasir, J., Gaft, A., and Slavin, S. (2003). Reconstruction of cartilage, bone, and hematopoietic microenvironment with demineralized bone matrix and bone marrow cells. *Stem Cells*, 21, 588-597

[43] Takahashi, Y., Yamamoto, M., and Tabata, Y. (2005). Osteogenic differentiation of mesenchymal stem cells in biodegradable sponges composed of gelatin and beta-tricalcium phosphate. *Biomaterials*, 26, 3587-3596

[44] Harris, C. T., and Cooper, L. F. (2004). Comparison of bone graft matrices for human mesenchymal stem cell-directed osteogenesis. *J Biomed Mater Res A*, 68, 747-755

[45] Haynesworth, S. E., Goshima, J., Goldberg, V. M., and Caplan, A. I. (1992). Characterization of cells with osteogenic potential from human marrow. *Bone*, 13, 81-88

[46] Gronthos, S., and Simmons, P. J. (1995). The growth factor requirements of STRO-1-positive human bone marrow stromal precursors under serum-deprived conditions in vitro. *Blood*, 85, 929-940.

[47] Bianchi, G., Banfi, A., Mastrogiacomo, M., Notaro, R., Luzzatto, L., Cancedda, R., and Quarto, R. (2003). Ex vivo enrichment of mesenchymal cell progenitors by fibroblast growth factor 2. *Exp Cell Res*, 287, 98-105

[48] Saito, A., Suzuki, Y., Ogata, S., Ohtsuki, C., and Tanihara, M. (2005). Accelerated bone repair with the use of a synthetic BMP-2-derived peptide and bone-marrow stromal cells. *J Biomed Mater Res A*, 72, 77-82

[49] Dennis, J. E., Haynesworth, S. E., Young, R. G., and Caplan, A. I. (1992). Osteogenesis in marrow-derived mesenchymal cell porous ceramic composites transplanted subcutaneously: effect of fibronectin and laminin on cell retention and rate of osteogenic expression. *Cell Transplant*, 1, 23-32

[50] Cowan, C. M., Shi, Y. Y., Aalami, O. O., Chou, Y. F., Mari, C., Thomas, R., Quarto, N., Contag, C. H., Wu, B., and Longaker, M. T. (2004). Adipose-derived adult stromal cells heal critical-size mouse calvarial defects. *Nat Biotechnol*, 22, 560-567

[51] Nixon, A. J., Brower-Toland, B. D., Bent, S. J., Saxer, R. A., Wilke, M. J., Robbins, P. D., and Evans, C. H. (2000). Insulinlike growth factor-I gene therapy applications for cartilage repair. *Clin Orthop*, S201-213

[52] Krebsbach, P. H., Gu, K., Franceschi, R. T., and Rutherford, R. B. (2000). Gene therapy-directed osteogenesis: BMP-7-transduced human fibroblasts form bone in vivo. *Hum Gene Ther*, 11, 1201-1210

[53] Okubo, Y., Bessho, K., Fujimura, K., Kaihara, S., Iizuka, T., and Miyatake, S. (2001). The time course study of osteoinduction by bone morphogenetic protein-2 via adenoviral vector. *Life Sci*, 70, 325-336

[54] Partridge, K., Yang, X., Clarke, N. M., Okubo, Y., Bessho, K., Sebald, W., Howdle, S. M., Shakesheff, K. M., and Oreffo, R. O. (2002). Adenoviral BMP-2 gene transfer in mesenchymal stem cells: in vitro and in vivo bone formation on biodegradable polymer scaffolds. *Biochem Biophys Res Commun*, 292, 144-152

[55] Li, J. Z., Hankins, G. R., Kao, C., Li, H., Kammauff, J., and Helm, G. A. (2003). Osteogenesis in rats induced by a novel recombinant helper-dependent bone morphogenetic protein-9 (BMP-9) adenovirus. *J Gene Med*, 5, 748-756

[56] Dayoub, H., Dumont, R. J., Li, J. Z., Dumont, A. S., Hankins, G. R., Kallmes, D. F., and Helm, G. A. (2003). Human mesenchymal stem cells transduced with recombinant bone morphogenetic protein-9 adenovirus promote osteogenesis in rodents. *Tissue Eng*, 9, 347-356

[57] Chang, S. C., Chuang, H. L., Chen, Y. R., Chen, J. K., Chung, H. Y., Lu, Y. L., Lin, H. Y., Tai, C. L., and Lou, J. (2003). Ex vivo gene therapy in autologous bone marrow stromal stem cells for tissue-engineered maxillofacial bone regeneration. *Gene Ther*, 10, 2013-2019

[58] Gysin, R., Wergedal, J. E., Sheng, M. H., Kasukawa, Y., Miyakoshi, N., Chen, S. T., Peng, H., Lau, K. H., Mohan, S., and Baylink, D. J. (2002). Ex vivo gene therapy with stromal cells transduced with a retroviral vector containing the BMP4 gene completely heals critical size calvarial defect in rats. *Gene Ther*, 9, 991-999

[59] Lieberman, J. R., Le, L. Q., Wu, L., Finerman, G. A., Berk, A., Witte, O. N., and Stevenson, S. (1998). Regional gene therapy with a BMP-2-producing murine stromal cell line induces heterotopic and orthotopic bone formation in rodents. *J Orthop Res*, 16, 330-339

[60] Gronthos, S., Chen, S., Wang, C. Y., Robey, P. G., and Shi, S. (2003). Telomerase accelerates osteogenesis of bone marrow stromal stem cells by upregulation of CBFA1, osterix, and osteocalcin. *J Bone Miner Res*, 18, 716-722

[61] Shi, S., Gronthos, S., Chen, S., Reddi, A., Counter, C. M., Robey, P. G., and Wang, C. Y. (2002). Bone formation by human postnatal bone marrow stromal stem cells is enhanced by telomerase expression. *Nat Biotechnol*, 20, 587-591

[62] Simonsen, J. L., Rosada, C., Serakinci, N., Justesen, J., Stenderup, K., Rattan, S. I., Jensen, T. G., and Kassem, M. (2002). Telomerase expression extends the proliferative life-span and maintains the osteogenic potential of human bone marrow stromal cells. *Nat Biotechnol*, 20, 592-596.

[63] Burns, J. S., Abdallah, B. M., Guldberg, P., Rygaard, J., Schroder, H. D., and Kassem, M. (2005). Tumorigenic heterogeneity in cancer stem cells evolved from long-term cultures of telomerase-immortalized human mesenchymal stem cells. *Cancer Res*, 65, 3126-3135

[64] Friedenstein, A. Y. (1968). Induction of bone tissue by transitional epithelium. *Clin Orthop*, 59, 21-37.

[65] Friedenstein, A. Y., Lalykina, K. S., and Tolmacheva, A. A. (1967). Osteogenic activity of peritoneal fluid cells induced by transitional epithelium. *Acta Anat*, 68, 532-549

[66] Gronthos, S., Mankani, M., Brahim, J., Robey, P. G., and Shi, S. (2000). Postnatal human dental pulp stem cells (DPSCs) in vitro and invivo. *Proc Natl Acad Sci U S A*, 97, 13625-13630.

[67] Kuznetsov, S. A., Mankani, M. H., Gronthos, S., Satomura, K., Bianco, P., and Robey, P. G. (2001). Circulating skeletal stem cells. *J Cell Biol*, 153, 1133-1140.

[68] Young, H. E., Steele, T. A., Bray, R. A., Hudson, J., Floyd, J. A., Hawkins, K., Thomas, K., Austin, T., Edwards, C., Cuzzourt, J., Duenzl, M., Lucas, P. A., and Black, A. C., Jr. (2001). Human reserve pluripotent mesenchymal stem cells are present in the connective tissues of skeletal muscle and dermis derived from fetal, adult, and geriatric donors. *Anat Rec*, 264, 51-62.

[69] Zuk, P. A., Zhu, M., Mizuno, H., Huang, J., Futrell, J. W., Katz, A. J., Benhaim, P., Lorenz, H. P., and Hedrick, M. H. (2001). Multilineage cells from human adipose tissue: implications for cell-based therapies. *Tissue Eng*, 7, 211-228

[70] Gimble, J. M., and Guilak, F. (2003). Differentiation potential of adipose derived adult stem (ADAS) cells. *Curr Top Dev Biol*, 58, 137-160

[71] Miura, M., Gronthos, S., Zhao, M., Lu, B., Fisher, L. W., Robey, P. G., and Shi, S. (2003). SHED: stem cells from human exfoliated deciduous teeth. *Proc Natl Acad Sci U S A*, 100, 5807-5812

[72] Tuli, R., Tuli, S., Nandi, S., Wang, M. L., Alexander, P. G., Haleem-Smith, H., Hozack, W. J., Manner, P. A., Danielson, K. G., and Tuan, R. S. (2003). Characterization of multipotential mesenchymal progenitor cells derived from human trabecular bone. *Stem Cells*, 21, 681-693

[73] Sakaguchi, Y., Sekiya, I., Yagishita, K., and Muneta, T. (2005). Comparison of human stem cells derived from various mesenchymal tissues: superiority of synovium as a cell source. *Arthritis Rheum*, 52, 2521-2529

[74] Sun, J. S., Wu, S. Y., and Lin, F. H. (2005). The role of muscle-derived stem cells in bone tissue engineering. *Biomaterials*, 26, 3953-3960

[75] Halvorsen, Y. D., Franklin, D., Bond, A. L., Hitt, D. C., Auchter, C., Boskey, A. L., Paschalis, E. P., Wilkison, W. O., and Gimble, J. M. (2001). Extracellular matrix mineralization and osteoblast gene expression by human adipose tissue-derived stromal cells. *Tissue Eng*, 7, 729-741

[76] Tholpady, S. S., Katz, A. J., and Ogle, R. C. (2003). Mesenchymal stem cells from rat visceral fat exhibit multipotential differentiation in vitro. *Anat Rec A Discov Mol Cell Evol Biol*, 272, 398-402

[77] Wickham, M. Q., Erickson, G. R., Gimble, J. M., Vail, T. P., and Guilak, F. (2003). Multipotent stromal cells derived from the infrapatellar fat pad of the knee. *Clin Orthop Relat Res*, 196-212

[78] Nathan, S., Das De, S., Thambyah, A., Fen, C., Goh, J., and Lee, E. H. (2003). Cell-based therapy in the repair of osteochondral defects: a novel use for adipose tissue. *Tissue Eng*, 9, 733-744

[79] Hicok, K. C., Du Laney, T. V., Zhou, Y. S., Halvorsen, Y. D., Hitt, D. C., Cooper, L. F., and Gimble, J. M. (2004). Human adipose-derived adult stem cells produce osteoid in vivo. *Tissue Eng*, 10, 371-380

[80] Shi, S., Robey, P. G., and Gronthos, S. (2001). Comparison of human dental pulp and bone marrow stromal stem cells by cDNA microarray analysis. *Bone*, 29, 532-539.

[81] Rubio, D., Garcia-Castro, J., Martin, M. C., de la Fuente, R., Cigudosa, J. C., Lloyd, A. C., and Bernad, A. (2005). Spontaneous human adult stem cell transformation. *Cancer Res*, 65, 3035-3039

[82] Fernandez, M., Simon, V., Herrera, G., Cao, C., Del Favero, H., and Minguell, J. J. (1997). Detection of stromal cells in peripheral blood progenitor cell collections from breast cancer patients. *Bone Marrow Transplant*, 20, 265-271

[83] Zvaifler, N. J., Marinova-Mutafchieva, L., Adams, G., Edwards, C. J., Moss, J., Burger, J. A., and Maini, R. N. (2000). Mesenchymal precursor cells in the blood of normal individuals. *Arthritis Res*, 2, 477-488

[84] Goodwin, H. S., Bicknese, A. R., Chien, S. N., Bogucki, B. D., Quinn, C. O., and Wall, D. A. (2001). Multilineage differentiation activity by cells isolated from umbilical cord blood: expression of bone, fat, and neural markers. *Biol Blood Marrow Transplant*, 7, 581-588

[85] Gang, E. J., Hong, S. H., Jeong, J. A., Hwang, S. H., Kim, S. W., Yang, I. H., Ahn, C., Han, H., and Kim, H. (2004). In vitro mesengenic potential of human umbilical cord blood-derived mesenchymal stem cells. *Biochem Biophys Res Commun*, 321, 102-108

[86] Lee, O. K., Kuo, T. K., Chen, W. M., Lee, K. D., Hsieh, S. L., and Chen, T. H. (2004). Isolation of multipotent mesenchymal stem cells from umbilical cord blood. *Blood*, 103, 1669-1675

In: Progress in Stem Cell Research
Editor: Prasad S. Koka, pp. 63-76

ISBN: 978-1-60456-065-7
© 2008 Nova Science Publishers, Inc.

Chapter 4

ADULT NEURAL STEM CELLS AND CELLULAR THERAPY

Philippe Taupin[*]

National Neuroscience Institute, Singapore
National University of Singapore
Nanyang Technological University, Singapore

ABSTRACT

Considerable efforts and means have been invested to find treatments for neurological diseases and injuries, yet there is still no cure for these ailments and new alternatives for therapy must be explored. Because they generate the main phenotypes of the central nervous system (CNS), neural stem cells (NSCs) hold the promise to cure a broad range of CNS diseases and injuries. With the confirmation that neurogenesis occurs in the adult brain, and the recent isolation and characterization *in vitro* of neural progenitor and stem cells from the adult CNS, new avenues for the treatment of neurological diseases and injuries are being considered. Cell therapeutic interventions may involve both *in vivo* stimulation and transplantation of neural progenitor and stem cells of the adult brain.

INTRODUCTION

Cellular therapy is the replacement of unhealthy or damaged cells or tissues by new ones. Because neurodegenerative diseases, cerebral strokes, and traumatic injuries to the CNS produce neurological deficits that result from neuronal loss, cell therapy is a prominent area of investigation for the treatment of neurological diseases and injuries. Cell types of various sources and merits have been considered for cellular therapy in the CNS. Until recently, strategies developed for cellular therapy to the CNS involved heterologous transplantation,

---

[*]Correspondence: 11 Jalan Tan Tock Seng, Singapore 308433. Tel. (65) 6357 - 7533. Fax (65) 6256 - 9178. Email obgpjt@nus.edu.sg

requiring to find a tissue-compatible donor or to administer drugs that suppress the immune system to prevent tissue rejection.

The recent confirmation that neurogenesis occurs in the adult brain and NSCs reside in the adult CNS gives new opportunities for cellular therapy in the CNS. The existence of NSCs in the adult CNS suggests that the CNS has the potential to self-repair. Hence, tremendous efforts are being devoted to study how endogenous neural progenitor and stem cells behave in the diseased brain, and to stimulate endogenous neurogenesis at the sites of degeneration. Neural progenitor and stem cells have also been isolated and expanded *in vitro* from the adult brain, allowing to perform autologous transplantation in the adult CNS. Thus, the recent confirmation that neurogenesis occurs in the adult brain and NSCs reside in the adult CNS opens new opportunities for cellular therapy in the CNS.

ADULT NEUROGENESIS AND NEURAL STEM CELLS

Neurogenesis occurs mainly in two areas of the adult mammalian brain, the dentate gyrus (DG) of the hippocampus, and the subventricular zone (SVZ), in several species including human [1-3]. In the DG, newly generated neuronal cells in the subgranular zone (SGZ) migrate to the granular layer, where they differentiate into mature neuronal cells, and extend axonal projections to the CA3 area. In the SVZ, cells are generated in the anterior part of the SVZ, and migrate to the olfactory bulb (OB), trough the rostro-migratory stream (RMS), where they differentiate into interneurons of the OB. Newly generated neuronal cells in the DG and OB establish functional connections with neighboring cells [1]. Quantitative studies showed that, though a significant fraction of newly generated neuronal cells in the DG and SVZ undergo programmed cell death [4, 5], as many as 9,000 new neuronal cells - or 0.1% of the granule cell population - are generated per day in the DG, and 65.3-76.9% of the bulbar neurons are replaced during a 6 weeks period in young adult rodents [6, 7]. The neuronal cells born during adulthood that survive to maturity and become integrated into circuits are very stable, and can survive for extended period of time; for at least 2 years in the human DG [2]. Thus, they may permanently and functionally replace cells born during development.

Neurogenesis may also occur, albeit at lower levels, in other areas of the brain, such as the Ammon's horn CA1, neocortex and substantia nigra (SN) in certain species [8-10]. However, some of these reports have been contradicted by other studies, and need to be further investigated [11-14]. In the adult spinal cord, recent studies have confirmed that gliogenesis, but not neurogenesis, occurs throughout the cord [15, 16].

Experimental studies show that the rate of neurogenesis in the DG and SVZ is modulated by various physiological and pathological conditions, as well as environmental stimuli. For example, stress, neuroinflammation and aging decrease neurogenesis in the DG, voluntary running increases neurogenesis in the DG, whereas exposure to odor deprivation or to an environment enriched in odors decreases or increases neurogenesis in the OB, respectively [17]. This modulation of neurogenesis suggests the implication of the hippocampus and SVZ in these processes. Since newly generated neural cells in the adult brain can survive for extended period of time, the modulation of neurogenesis may have long-term consequences on the architecture and functioning of the CNS.

Investigators have attempted to define the function of newly generated neuronal cells in the adult brain. Evidences suggest that newly generated neuronal cells in the hippocampus may be involved in learning and memory [18], such as in the formation of trace memories, a form of memory that depends on the hippocampus [19]. Newly generated neuronal cells in the hippocampus may also be involved in depression [20, 21]. Stress is an important causal factor in precipitating episodes of depression, and decreases hippocampal neurogenesis [22]. It is hypothesized that the waning and waxing of neurogenesis in the hippocampal formation are important causal factors, respectively, in the precipitation of, and recovery from, episodes of clinical depression [23].

It is hypothesized that newly generated neuronal cells in the adult brain originate from residual NSCs. NSCs are the self-renewing, multipotent cells that generate neurons, astrocytes, and oligodendrocytes in the nervous system [24] (Fig. 1). Neural progenitor and stem cells have been isolated and characterized *in vitro* from various areas, neurogenic and non-neurogenic, of the adult CNS, including the spinal cord, suggesting that NSCs reside throughout the adult CNS.

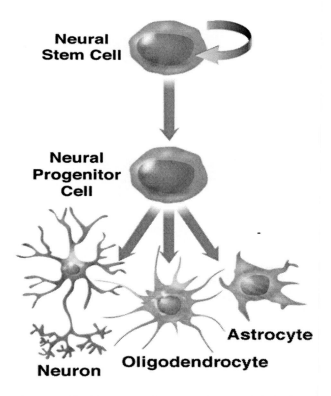

Figure 1. Neural stem cells. Neurogenesis occurs in the adult brain. It is hypothesized that newly generated neuronal cells in the adult brain originate from residual neural stem cells (NSCs). NSCs are the self-renewing, multipotent cells that generate neurons, astrocytes, and oligodendrocytes in the nervous system. Neural progenitor and stem cells have been isolated and characterized *in vitro* from various areas, neurogenic and non-neurogenic, of the adult CNS, suggesting that NSCs reside throughout the adult CNS. Neural progenitor cells are multipotent cells, with limited self-renewing capacity. The origin and identity of NSCs remain to be determined.

The origin and identity of NSCs remain source of debates and controversies [1]. Though recent reports further support an astroglial origin for the newly generated neuronal cells [25-29], NSCs remain to be unequivocally identified in the adult brain. There are currently no specific markers of adult NSCs. The intermediate neurofilament nestin, the transcription factors sox-2, oct-3/4, and the RNA binding protein Musashi 1 are markers for neural progenitor and stem cells, but also label population of glial cells [30-36]. Though much questions remain to be answered, the confirmation that neurogenesis occurs in the adult brain and that NSCs reside in the adult CNS have tremendous implication for cellular therapy: the adult CNS has the potential to repair itself.

ADULT NEURAL STEM CELLS AND CELLULAR THERAPY

With the confirmation that neurogenesis occurs in the adult brain, and the recent isolation and characterization *in vitro* of neural progenitor and stem cells from the adult CNS, new avenues for the treatment of neurological diseases and injuries are being considered. Cell therapeutic interventions may involve both *in vivo* stimulation and transplantation of neural progenitor and stem cells.

Stimulation of Endogenous Neural Progenitor Cells

Recent evidences show that new neuronal cells are generated at sites of degeneration in the diseased brain and after CNS injuries. Curtis et al. (2003) and Tattersfield et al. (2004) reported an increase in SVZ neurogenesis, leading to the migration of neural progenitor cells and the formation of new neuronal cells in the damaged areas of the striatum in Huntington's disease (HD) patients, and in animal model of HD (quinolinic acid lesion) [37, 38]. After experimental strokes (middle cerebral artery occlusion), new neuronal cells are detected at the major sites of degeneration, such as the striatum and the cortex [39-42]. Cell tracking studies revealed that these newly generated neuronal cells at the sites of degeneration originate from the SVZ. The newly generated cells migrate partially through the RMS to the sites of degeneration, where they differentiate, within 5 weeks, into the phenotypes of the degenerated nerve cells [37, 38, 43, 44]. Though this regenerative process is limited – estimated at 0.2% of the degenerated nerve cells in the striatum after focal ischemia [43]-, these evidences overturn the long-held dogma that the adult brain cannot renew itself after injuries [1, 24]. Several hypotheses can explain the limited capacity of the CNS to recover after injuries. The number of new neurons generated may be too low to compensate for the neuronal loss. The neuronal cells that are produced are non-functional because they do not develop into fully mature neurons, because they do not develop into the right type of neurons, or because they do not integrate into the surviving brain circuitry. The generation of new neuronal cells at the sites of injury would then represent an attempt by the CNS to repair itself, further highlighting the potential of the CNS for regeneration.

The SVZ origin of these newly generated neuronal cells suggests that conditions enhancing SVZ neurogenesis could promote regeneration and functional recovery after CNS injuries. Several molecules and factors have been reported to enhance SVZ neurogenesis in rodents. Trophic factors such as epidermal growth factor and basic fibroblast growth factor, administered by intracerebroventricular or subcutaneous injection, stimulate neurogenesis in the adult SVZ [45-47]. Exogenous substances, such as Ginko biloba extract -an herbal plant used medicinally-, stimulates neurogenesis in the OB [48]. Transforming growth factor-α, which infusion into the adult rat striatum leads to migration of neuronal progenitor cells from the SVZ and to the infusion site [49]. Nitric oxide donor [50, 51], sildenafil (Viagra) [52], glutamate [53], statins [54], erythropoietin [55], heparin-binding epidermal growth factor-like growth factor [56], vascular endothelial growth factor [57], epidermal growth factor [58, 59] promote neurogenesis in the SVZ and improve neurological function after experimental injuries in rodents, such as strokes. These molecules and factors are potential candidates for cellular therapy in the CNS.

Alternatively, since evidences suggest that NSCs may reside in neurogenic and non-neurogenic areas, the stimulation of neural progenitor and stem cells locally may also provide a strategy to promote regeneration of the CNS. Factors such as platelet-derived growth factor and brain-derived neurotrophic factor induce striatal neurogenesis in adult rats with 6-hydroxydopamine lesions, with no indications of any newly born cells differentiating into dopaminergic neurons following growth factor treatment [60]. Though neurogenesis in the SN remains the source of controversies [12-14], such factors may prove to be beneficial for recovery in Parkinson's disease. Future investigations will aim at identifying factors promoting neurogenesis in non-neurogenic areas.

The identification of the SVZ as a source of newly generated neuronal cells at the sites of degeneration, after injuries, present several features that can benefit cellular therapy in the CNS. First, in the intact CNS and after injuries, a significant proportion of newly generated neuronal progenitor cells in the SVZ undergo programmed cell death rather than achieving maturity -e.g. 80% of the new neuronal cells that are generated in the SVZ after stroke in rats die within the first weeks after the insult- [4, 5, 53]. This transient increase in newly generated neuronal progenitor cells provides a window of opportunity when the newly generated cells could be salvaged, and directed to participate in the regeneration process. Factors preventing cell death, such as caspases [61-63], would thus also be potentially beneficial for cellular therapy, alone or in combination with other condition promoting SVZ neurogenesis, such as the administration of trophic factors and/or environmental enrichment. Second, the identification of the SVZ, along the ventricles, as the source of neural progenitor and stem cells with regenerative potential after injuries also suggests that molecules and factors could be administered either by systemic, intracerebroventricular or subcutaneous injection, or through the cerebrospinal fluid (CSF) to promote neurogenesis in the brain [45-47], but also in the spinal cord [64], as the central canal is a presumed location of putative NSCs [16]. Such procedures that are less invasive would be beneficial for the treatment of the injured patients.

Future studies will aim at better understanding the molecular and cellular cascades involved in adult neuronal progenitor and stem cells proliferation, migration and fate determination, in the injured brain, to promote regeneration. For example, neuroinflammation inhibits neurogenesis [65, 66], and is a component of the secondary reaction after injury. Hence, strategies promoting neurogenesis after injuries would consist in reducing the events that regulate negatively neurogenesis, such as neuroinflammation. Thus, anti-inflammatory treatments may be considered to promote neurogenesis and functional recovery after injury.

Adult-Derived Neural Progenitor and Stem Cells as a Source of Tissue for Transplantation

Adult neural progenitor and stem cells can be isolated from human *post-mortem* tissues [67, 68], potentially allowing the generation of neural progenitor and stem cells from multiple sources for cellular therapy. Alternatively, neural progenitor and stem cells could be isolated from an undamaged area of the patient's brain, expanded *in vitro*, and grafted back to the degenerated area(s) (Fig. 2). Though such strategy would carry secondary risks associated with brain surgery, autologous transplantation would obviate the need to find a matching donor for the tissues, limiting rejection risk of the grafted tissues, or to administer drugs that suppress the immune system, such as cyclosporine. Hence, greatly enhancing the chance of cellular integration in the patient, and recovery. Neural progenitor and stem cells have been isolated and characterized *in vitro* from various areas, neurogenic and non-neurogenic, of the adult CNS, such as the hippocampus, SVZ, striatum, septum, spinal cord, SN [1, 12]. Whether neural progenitor and stem cells isolated from divers brain areas are equivalent and have the same potential remain to be determined. Nonetheless, experimental studies in rodents have shown that neural progenitor and stem cells isolated from the adult CNS grafted in heterotypic areas integrate and differentiate into neuronal cells of the host brain areas - within 2 months- [69-75]. The ability of the cells to differentiate into neuronal phenotypes of the target areas in heterotypic transplantation supports autologous transplantation as a possible strategy for cellular therapy in the CNS.

ADULT NEURAL STEM CELLS A MODEL OF CHOICE FOR CELLULAR THERAPY FOR CNS DISEASES AND INJURIES

Cell types of various sources and merits, such as cells derived from embryos -embryonic stem cells-, from fetuses, or from tissues and organs, have been considered for cellular therapy in the CNS. Because they do not carry ethical and political concerns, and allow rewiring of the CNS, adult NSCs offer of model of choice for cellular therapy. Beside the ethical and political concerns, NSCs offer a powerful tool for cellular therapy, particularly for cellular trans-lantation.

Cell transplantation aims mainly at delivering cells at specific sites. This is particularly suitable for the treatment of diseases and injuries where the degeneration is limited to mainly one area, such as neurodegenerative diseases like Parkinson's disease, and after traumatic injuries to the CNS [76, 77]. When the degeneration is widespread, such as in neurodegenerative diseases like Alzheimer's disease, HD and multiple sclerosis, such strategy is not applicable. Neural progenitor and stem cells migrate to tumor [78], injured [79-81], and diseased sites [82] when transplanted into the CNS, or administered either by systemic injection, or through the CSF. A recent study in an animal model of multiple sclerosis has reported that systemic injection of neural progenitors and stem cells may provide significant clinical benefits for these disease [82]. Thus, NSC therapy may provide a therapeutic tool for the treatment of a broad range of neurological diseases and injuries, particularly for neurodegenerative diseases. Such migratory properties of NSCs can be used as a general mode for administering neural progenitor and stem cells for cellular therapy, avoiding surgical procedures, and their associated risks and secondary effects. Indeed, systemic injection and injection through CSF are regarded as promising ways to administer NSCs for cellular therapy [83, 84]. Grafted NSCs may also promote functional recovery by promoting the survival of injured neuronal cells through the secretion of neurotrophic factors [85-89], and its interaction with the injured brain [90], further underlining the relevance of NSC transplantation for cellular therapy in the CNS.

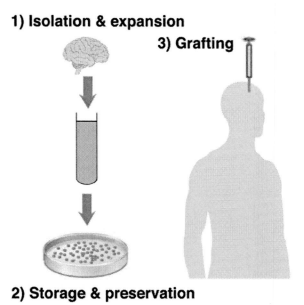

Figure 2. Cellular therapy. The isolation and characterization of neural progenitor and stem cells from the adult brain open new opportunities for cellular transplantation in the CNS. Neural progenitor and stem cells can be isolated, from various areas of the adult CNS, and cultured *in vitro*. Expanded cells can be maintained for weeks in culture, frozen, and stored, allowing the long-term preservation of the neural progenitor and stem cells to be used for cellular therapy. The ability to isolate neural progenitor and stem cells from the adult brain opens the possibility to perform autologous graft by isolating the patients' neural progenitor and stem cells, hence limiting the risk of tissue rejection and obviating the need to find a matching donor.

CONCLUSION

The recent confirmation that neurogenesis occurs in the adult brain, and isolation and characterization *in vitro* of neural progenitor and stem cells from the adult CNS, open new opportunities for cellular therapy in the CNS. Adult-derived neural progenitor and stem cells circumvent the ethical and political concerns associated to their embryonic and fetal counterparts, and offer the opportunity to treat a broad range of CNS diseases and injuries, making adult NSCs a model of choice for cellular therapy in the CNS.

ACKNOWLEDGMENTS

P.T. is supported by grants from the NMRC, BMRC, and the Juvenile Diabetes Research Foundation.

REFERENCES

[1] Taupin P, Gage FH. (2002) Adult neurogenesis and neural stem cells of the central nervous system in mammals. *J Neurosci Res*. 69, 745-9.

[2] Eriksson PS, Perfilieva E, Bjork-Eriksson T, Alborn AM, Nordborg C, Peterson DA, Gage FH. (1998) *Neurogenesis in the adult human hippocampus. Nat* Med. 4, 1313-7.

[3] Sanai N, Tramontin AD, Quinones-Hinojosa A, Barbaro NM, Gupta N, Kunwar S, Lawton MT, McDermott MW, Parsa AT, Manuel-Garcia Verdugo J, Berger MS, Alvarez-Buylla A. (2004) Unique astrocyte ribbon in adult human brain contains neural stem cells but lacks chain migration. *Nature*. 427, 740-4.

[4] Morshead CM, van der Kooy D. (1992) Postmitotic death is the fate of constitutively proliferating cells in the subependymal layer of the adult mouse brain. *J Neurosci*. 12, 249-56.

[5] Cameron HA, McKay RD. (2001) Adult neurogenesis produces a large pool of new granule cells in the dentate gyrus. *J Comp Neurol*. 435, 406-17.

[6] Kempermann G, Kuhn HG, Gage FH. (1997) More hippocampal neurons in adult mice living in an enriched environment. *Nature*. 386, 493-5.

[7] Kato T, Yokouchi K, Fukushima N, Kawagishi K, Li Z, Moriizumi T. (2001) Continual replacement of newly-generated olfactory neurons in adult rats. *Neurosci Lett*. 307, 17-20.

[8] Rietze R, Poulin P, Weiss S. (2000) Mitotically active cells that generate neurons and astrocytes are present in multiple regions of the adult mouse hippocampus. *J Comp Neurol*. 424, 397-408.

[9] Gould E, Reeves AJ, Graziano MS, Gross CG. (1999) Neurogenesis in the neocortex of adult primates. *Science*. 286, 548-52.

[10] Zhao M, Momma S, Delfani K, Carlen M, Cassidy RM, Johansson CB, Brismar H, Shupliakov O, Frisen J, Janson AM. (2003) Evidence for neurogenesis in the adult mammalian substantia nigra. *Proc Natl Acad Sci USA*. 100, 7925-30.

[11] Kornack DR, Rakic P. (2001) Cell proliferation without neurogenesis in adult primate neocortex. *Science*. 294, 2127-30.

[12] Lie DC, Dziewczapolski G, Willhoite AR, Kaspar BK, Shults CW, Gage FH. (2002) The adult substantia nigra contains progenitor cells with neurogenic potential. *J Neurosci*. 22, 6639-49.

[13] Lindvall O, McKay R. (2003) Brain repair by cell replacement and regeneration. *Proc Natl Acad Sci USA*. 100, 7430-1.

[14] Frielingsdorf H, Schwarz K, Brundin P, Mohapel P. (2004) No evidence for new dopaminergic neurons in the adult mammalian substantia nigra. *Proc Natl Acad Sci USA*. 101, 10177-82.

[15] Adrian EK Jr, Walker BE. (1962) Incorporation of thymidine-H3 by cells in normal *and injured mouse spinal cord. J Neuropathol Exp Neurol.* 21, 597-609.

[16] Horner PJ, Power AE, Kempermann G, Kuhn HG, Palmer TD, Winkler J, Thal LJ, Gage FH. (2000) Proliferation and differentiation of progenitor cells throughout the intact adult rat spinal cord. *J Neurosci.* 20, 2218-28.

[17] Taupin P. (2005) Adult neurogenesis in the mammalian central nervous system: functionality and potential clinical interest. *Med Sci Monit.* 11, RA247-52.

[18] Shors TJ, Townsend DA, Zhao M, Kozorovitskiy Y, Gould E. (2002) Neurogenesis may relate to some but not all types of hippocampal-dependent learning. *Hippocampus.* 12, 578-84.

[19] Shors TJ, Miesegaes G, Beylin A, Zhao M, Rydel T, Gould E. (2001) Neurogenesis in the adult is involved in the formation of trace memories. Nature. 410, 372-6. Erratum in: (2001) *Nature.* 414, 938.

[20] Malberg JE, Eisch AJ, Nestler EJ, Duman RS. (2000) Chronic antidepressant treatment increases neurogenesis in adult rat hippocampus. *J Neurosci.* 20, 9104-10.

[21] Santarelli L, Saxe M, Gross C, Surget A, Battaglia F, Dulawa S, Weisstaub N, Lee J, Duman R, Arancio O, Belzung C, Hen R. (2003) Requirement of hippocampal neurogenesis for the behavioral effects of antidepressants. *Science.* 301, 805-9.

[22] Malberg JE, Duman RS. (2003) Cell proliferation in adult hippocampus is decreased by inescapable stress: reversal by fluoxetine treatment. *Neuropsycho-harmacology.* 28, 1562-71.

[23] Jacobs BL, Praag H, Gage FH. (2000) Adult brain neurogenesis and psychiatry: a novel theory of depression. *Mol Psychiatry.* 5, 262-9.

[24] Gage FH. (2000) Mammalian neural stem cells. *Science.* 287, 1433-8.

[25] Heins N, Malatesta P, Cecconi F, Nakafuku M, Tucker KL, Hack MA, Chapouton P, Barde YA, Gotz M. (2002) Glial cells generate neurons: the role of the transcription facto Pax6. *Nat Neurosci.* 5, 308-15.

[26] Wei LC, Shi M, Chen LW, Cao R, Zhang P, Chan YS. (2002) Nestin-containing cells express glial fibrillary acidic protein in the proliferative regions of central nervous system of postnatal developing and adult mice. *Brain Res Dev Brain Res.* 139, 9-17.

[27] Morshead CM, Garcia AD, Sofroniew MV, van Der Kooy D. (2003) The ablation of glial fibrillary acidic protein-positive cells from the adult central nervous system results in the loss of forebrain neural stem cells but not retinal stem cells. *Eur J Neurosci.* 18, 76-84.

[28] Imura T, Kornblum HI, Sofroniew MV. (2003) The predominant neural stem cell isolated from postnatal and adult forebrain but not early embryonic forebrain expresses GFAP. *J Neurosci.* 23, 2824-32.

[29] Garcia AD, Doan NB, Imura T, Bush TG, Sofroniew MV. (2004) GFAP-expressing progenitors are the principal source of constitutive neurogenesis in adult mouse forebrain. *Nat Neurosci.* 7, 1233-41.

[30] Lendahl U, Zimmerman LB, McKay RD. (1990) CNS stem cells express a new class of intermediate filament protein. *Cell.* 60, 585–95.

[31] Sakakibara S, Imai T, Hamaguchi K, Okabe M, Aruga J, Nakajima K, Yasutomi D, Nagata T, Kurihara Y, Uesugi S, Miyata T, Ogawa M, Mikoshiba K, Okano H. (1996) Mouse-Musashi-1, a neural RNA-binding protein highly enriched in the mammalian CNS stem cell. *Dev Biol.* 176, 230-42.

[32] Doetsch F, Caille I, Lim DA, Garcia-Verdugo JM, Alvarez-Buylla A. (1999) Subventricular zone astrocytes are neural stem cells in the adult mammalian brain. *Cell.* 97, 703-16.

[33] Zappone MV, Galli R, Catena R, Meani N, De Biasi S, Mattei E, Tiveron C, Vescovi AL, Lovell-Badge R, Ottolenghi S, Nicolis SK. (2000) Sox2 regulatory sequences direct expression of a (beta)-geo transgene to telencephalic neural stem cells and precursors of the mouse embryo, revealing regionalization of gene expression in CNS stem cells. *Development.* 127, 2367-82.

[34] Kaneko Y, Sakakibara S, Imai T, Suzuki A, Nakamura Y, Sawamoto K, Ogawa Y, Toyama Y, Miyata T, Okano H. (2000) Musashi1: an evolutionally conserved marker for CNS progenitor cells including neural stem cells. *Dev Neurosci.* 22, 139-53.

[35] Okuda T, Tagawa K, Qi ML, Hoshio M, Ueda H, Kawano H, Kanazawa I, Muramatsu M, Okazawa H. (2004) Oct-3/4 repression accelerates differentiation of neural progenitor cells in vitro and in vivo. *Brain Res Mol Brain Res.* 132, 18-30.

[36] Komitova M, Eriksson PS. (2004) Sox-2 is expressed by neural progenitors and astroglia in the adult rat brain. *Neurosci Lett.* 369, 24-7.

[37] Curtis MA, Penney EB, Pearson AG, van Roon-Mom WM, Butterworth NJ, Dragunow M, Connor B, Faull RL. (2003) Increased cell proliferation and neurogenesis in the adult human Huntington's disease brain. *Proc Natl Acad Sci USA.* 100, 9023-7.

[38] Tattersfield AS, Croon RJ, Liu YW, Kells AP, Faull RL, Connor B. (2004) Neurogenesis in the striatum of the quinolinic acid lesion model of Huntington's disease. *Neurosci.* 127, 319-32.

[39] Zhang RL, Zhang ZG, Zhang L, Chopp M. (2001) Proliferation and differentiation of progenitor cells in the cortex and the subventricular zone in the adult rat after focal cerebral ischemia. *Neurosci.* 105, 33-41.

[40] Jiang W, Gu W, Brannstrom T, Rosqvist R, Wester P. (2001) Cortical neurogenesis in adult rats after transient middle cerebral artery occlusion. *Stroke.* 32, 1201-7.

[41] Parent JM, Vexler ZS, Gong C, Derugin N, Ferriero DM. (2002) Rat forebrain neurogenesis and striatal neuron replacement after focal stroke. *Ann Neurol.* 52, 802-13.

[42] Li Y, Chen J, Chopp M. (2002) Cell proliferation and differentiation from ependymal, subependymal and choroid plexus cells in response to stroke in rats. *J Neurol Sci.* 193, 137-46.

[43] Arvidsson A, Collin T, Kirik D, Kokaia Z, Lindvall O. (2002) Neuronal replacement from endogenous precursors in the adult brain after stroke. *Nat Med.* 8, 963-70.

[44] Jin K, Sun Y, Xie L, Peel A, Mao XO, Batteur S, Greenberg DA. (2003) Directed migration of neuronal precursors into the ischemic cerebral cortex and striatum. *Mol Cell Neurosci.* 24, 171-89.

[45] Craig CG, Tropepe V, Morshead CM, Reynolds BA, Weiss S, van der Kooy D. (1996) In vivo growth factor expansion of endogenous subependymal neural precursor cell populations in the adult mouse brain. *J Neurosci.* 16, 2649-58.

[46] Kuhn HG, Winkler J, Kempermann G, Thal LJ, Gage FH. (1997) Epidermal growth factor and fibroblast growth factor-2 have different effects on neural progenitors in the adult rat brain. *J Neurosci.* 17, 5820-9.

[47] Wagner JP, Black IB, DiCicco-Bloom E. (1999) Stimulation of neonatal and adult brain neurogenesis by subcutaneous injection of basic fibroblast growth factor. *J Neurosci.* 19, 6006-16.

[48] Didier A, Jourdan F. (2002) The Ginkgo biloba extract modulates the balance between proliferation and differentiation in the olfactory epithelium of adult mice following bulbectomy. *Cell Mol Biol* (Noisy-le-grand). 48, 717-23.

[49] Fallon J, Reid S, Kinyamu R, Opole I, Opole R, Baratta J, Korc M, Endo TL, Duong A, Nguyen G, Karkehabadhi M, Twardzik D, Patel S, Loughlin S. (2000) In vivo induction of massive proliferation, directed migration, and differentiation of neural cells in the adult mammalian brain. Proc Natl Acad Sci USA. 97, 14686-91. Erratum in: (2001) *Proc Natl Acad Sci USA*. 98, 8157.

[50] Zhang R, Zhang L, Zhang Z, Wang Y, Lu M, Lapointe M, Chopp M. (2001) A nitric oxide donor induces neurogenesis and reduces functional deficits after stroke in rats. *Ann Neurol*. 50, 602-11.

[51] Chen J, Li Y, Zhang R, Katakowski M, Gautam SC, Xu Y, Lu M, Zhang Z, Chopp M. (2004) Combination therapy of stroke in rats with a nitric oxide donor and human bone marrow stromal cells enhances angiogenesis and neurogenesis. *Brain Res*. 1005, 21-8.

[52] Zhang R, Wang Y, Zhang L, Zhang Z, Tsang W, Lu M, Zhang L, Chopp M. (2002) Sildenafil (Viagra) induces neurogenesis and promotes functional recovery after stroke in rats. *Stroke*. 33, 2675-80.

[53] Arvidsson A, Kokaia Z, Lindvall O. (2001) N-methyl-D-aspartate receptor-mediated increase of neurogenesis in adult rat dentate gyrus following stroke. *Eur J Neurosci*. 14, 10-8.

[54] Chen J, Zhang ZG, Li Y, Wang Y, Wang L, Jiang H, Zhang C, Lu M, Katakowski M, Feldkamp CS, Chopp M. (2003) Statins induce angiogenesis, neurogenesis, and synaptogenesis after stroke. *Ann Neurol*. 53, 743-51.

[55] Wang L, Zhang Z, Wang Y, Zhang R, Chopp M. (2004) Treatment of stroke with erythropoietin enhances neurogenesis and angiogenesis and improves neurological function in rats. *Stroke*. 35, 1732-7.

[56] Jin K, Sun Y, Xie L, Childs J, Mao XO, Greenberg DA. (2004) Post-ischemic administration of heparin-binding epidermal growth factor-like growth factor (HB-EGF) reduces infarct size and modifies neurogenesis after focal *cerebral ischemia in the rat. J Cereb Blood Flow Metab*. 24, 399-408.

[57] Sun Y, Jin K, Xie L, Childs J, Mao XO, Logvinova A, Greenberg DA. (2003) VEGF-induced neuroprotection, neurogenesis, and angiogenesis after focal cerebral ischemia. *J Clin Invest*. 111, 1843-51.

[58] Teramoto T, Qiu J, Plumier JC, Moskowitz MA. (2003) EGF amplifies the replacement of parvalbumin-expressing striatal interneurons after ischemia. *J Clin Invest*. 111, 1125-32.

[59] Nakatomi H, Kuriu T, Okabe S, Yamamoto S, Hatano O, Kawahara N, Tamura A, Kirino T, Nakafuku M. (2002) Regeneration of hippocampal pyramidal neurons after ischemic brain injury by recruitment of endogenous neural progenitors. *Cell*. 110, 429-41.

[60] Mohapel P, Frielingsdorf H, Haggblad J, Zachrisson O, Brundin P. (2005) Platelet-Derived Growth Factor (PDGF-BB) and Brain-Derived Neurotrophic Factor (BDNF) induce striatal neurogenesis in adult rats with 6-hydroxydopamine lesions. *Neuroscience*. 132, 767-76.

[61] Namura S, Zhu J, Fink K, Endres M, Srinivasan A, Tomaselli KJ, Yuan J, Moskowitz MA. (1998) Activation and cleavage of caspase-3 in apoptosis induced by experimental cerebral ischemia. *J Neurosci*. 18, 3659-68.

[62] Pompeiano M, Blaschke AJ, Flavell RA, Srinivasan A, Chun J. (2000) Decreased apoptosis in proliferative and postmitotic regions of the Caspase 3-deficient embryonic central nervous system. *J Comp Neurol*. 423, 1-12.

[63] Ekdahl CT, Mohapel P, Elmer E, Lindvall O. (2001) Caspase inhibitors increase short-term survival of progenitor-cell progeny in the adult rat dentate gyrus following status epilepticus. *Eur J Neurosci*. 14, 937-45.

[64] Martens DJ, Seaberg RM, van der Kooy D. (2002) In vivo infusions of exogenous growth factors into the fourth ventricle of the adult mouse brain increase the proliferation of neural progenitors around the fourth ventricle and the central canal of the spinal cord. *Eur J Neurosci*. 16, 1045-57.

[65] Monje ML, Toda H, Palmer TD. (2003) Inflammatory blockade restores adult hippocampal neurogenesis. *Science*. 302, 1760-5.

[66] Ekdahl CT, Claasen JH, Bonde S, Kokaia Z, Lindvall O. (2003) Inflammation is detrimental for neurogenesis in adult brain. *Proc Natl Acad Sci USA*. 100, 13632-7.

[67] Palmer TD, Schwartz PH, Taupin P, Kaspar B, Stein SA, Gage FH. (2001) Cell culture. Progenitor cells from human brain after death. *Nature*. 411, 42-3.

[68] Schwartz PH, Bryant PJ, Fuja TJ, Su H, O'Dowd DK, Klassen H. (2003) Isolation and characterization of neural progenitor cells from post-mortem human cortex. *J Neurosci Res*. 74, 838-51.

[69] Gage FH, Coates PW, Palmer TD, Kuhn HG, Fisher LJ, Suhonen JO, Peterson DA, Suhr ST, Ray J. (1995) Survival and differentiation of adult neuronal progenitor cells transplanted to the adult brain. *Proc Natl Acad Sci USA*. 92, 11879-83.

[70] Suhonen JO, Peterson DA, Ray J, Gage FH. (1996) Differentiation of adult hippocampus-derived progenitors into olfactory neurons *in vivo*. *Nature*. 383, 624-27.

[71] Takahashi M, Palmer TD, Takahashi J, Gage FH. (1998) Widespread integration and survival of adult-derived neural progenitor cells in the developing optic retina. *Mol Cell Neurosci*. 12, 340-8.

[72] Shihabuddin LS, Horner PJ, Ray J, Gage FH. (2000) Adult spinal cord stem cells generate neurons after transplantation in the adult dentate gyrus. *J Neurosci*. 20, 8727-35.

[73] Young MJ, Ray J, Whiteley SJ, Klassen H, Gage FH. (2000) Neuronal differentiation and morphological integration of hippocampal progenitor cells transplanted to the retina of immature and mature dystrophic rats. *Mol Cell Neurosci*. 16, 197-205.

[74] .Akiyama Y, Honmou O, Kato T, Uede T, Hashi K, Kocsis JD. (2001) Transplantation of clonal neural precursor cells derived from adult human brain establishes functional peripheral myelin in the rat spinal cord. *Exp Neurol*. 167, 27-39.

[75] Vroemen M, Aigner L, Winkler J, Weidner N. (2003) Adult neural progenitor cell grafts survive after acute spinal cord injury and integrate along axonal pathways. *Eur J Neurosci*. 18, 743-51.

[76] Armstrong RJ, Tyers P, Jain M, Richards A, Dunnett SB, Rosser AE, Barker RA. (2003) Transplantation of expanded neural precursor cells from the developing pig ventral mesencephalon in a rat model of Parkinson's disease. *Exp Brain Res*. 151, 204-17.

[77] Lepore AC, Bakshi A, Swanger SA, Rao MS, Fischer I. (2005) Neural precursor cells can be delivered into the injured cervical spinal cord by intrathecal injection at the lumbar cord. *Brain Res*. 1045, 206-16.

[78] Brown AB, Yang W, Schmidt NO, Carroll R, Leishear KK, Rainov NG, Black PM, Breakefield XO, Aboody KS. (2003) Intravascular delivery of neural stem cell lines to target intracranial and extracranial tumors of neural and non-neural origin. *Hum Gene Ther*. 14, 1777-85.

[79] Macklis JD. (1993) Transplanted neocortical neurons migrate selectively into regions of neuronal degeneration produced by chromophore-targeted laser photolysis. *J Neurosci*. 13, 3848-63.

[80] Veizovic T, Beech JS, Stroemer RP, Watson WP, Hodges H. (2001) Resolution of stroke deficits following contralateral grafts of conditionally immortal neuroepithelial stem cells. *Stroke*. 32, 1012-9.

[81] Boockvar JA, Schouten J, Royo N, Millard M, Spangler Z, Castelbuono D, Snyder E, O'Rourke D, McIntosh T. (2005) Experimental traumatic brain injury modulates the survival, migration, and terminal phenotype of transplanted epidermal growth factor receptor-activated neural stem cells. *Neurosurgery*. 56, 163-71.

[82] Pluchino S, Quattrini A, Brambilla E, Gritti A, Salani G, Dina G, Galli R, Del Carro U, Amadio S, Bergami A, Furlan R, Comi G, Vescovi AL, Martino G. (2003) Injection of adult neurospheres induces recovery in a chronic model of multiple sclerosis. *Nature*. 422, 688-94.

[83] Wu S, Suzuki Y, Kitada M, Kataoka K, Kitaura M, Chou H, Nishimura Y, Ide C. (2002) New method for transplantation of neurosphere cells into injured spinal cord through cerebrospinal fluid in rat. *Neurosci Lett*. 318, 81-4.

[84] Fujiwara Y, Tanaka N, Ishida O, Fujimoto Y, Murakami T, Kajihara H, Yasunaga Y, Ochi M. (2004) Intravenously injected neural progenitor cells of transgenic rats can migrate to the injured spinal cord and differentiate into neurons, astrocytes and oligodendrocytes. *Neurosci Lett*. 366, 287-91.

[85] Ourednik J, Ourednik V, Lynch WP, Schachner M, Snyder EY. (2002) Neural stem cells display an inherent mechanism for rescuing dysfunctional neurons. *Nat Biotechnol*. 20, 1103-10.

[86] Lu P, Jones LL, Snyder EY, Tuszynski MH. (2003) Neural stem cells constitutively secrete neurotrophic factors and promote extensive host axonal growth after spinal cord injury. *Exp Neurol*. 181, 115-29.

[87] Llado J, Haenggeli C, Maragakis NJ, Snyder EY, Rothstein JD. (2004) Neural stem cells protect against glutamate-induced excitotoxicity and promote survival of injured motor neurons through the secretion of neurotrophic factors. *Mol Cell Neurosci*. 27, 322-31.

[88] Yan J, Welsh AM, Bora SH, Snyder EY, Koliatsos VE. (2004) Differentiation and tropic/trophic effects of exogenous neural precursors in the adult spinal cord. *J Comp Neurol*. 480, 101-14.

[89] Pfeifer K, Vroemen M, Blesch A, Weidner N. (2004) Adult neural progenitor cells provide a permissive guiding substrate for corticospinal axon growth following spinal cord injury. *Eur J Neurosci*. 20, 1695-704.

[90] Park KI, Teng YD, Snyder EY. (2002) The injured brain interacts reciprocally with neural stem cells supported by scaffolds to reconstitute lost tissue. *Nat Biotechnol.* 20, 1111-7.

In: Progress in Stem Cell Research
Editor: Prasad S. Koka, pp. 77-90

ISBN: 978-1-60456-065-7
© 2008 Nova Science Publishers, Inc.

Chapter 5

THE CARDIOGENIC POTENTIAL OF MOUSE AND HUMAN EMBRYONIC STEM CELLS: COGNITIVE RESEARCH TO ENVISION THE THERAPEUTIC USE OF THE CELLS

Michel Pucéat[2]

CNRS FRE2593, Centre de Recherche de Biochimie Macromoléculaire
Montpellier, France

ABSTRACT

Embryonic stem cells (ESC) have become attractive for prospective cell therapy of degenerative diseases. Both mouse and human embryonic stem cell lines provide also a powerful biological system to study the early stages of mouse and human development. More specifically, the heart is the first functional organ to develop in the embryo. Cardiac congenital and genetic diseases are the most frequent inborn defects in the foetus. Mouse ES cells recapitulate the genetic programme of the first stages of cardiac cell differentiation. They can give rise to all cardiac phenotypes. They thus represent a precious cell model to better comprehend these diseases. The early stages of development of the primate embryo share many similarities with mouse embryogenesis. However, differences also exist including the temporal and spatial patterns of gene expression. Little is known about the cardiogenic potential of human ES cells. This overview discusses the true potential of cardiogenesis of both mouse and human ES cells and proposes future lines of research within the prospective of developmental biology and therapeutic use.

[2] Correspondence: M. Pucéat, CRBM, CNRS FRE 2593, 1919, route de Mende 34293, Montpellier, France
Phone: (33) 4 67 61 34 32; Fax: (33) 4 67 52 15 59 michel.puceat@crbm.cnrs.fr

INTRODUCTION: THE NEED FOR STEM CELL THERAPIES IN CARDIOLOGY

Heart failure emerges as an epidemic in the industrialized world. According to The World Health Organisation (WHO), 16.6 millions of people die of cardiovascular diseases each year and more than 600 millions are at high risk of heart attack, stroke and cardiac failure. The WHO predicts a three fold increase in mortality from cardiac diseases by 2020. Most of chronic heart diseases develop following cardiac stroke and as consequences of both cardiomyopathies and congenital diseases. These pathologies are also associated with muscle myopathies such as Duchenne muscular dystrophies, X-linked dilated myopathies and some forms of Becker muscular dystrophies [1]. It is worth pointing out that congenital heart diseases are the most common inborn defects likely because the heart is the first organ to develop. Adult patients with congenital heart diseases represent an expanding population [2]. Although surgical repair has greatly improved and relieved most of the symptoms, more and more patients still suffer from a myocardial degeneration process when they get older [3]. The clinical picture shared by all these cardiac diseases includes a degeneration of myocytes replaced by interstitial fibrosis [4, 5]. Mammalian cardiomyocytes are terminally differentiated, with a limited mitotic activity [6]. They are thus unable to regenerate a diseased myocardium. An external source of cells is required to repair a damaged myocardium. The origin of cells to be transplanted is still under debate and has been the subject of several overviews for the last years [7-9]. In the following, I will specifically focus on embryonic stem cells and their cardiogenic potential.

In a recent report, Nadia Rosenthal [10] envisioned a science fiction scenario in which a patient featuring heart failure is transplanted with personalised embryonic stem cells (ESC) engineered by nuclear transfer [11, 12]. The cells meet the right growth factors *in situ* and regenerate his damaged myocardium (Figure 1). How far are we to make this dream becoming reality at the bedside of patients? Will we need somatic nuclear transfer to engineer immunologically tolerant so called customized ESCs? What is the genuine cardiogenic potential of hESC lines? These issues are reviewed and discussed.

CARDIAC POTENTIAL OF EMBRYONIC STEM CELLS

Immature and full of potential, ESCs are capable to recapitulate the first stages of heart development including specification and differentiation toward a cardiac phenotype. A pioneering paper [13] ten years ago, reported *in vitro* that mouse ESCs were able to differentiate toward all cardiac cell types (i.e, atrial ventricular, conduction or pacemaker cells). Using mouse ESC clones engineered to express reporter genes under specific cardiac promoters, we could more recently track in embryoid bodies, a three dimensional *in vitro* structure recapitulating the three embryonic layers, contractile ventricular cells [14, 15] or non-contractile pacemaker cells [16]. One of the major advantages of mouse ES cells including the D3 [13], R1 and CGR8 [14] cell lines is that they feature a great potential of cardiac differentiation. Furthermore their fate can be directed toward a cardiac lineage by using BMP2 (bone morphogenetic protein) or TGFβ [15], two members of the TGFβ superfamily secreted by the endoderm [17], or after co-culture with endodermal cells.

Under these experimental conditions, ESC-derived cardiomyo-cytes are capable to align their sarcomeric units as observed *in vivo* in the myocardium (Figure 2). BMP2, the most efficient cardiogenic factor when used at low concentration is a well conserved cardiogenic morphogen through the evolution. Dpp, the drosophila homolog of BMP2, favors formation of the mesoderm including the heart [18]. Similar effects have been observed in zebrafish [19], xenopus [20, 21] and chicken [22]. It is thus expected that BMP2 can direct the fate of human ESCs toward a cardiac lineage although this remains to be determined.

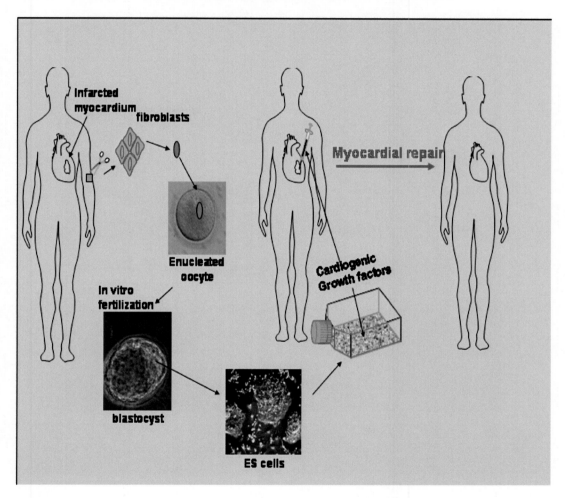

Figure 1. An envisioned scenario for cell therapy of heart failure. Nuclear somatic transfer to customize hESCs. After enucleation, the oocyte receives the nucleus of a fibroblast isolated from a patient. After in vitro fertilisation, the oocyte will develop up to the stage of the blastocyst. An ESC line can be derived. Following growth factor induced-cardiac commitment, the hESCs will be transplanted into the myocardium of the patient allowing for its repair

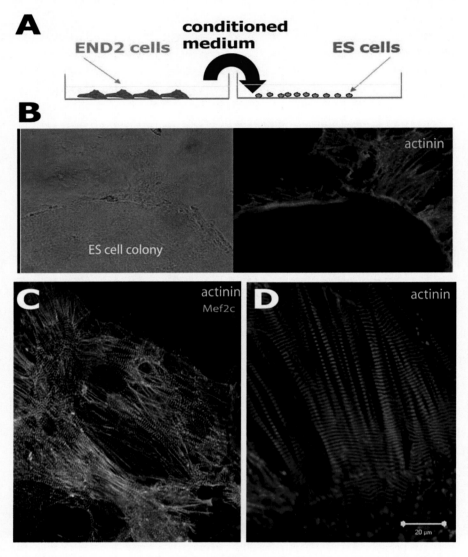

Figure 2. Mouse ESCs were cultured with conditioned medium from END2 cell line (A) for 7 days. After 4 days cells at the border of the colony differentiate into cardiomyocytes expressing actinin (B). After 5 days, sarcomeric units were organised in Mef2c-positive cells (C). After one week, alignment of sarcomeric units was observed (D).

Ours and other studies have demonstrated the cardiogenic potential of mouse ESCs *in vivo* after transplantation in damaged myocardium. We have uncovered that undifferentiated mouse ESCs cultured at high density or committed to the cardiogenic fate by factors of the TGFβ superfamily, engrafted into immunocompetent rat infarcted myocardium are capable to respond to growth factors of the same family, present in the scar environment. The cells differentiate into functional cardiomyocytes and improve myocardial function [15], even in a long term [23]. Importantly, we never observed any teratomas in transplanted rats. Similar results were recently found after transplantation of cardiac committed ESCs into allogenic hosts [24]. These findings point out an immune privilege of ESCs and their cardiac progeny, an advantage that could overcome the need for somatic nuclear transfer to engineer "autologous like" cells. Several hypothesis exist to account for this privilege: (i) the low levels of major histo-compatibility complex molecules (MHC) in early-differentiated ESCs and their differentiated derivatives as well as the lack of co-stimulatory molecules and of natural killer lysis receptors [25]; (ii) a local immunosuppressive effect mediated by cell-to-cell contact or soluble factors, as described for mesenchymal stem cells [26]; (iii) an induction of tolerance as reported following injection of rat ESC-like cells into fully MHC-mismatched recipients with functional thymus [27-29]. The proposed mechanisms for this host "stealth immune tolerance" [30] remain however to be further investigated to fully comprehend its molecular basis prior to foresee the use of hESCs in allogenic patients.

In contrast, continued proliferation and formation of tumors occurred upon transplantation of ESC lines engineered to be unresponsive to endogenous BMP2 or TGFβ signaling through expression of Noggin or a dominant negative mutant of the TGFβRII, respectivelyβ [15]. These ESC-derived tumors are teratomas consisting of cartilaginous, glandular and germ cell types indicating that in the absence of specific signaling differentiation is random.

The risk of tumorogenesis in the heart is reduced by several compounding factors. Indeed, primary tumors or metastasis are rarely observed in the heart [31] indicating that the myocardium is an unfavorable environment for unregulated cell proliferation. Furthermore, mouse ESCs lose their tumorigenic potential when pluripotency is no longer supported by the influence of Leukemia Inhibitory Factor (LIF), a cytokine used in culture to maintain the undifferentiated state. This likely results from upregulation of D cyclins and cyclin-dependent kinase inhibitors [32], which we observed after challenging ESCs with TGFβ or BMP2 (unpublished data) and forcing cell dependence upon activation of mitogen-activated protein (MAP) kinases [33] by growth factors like TGFβ. In fact, it was known for a long time that grafts of embryonic tissue also lose the capacity to form tumors early after differentiation [34] when they acquire control of their proliferation by extracellular signal regulated kinases (ERKs). It is thus not surprising that a similar scenario takes place after cardiac commitment of ESC.

When transplanted into immuno-depressed hosts without guiding their fate, the cells form a teratoma [9]. These results were somehow expected as discussed above and further suggest that the cardiac environment of non-infarcted myocardium of immuno-tolerant recipients does not provide enough cardiogenic factors required for differentiation of mouse ESCs. Furthermore it further points out the major role of cardiac commitment of cells before transplantation into a recipient animal. We recently carried out similar xenogeneic cell transplantation experiments, engrafting BMP2-cardiac committed ESCs into sheep failing heart. We still observed differentiation of ESCs into functional cardiac cells resulting in a significant gain in myocardial function without formation of any teratomas. The cells were tolerated even in the absence of immunosuppression [35], further suggesting the immune privilege of these embryonic cells. These finding are undoubtedly promising for the use of ESCs in regenerative medicine.

Others and we aim at obtaining similar results with primate non-human and human ESCs. Primate ESCs turn out however to be more labor intensive than mouse ESCs. So far, several laboratories have reported the cardiogenic potential of hESCs. Kehat et al [36] were the first to demonstrate that hESC could differentiate in cardiomyocytes. However, using different stage-specific cardiac markers and electrophysiology, they found that these cells did not mature but remained at a very early stage of differentiation. Furthermore, the percentage of embryoid bodies that feature contractile areas was very low. These data were confirmed by Xu et al [37] using several ESC lines (H1, H7, H9, H9.1 and H9.2). In 2003, He et al [38] used electrophysiology and demonstrated that hESCs could give rise to atrial, ventricular as well as nodal cells. Still, the number of cardiomyocytes generated from hESCs was poor. However, hESC–derived cardiomyocytes mostly featured an early cardiac phenotype associated with a spontaneous electrical activity. Although this property is used to generate biological cell-based pacemaker [39, 40], this should be only a transient characteristic. The cells should differentiate later on toward a quiescent cardiac phenotype. Differentiation of hESCs into a mature ventricular cell does not appear to be as spontaneous as for mouse ESCs. Additional extrinsic factors may be required to achieve this goal. In fact, very few attempts have been made to improve spontaneous differentiation of hESC toward a cardiogenic lineage. So far, one study showed that TGFβ and activin direct the fate of hESC toward a mesodermal lineage [41] and a second one reported that endodermal cells (END-2) [42], likely to secrete cardiogenic factors including TGFβ, FGFs and BMP2, favor cardiac differentiation. Much experimental effort should be devoted to this key issue.

TRANSCRIPTIONAL REGULATION OF ESC CARDIAC SPECIFICATION

In the embryo, the heart is the first organ to develop. Similarly, cardiomyocytes are among the first cell type to differentiate *in vitro* from ES cells. In murine embryogenesis, numerous cardiac–restricted transcription factors are induced in the heart field. These include Mesp1,2, Tbx genes, Nkx2.5, GATA4, GATA6 and Mef2c [43]. A similar genetic program is switched on in spontaneously differentiating ESCs [14, 44]. These transcription factors work in concert together with the serum responsive factor (SRF) to specify the cardiac lineage [45]. More recently, two heart fields have been described in mouse embryos. The primary heart field gives rise to the left ventricle while the secondary or anterior heart field gives rise to the right ventricle, the atria and the outflow tract [46]. It is still unknown whether ESCs are capable to generate both heart fields. The search of specific markers of each heart field (i.e., FoxH1, Tbx1, and Isl1 for the anterior field for example) in embryoid bodies will be important to address this issue.

Two cardiogenic transcriptional pathways regulating expression of the cardiac specific genes mentioned above have been described so far in murine cardiogenesis. Nodal, a factor belonging to the TGFβ superfamily is expressed in blastocysts and commit the cells of the epiblast toward a mesodermal cardiogenic fate [47]. Later on, another member of the TGFβ superfamily, the bone morphogenetic 2 (BMP2) has been shown to play a key role in cardiogenesis [43]. The BMP-dependent pathway activates Smad proteins and downstream effectors including cardiac transcription factors such as Nkx2.5 and Mef2c [48]. These transcription factors interact to activate the cardiac transcriptional programme. For example, GATA and Smad 1 et 4 cooperate to transactivate Nkx2.5 [49]. Smad proteins regulate transcription of Mef2c [50] and GATA4 recruits Mef2c on promoters of cardiac genes [51]. GATA4, Nkx2.5 and « serum response factor» (SRF) are all required for the cardiogenic fate [52].

We have recently uncovered another BMP independent cardiogenic pathway in mouse ESCs in which LEK1, a mouse and human ortholog of CMF1 (chicken cardiomyogenic factor 1) [53] binding the retinoblastoma protein (Rb) plays a major role. We found that Rb-/- ES cells, siRNA- and antisense-mediated LEK1 knock-down ES cells share the same cardiac phenotype while differentiating. A dramatic delay in the process of cardiac differentiation was observed in both cell types. Most of mesodermal and cardiac specific genes are downregulated resulting in impaired myofibrillogenesis and in turn, beating activity of the cells at early stages of differentiation. Interestingly, both phenotypes are rescued by activation of the canonical cardiogenic BMP-dependent pathway. In the presence of both Rb and LEK1, a block in interaction between these proteins by expressing a peptide mimicking the Rb binding domain of LEK1 in the nucleus of differentiating ES cells recapitulated the delay in cardiac cell differentiation [54]. Interaction of Rb with LEK1 is thus required to specify stem cells toward a cardiac lineage at an earlier stage than the BMP-dependent pathway. Whether these transcriptional pathways are functional in hESCs is under investigation in the laboratory.

DIFFERENCES IN EARLY CARDIAC DEVELOPMENT OF MOUSE AND PRIMATE EMBRYO

Both mouse and primate embryonic cell lines are derived from the inner cell mass of the blastocyst. Propagation of both types of cell lines required specific conditions in relation to the molecular mechanisms underlying their pluripotency and self renewal. These mechanisms implicate the LIF and the JAK/STAT pathway, and the transcription factors Oct-4 and Nanog in mouse. In LIF-independent primate ESCs, Oct-4 and Nanog still play a key role as gatekeepers of their pluripotency while growth factors including FGF2 and members of the TGFβ superfamily also participate in maintaining the pluripotency of cells (reviewed by Rao and Stice [55]).

There is a general agreement that mouse ESCs recapitulate the differentiation potential of the inner cell mass. Mouse ESCs participate in chimera formation following injection in blastocysts fully demonstrating their pluripotency. So far such a potential of primate ESCs is unknown in non human primates. Generation of teratoma after implantation of primate ESCs into immunosuppressed mice is the only index of pluripotency although it does not predict the functionality of differentiated cells. Several observations support the idea that the phenotype of mouse ESCs might be different from the one of primate ESCs. The three embryonic layers are formed after 14 days in human and 6 days in mouse. Considering 5-9 months gestation in primates versus 3 weeks in mouse, the difference may not appear as so important. However, it is crucial to keep in mind that at day 7, cardiac progenitors are clearly clustered in the cardiac crescent in mouse embryos, while human embryo has just finished formation of extraembryonic membranes. Nevertheless, cell beating activity, an index of the first functional cardiac cells is observed at one week in mouse [56] and at three weeks in humans [57, 58]. However, the early stages of embryonic development in primate feature some peculiar differences with the ones in mouse, which could account for potential differences in differentiation capabilities between mouse and primate ESCs. Importantly, transition from maternal to zygote gene expression occurs later in human embryo than in mice. The mouse blastocyst forms one cleavage later than the human (reviewed by Pera and Troumson [59]). It is also interesting to note that the major genome activation occurs between six and eight cells in primates but at the two cells stage in mouse [60]. Major differences have been observed in the *in vitro* model of ESCs maybe reflecting the differences observed between species at the early embryonic stages. Oct-4 is no longer detectable in day 5 embryoid bodies generated from mouse ESCs (our unpublished data) while it is still highly expressed in day 10 human embryoid bodies. Similarly α-foeto protein, an endodermal marker expressed very early in mouse ESCs (i.e. in undifferentiated cells, our unpublished data) starts to be expressed only in day 10-30 human embryoid bodies [61]. This gene expression profiling suggests major differences in the timing of differentiation of mouse and human ESCs.

Mouse ESCs have been shown to generate the primitive ectoderm (early primitive ectodermal like cells, EPL cells), a post gastrulation structure deriving from cavitation of the epiblast in vivo and giving rise to the three embryonic layers ectoderm, mesoderm and endoderm [62]. Non human primate ESCs also form embryoid bodies ressembling the post-implantation embryo, including the formation of the early primitive streak, an amnion and a yolk sac [63] as well as the epiblast generating the mesoderm [64]. This strongly suggests that both mouse and human ESC represent a suitable model of embryonic development.

More specifically, while studies on the dysfunctional genetics of human cardiac development have suggested that key cardiac genes may be conserved in both mouse and primate [65], and that comparison of gene expression pattern in both mouse and primate have shown some compelling similarities, there are also some key differences that should be kept in mind [66].

PROSPECTIVE RESEARCH

There are still many lines of research that need to be investigated to better characterize and understand the cardiogenic potential of ESCs. First, the cardiogenic transcriptional networks established in mouse including in the ESC model remains to be substantiated in human ESCs. Second, The dynamic of transcription factors to bind each other in a concerted action and/or to genes promoters to direct the fate of ESCs is conditioned by accessibility of their targets and thus by chromatin structure. Indeed, genes residing in heterochromatin (containing repressive factors) are silent while genes located in euchromatin (including activating factors) are turned on. Chromatin remodelling is thus required to activate transcriptional pathways. Multiprotein complexes are the key molecular components to modify the structure of chromatin. These include DNA cytosine methyltransferase (Dnmt), Methyl CpG-binding protein (MECP2, MBDs and Kaiso), histone modification enzymes (HAT Histone acetyl transferase, HDAC Histone deacetylase, HMT, Histone methyltransferase) and ATP-dependent remodelling enzyme [67]. ESCs indeed contain robust chromatin-remodeling activities [68]. A complex formed by specific components might be a key element to ensure proper transactivation of genes and in turn to set a developmental genetic programme toward cardiac cell differentiation. Further investigation will elucidate these transcriptional mechanisms.

Third, one has to keep in mind that protein-coding regions represent roughly 2 % of the total human genome with additional surrounding sequence being transcribed into RNA either in the form of introns or as 5'- or 3'-untranslated regions of mRNA. A great proportion of non-coding DNA is transcribed into functional non-coding RNAs including micro (mi)RNAs. miRNAs are short RNAs that downregulate protein expression by promoting the degradation of mRNAs [69]. Specific expression of miRNAs as early as in embryonic stem cells (ESCs) [70, 71] and in different adult mouse tissues including heart-specific miRNAs [72], suggests that they also determine cell lineage and the mature phenotype. Expression and regulation of these miRNAs as well as identification of their targets, in a context of ESC differentiation would shed light to their role and would open a new concept of regulation of developmental pathways.

Derivation of hESC lines from blastocysts harboring a genetic disease is one of the most challenging aspects of biology of ESCs. Indeed, using mouse ESCs, we [73] have been the first laboratory to develop a cell model of cardiomyopathy that turned out to be very powerful to delineate the molecular mechanisms underlying the extent of the severity of the disease at very early stages of development.

HESC lines have already been derived after preimplantation diagnostic of genetic diseases including mucoviscidosis [74]. Undoubtedly, research carried out on such cell lines including the establishment of their differentiation potential will greatly help in understanding the molecular basis of genetic diseases.

Finally, in the prospective of potential therapeutic trials using hESCs, transplantation of cardiac committed hESC in a non human primate model of heart failure is mandatory to determine *in vivo* the fate of stem cells, their differentiation status and tolerance by the recipient. Such experiments are on going in the laboratory. They should provide us with precious information as to the requirement or not of somatic nuclear transfer to customize hESCs, a feasible process but with potential unexpected problems [75].

Potential of ESCs has opened a new area of biology with still unexpected applications. These cells are still to surprise us. However, we have to learn more from and be inspired by embryology to better comprehend and to instruct the fate of ESCs. It is still difficult to predict what will be the fate of ESCs after in vivo engraftment. More basic science is required to fill the gap between bench work and regenerative medicine. Once again in biology, we have to remember Claude Bernard: "At the origin of knowledge, there is an idea, a thought, then, the experience comes to confirm the idea".

REFERENCES

[1]   Megeney LA, Kablar B, Perry RL, Ying C, May L, Rudnicki MA. Severe cardiomyopathy in mice lacking dystrophin and MyoD. *Proc Natl Acad Sci USA*, (1999) 96, 220-5.

[2]   Wu JC, Child JS. Common *congenital heart disorders in adults.* Curr Probl Cardiol, (2004) 29, 641-700.

[3]   Bolger AP, Gatzoulis MA. Towards defining heart failure in adults with congenital heart disease. *Int J Cardiol, (2004) 97 Suppl* 1, 15-23.

[4]   Schonberger J, Seidman CE, Levy H, Grunig E, Sangwatanaroj S, Fatkin D, MacRae C, Stacker H, Halpin C, Eavey R, Philbin EF, Katus H, Seidman JG. Many roads lead to a broken heart: the genetics of dilated cardiomyopathy. *Am J Hum Genet,* (2001) 69, 249-60.

[5]   Cox G, Kunkel L. Dystrophies and heart disease. *Curr Opin Cardiol.*, (1997) 12, 229-343.

[6]   Beltrami AP, Urbanek K, Kajstura J, Yan SM, Finato N, Bussani R, Nadal-Ginard B, Silvestri F, Leri A, Beltrami CA, Anversa P. Evidence that human cardiac myocytes divide after myocardial infarction. *N Engl J Med,* (2001) 344, 1750-7.

[7]   Menard C, Grey C, Mery A, Zeineddine D, Aimond F, Puceat M. Cardiac specification of embryonic stem cells. *J Cell Biochem,* (2004) 93, 681-7.

[8]   Mathur A, Martin JF. Stem cells and repair of the heart. *Lancet,* (2004) 364, 183-92.

[9]   Laflamme MA, Murry CE. Regenerating the heart. *Nat Biotechnol,* (2005) 23, 845-56.

[10] Rosenthal N. Youthful prospects for human stem-cell therapy. *EMBO reports,* (2005) 6, S30-S34.

[11] Hwang WS, Lee BC, Lee CK, Kang SK. Human embryonic stem cells and therapeutic cloning. *J Vet Sci,* (2005) 6, 87-96.

[12] Hwang WS, Roh SI, Lee BC, Kang SK, Kwon DK, Kim S, Kim SJ, Park SW, Kwon HS, Lee CK, Lee JB, Kim JM, Ahn C, Paek SH, Chang SS, Koo JJ, Yoon HS, Hwang JH, Hwang YY, Park YS, Oh SK, Kim HS, Park JH, Moon SY, Schatten G. Patient-specific embryonic stem cells derived from human SCNT blastocysts. *Science,* (2005) 308, 1777-83.

[13] Maltsev VA, Wobus AM, Rohwedel J, Bader M, Hescheler J. Cardiomyocytes differentiated in vitro from embryonic stem cells developmentally express cardiac-specific genes and ionic currents. *Circ Res,* (1994) 75, 233-44.

[14] Meyer N, Jaconi M, Ladopoulou A, Fort P, Puceat M. A fluorescent reporter gene as a marker for ventricular specification in ES-derived cardiac cells. *FEBS Letter,* (2000) 478, 151-158.

[15] Behfar A, Zingman L, Hodgson D, Rauzier J, Kane G, Terzic A, Pucéat M. Stem cell differentiation requires a paracrine pathway in the heart. *FASEB J.,* (2002) 16, 1558-1566.

[16] Mery A, Aimond F, Menard C, Mikoshiba K, Michalak M, Puceat M. Initiation of Embryonic Cardiac Pacemaker Activity by Inositol 1,4,5 Trisphosphate-dependent Calcium Signaling. *Mol Biol Cell,* (2005) 9, 2414-23.

[17] Lough J, Sugi Y. Endoderm and heart development. *Dev Dyn,* (2000) 217, 327-42.

[18] Frasch M. Intersecting signalling and transcriptional pathways in Drosophila heart specification. *Semin Cell Dev Biol,* (1999) 10, 61-71.

[19] Reiter JF, Verkade H, Stainier DY. Bmp2b and Oep promote early myocardial differentiation through their regulation of gata5. *Dev Biol,* (2001) 234, 330-8.

[20] Breckenridge RA, Mohun TJ, Amaya E. A role for BMP signalling in heart looping morphogenesis in Xenopus. *Dev Biol,* (2001) 232, 191-203.

[21] Shi Y, Katsev S, Cai C, Evans S. BMP signaling is required for heart formation in vertebrates. *Dev Biol,* (2000) 224, 226-37.

[22] Andree B, Duprez D, Vorbusch B, Arnold HH, Brand T. BMP-2 induces ectopic expression of cardiac lineage markers and interferes with somite formation in chicken embryos. *Mech Dev,* (1998) 70, 119-31.

[23] Hodgson DM, Behfar A, Zingman LV, Kane GC, Terzic C, Alekseev AE, Pucéat M, Terzic A. Stable benefit of embryonic stem cell therapy in myocardial infarction. *Am. J. Physiol,* (2004) 287, H471-9.

[24] Kofidis T, de Bruin JL, Yamane T, Tanaka M, Lebl DR, Swijnenburg RJ, Weissman IL, Robbins RC. Stimulation of paracrine pathways with growth factors enhances embryonic stem cell engraftment and host-specific differentiation in the heart after ischemic myocardial injury. *Circulation*, (2005) 111, 2486-93.

[25] Drukker M, Benvenisty N. The immunogenicity of human embryonic stem-derived cells. Trends *Biotechnol*, (2004) 22, 136-41.

[26] Aggarwal S, Pittenger MF. Human mesenchymal stem cells modulate allogeneic immune cell responses. *Blood*, (2005) 105, 1815-22.

[27] Frandrich F, Lin X, Chai GX, Schulze M, Ganten D, Bader M, Holle J, Huang D-G, Parwaresch R, Zavazava N, Binas B. Preimplantation-stage stem cells induce long-term allogenic graft acceptance without supplementary host conditioning. *Nature Medecine*, (2002) 8, 171-178.

[28] Li L, Baroja ML, Majumdar A, Chadwick K, Rouleau A, Gallacher L, Ferber I, Lebkowski J, Martin T, Madrenas J, Bhatia M. Human embryonic stem cells possess immune-privileged properties. *Stem Cells*, (2004) 22, 448-56.

[29] Fabricius D, Bonde S, Zavazava N. Induction of stable mixed chimerism by embryonic stem cells requires functional Fas/FasL engagement. *Transplantation*, (2005) 79, 1040-4.

[30] Chiu RC. Xenogeneic cell transplant: fact or fancy? *Int J Cardiol, (2004) 95 Suppl 1*, S43-4.

[31] Beghetti M, Gow RM, Haney I, Mawson J, Williams WG, Freedom RM. Pediatric primary benign cardiac tumors: a 15-year review. *Am Heart J*, (1997) 134, 1107-14.

[32] Savatier P, Lapillonne H, van Grunsven LA, Rudkin BB, Samarut J. Withdrawal of differentiation inhibitory activity/leukemia inhibitory factor up-regulates D-type cyclins and cyclin-dependent kinase inhibitors in mouse embryonic stem cells. *Oncogene*, (1996) 12, 309-22.

[33] Burdon T, Stracey C, Chambers I, Nichols J, Smith A. Suppression of SHP-2 and ERK signalling promotes self-renewal of mouse embryonic stem cells. *Dev Biol*, (1999) 210, 30-43.

[34] Damajanov I, Solter D, Skreb N. Teratocarcinogenesis as related to the age of embryos grafted under the kidney capsule. *Roux arch. Dev. Biol.*, (1971) 173, 228-234.

[35] Ménard C, Hagège A, Agbulut O, Barro M, Morichetti C, Brasselet C, Bel A, Messas E, Bissery A, Bruneval P, Desnos M, Pucéat M, Menasché P. Transplantation of cardiac-committed mouse embryonic stem cells to infarcted sheep myocardium: a preclinical study.*The Lancet* (2005) 366:1005-12.

[36] Kehat I, Kenyagin-Karsenti D, Snir M, Segev H, Amit M, Gepstein A, Livne E, Binah O, Itskovitz-Eldor J, Gepstein L. Human embryonic stem cells can differentiate into myocytes with structural and functional properties of cardiomyocytes. *J Clin Invest*, (2001) 108, 407-14.

[37] Xu C, Police S, Rao N, Carpenter MK. Characterization and enrichment of cardiomyocytes derived from human embryonic stem cells. *Circ Res*, (2002) 91, 501-8.

[38] He JQ, Ma Y, Lee Y, Thomson JA, Kamp TJ. Human embryonic stem cells develop into multiple types of cardiac myocytes: action potential characterization. *Circ Res,* (2003) 93, 32-9.

[39] Kehat I, Khimovich L, Caspi O, Gepstein A, Shofti R, Arbel G, Huber I, Satin J, Itskovitz-Eldor J, Gepstein L. Electromechanical integration of cardiomyocytes derived from human embryonic stem cells. *Nat Biotechnol,* (2004) 22, 1282-1289.

[40] Xue T, Cho HC, Akar FG, Tsang SY, Jones SP, Marban E, Tomaselli GF, Li RA. Functional integration of electrically active cardiac derivatives from genetically engineered human embryonic stem cells with quiescent recipient ventricular cardiomyocytes: insights into the development of cell-based pacemakers. *Circulation,* (2005) 111, 11-20.

[41] Schuldiner M, Yanuka O, Itskovitz-Eldor J, Melton DA, Benvenisty N. Effects of eight growth factors on the differentiation of cells derived from human embryonic stem cells. *Proc Natl Acad Sci USA,* (2000) 97, 11307-12.

[42] Mummery C, Ward-van Oostwaard D, Doevendans P, Spijker R, van den Brink S, Hassink R, van der Heyden M, Opthof T, Pera M, de la Riviere AB, Passier R, Tertoolen L. Differentiation of human embryonic stem cells to cardiomyocytes: role of coculture with visceral endoderm-like cells. *Circulation,* (2003) 107, 2733-40.

[43] Solloway MJ, Harvey RP. Molecular pathways in myocardial development: a stem cell perspective. *Cardiovasc Res,* (2003) 58, 264-77.

[44] Fijnvandraat AC, Van Ginneken AC, Schumacher CA, Boehler KR, Lekanne Deprez RH, Christoffels VM, Moorman AF. Cardiomyocytes purified from differentiated embryonic stem cells exhibit characteristics of early chamber formation. *J. Mol. Cell. Cardiol.,* (2003) 35, 1461-1472.

[45] Cripps RM, Olson EN. Control of cardiac development by an evolutionarily conserved transcriptional network. *Dev Biol,* (2002) 246, 14-28.

[46] Kelly RG. Molecular inroads into the anterior heart field. *Trends Cardiovasc Med,* (2005) 15, 51-6.

[47] Schier AF. Nodal signaling in vertebrate development. *Annu Rev Cell Dev Biol,* (2003) 19, 589-621.

[48] Harvey RP. Patterning the vertebrate heart. *Nat Rev Genet,* (2002) 3, 544-56.

[49] Brown CO, 3rd, Chi X, Garcia-Gras E, Shirai M, Feng XH, Schwartz RJ. The cardiac determination factor, Nkx2-5, is activated by mutual cofactors GATA-4 and Smad1/4 via a novel upstream enhancer. *J Biol Chem,* (2004) 279, 10659-69.

[50] Quinn ZA, Yang CC, Wrana JL, McDermott JC. Smad proteins function as co-modulators for MEF2 transcriptional regulatory proteins. *Nucleic Acids Res,* (2001) 29, 732-42.

[51] Morin S, Charron F, Robitaille L, Nemer M. GATA-dependent recruitment of MEF2 proteins to target promoters. *EMBO J,* (2000) 19, 2046-55.

[52] Sepulveda JL, Vlahopoulos S, Iyer D, Belaguli N, Schwartz RJ. Combinatorial expression of GATA4, Nkx2-5, and serum response factor directs early cardiac gene activity. *J Biol Chem,* (2002) 277, 25775-82.

[53] Wei Y, Bader D, Litvin J. Identification of a novel cardiac-specific transcript critical for cardiac myocyte differentiation. *Development,* (1996) 122, 2779-89.

[54] Papadimou E, Menard C, Grey C, Puceat M. Interplay between the retinoblastoma protein and LEK1 specifies stem cells toward the cardiac lineage. *EMBO J,* (2005) 24, 1750-1761.

[55] Rao RR, Stice SL. Gene Expression Profiling of Embryonic Stem Cells Leads to Greater Understanding of Pluripotency and Early Developmental Events. *Biol Reprod,* (2004) , 71:1772-8.

[56] Porter GA, Jr., Machuck RF, Rivkees SA. Intracellular calcium plays an essential role in cardiac development. *Developmental Dynamics*, (2003) 227, 280-290.

[57] Schats R, Jansen CA, Wladimiroff JW. Embryonic heart activity: appearance and development in early human pregnancy. *Br J Obstet Gynaecol,* (1990) 97, 989-94.

[58] Tezuka N, Sato S, Kanasugi H, Hiroi M. Embryonic heart rates: development in early first trimester and clinical evaluation. *Gynecol Obstet Invest,* (1991) 32, 210-2.

[59] Pera MF, Trounson AO. Human embryonic stem cells: prospects for development. *Development,* (2004) 131, 5515-25.

[60] Latham KE. Mechanisms and control of embryonic genome activation in mammalian embryos. *Int Rev Cytol,* (1999) 193, 71-124.

[61] Dvash T, Mayshar Y, Darr H, McElhaney M, Barker D, Yanuka O, Kotkow KJ, Rubin LL, Benvenisty N, Eiges R. Temporal gene expression during differentiation of human embryonic stem cells and embryoid bodies. *Hum Reprod,* (2004) 19, 2875-83.

[62] Lake J, Rathjen J, Remiszewski J, Rathjen PD. Reversible programming of pluripotent cell differentiation. *J Cell Sci,* (2000) 113, 555-66.

[63] Thomson JA, Kalishman J, Golos TG, Durning M, Harris CP, Hearn JP. Pluripotent cell lines derived from common ma*rmoset (Callithrix jacchus) blastocysts.* Biol Reprod, (1996) 55, 254-9.

[64] Behr R, Heneweer C, Viebahn C, Denker HW, Thie M. Epithelial-mesenchymal transition in colonies of rhesus monkey embryonic stem cells: a model for processes involved in gastrulation. *Stem Cells,* (2005) 23, 805-16.

[65] Ryan K, Chin AJ. T-box genes and cardiac development. Birth Defects Res C Embryo Today, (2003) 69, 25-37.

[66] Zheng P, Patel B, McMenamin M, Reddy SE, Paprocki AM, Schramm RD, Latham KE. The primate embryo gene expression resource: a novel resource to facilitate rapid analysis of gene expression patterns in non-human primate oocytes and preimplantation stage embryos. *Biol Reprod,* (2004) 70, 1411-8.

[67] Li E. Chromatin modification and epigenetic reprogramming in mammalian development. Nat Rev Genet, (2002) 3, 662-73.

[68] Rasmussen TP. Embryonic stem cell differentiation: a chromatin perspective. *Reprod Biol Endocrinol,* (2003) 1, 100.

[69] Bartel DP. MicroRNAs: genomics, biogenesis, mechanism, and function. *Cell,* (2004) 116, 281-97.

[70] Houbaviy HB, Murray MF, Sharp PA. Embryonic stem cell-specific MicroRNAs. *Dev Cell,* (2003) 5, 351-8.

[71] Suh MR, Lee Y, Kim JY, Kim SK, Moon SH, Lee JY, Cha KY, Chung HM, Yoon HS, Moon SY, Kim VN, Kim KS. Human embryonic stem cells express a unique set of microRNAs. *Dev Biol,* (2004) 270, 488-98.

[72] Lagos-Quintana M, Rauhut R, Meyer J, Borkhardt A, Tuschl T. New microRNAs from mouse and human. *RNA,* (2003) 9, 175-9.

[73] Grey C, Mery A, Puceat M. Fine-tuning in Ca2+ homeostasis underlies progression of cardiomyopathy in myocytes derived from genetically modified embryonic stem cells. *Hum Mol Genet,* (2005) 14:1367-77

[74]   Pickering SJ, Minger SL, Patel M, Taylor H, Black C, Burns CJ, Ekonomou A, Braude PR. Generation of a human embryonic stem cell line encoding the cystic fibrosis mutation deltaF508, using preimplantation genetic diagnosis. *Reprod Biomed Online*, (2005) 10, 390-7.

[75]   Daley GQ. Customized human embryonic stem cells. *Nat Biotechnol,* (2005) 23, 826-828.

In: Progress in Stem Cell Research
Editor: Prasad S. Koka, pp. 91-117

ISBN: 978-1-60456-065-7
© 2008 Nova Science Publishers, Inc.

Chapter 6

HEMOPOIETIC STEM CELLS AND AUTOIMMUNITY: IMPAIRED MECHANISMS OF THYMIC SELECTION OR GENETIC PREDISPOSITION?

Masha Fridkis-Hareli[2,3,#], Joaquin Zúñiga[1, 3,4,#] and Edmond J. Yunis[1,2]*

[1]Department of Cancer Immunology and AIDS,
Dana Farber Cancer Institute, Boston MA, USA
[2]Department of Pathology, Harvard Medical School, Boston, MA, USA
[3]Instituto Nacional de Enfermedades Respiratorias, Mexico City

ABSTRACT

Thymus is the major site where hemopoietic stem cell progenitors develop into functionally mature T cells, which reconstitute the peripheral lymphocyte pool. Repopulation of the thymus by stem cells begins in the embryonic life and continues through adolescence. In the thymus, tolerance to self is established by elimination of autoreactive T lymphocytes expressing T cell receptors (TCR) with high affinity to self-peptides, the process known as negative selection, and by generation of regulatory T cells. Breakdown in tolerance toward self-antigens, together with complex genetic and environmental factors may lead to autoimmunity. In recent years, there have been advances in the understanding of molecular and cellular pathways controlling negative selection in the thymus and in the periphery, including the discovery of the genes

---

[3] Corresponding authors: Masha Fridkis-Hareli, Ph.D., Department of Cancer Immunology and AIDS, Dana Farber Cancer Institute, 44 Binney St, Boston, MA, 02115. Phone (617)632-3344, Fax (617)632-4468, E-mail: masha_fridkis-hareli@dfci.harvard.edu

[#] These authors contributed equally to this work

[4] Joaquin Zúñiga, Ph.D., Department of Cancer Immunology and AIDS, Dana Farber Cancer Institute, 44 Binney St, Boston, MA, 02115. Phone (617)632-3342, Fax (617)632-4468, E-mail:joaquin_zuniga@dfci.harvard.edu

[*] Edmond J. Yunis, M.D., Department of Cancer Immunology and AIDS, Dana Farber Cancer Institute, 44 Binney St, Boston, MA, 02115. Phone (617) 632-3347, Fax (617) 632-4468, E-mail: edmond_yunis@dfci.harvard.edu

mediating protection from autoimmune responses. In this review, we discuss the structure and function of the thymus as relates to the mechanisms of thymocyte development, selection and egress from the thymus, as well as the factors that mediate susceptibility to autoimmunity or the induction of tolerance. Unraveling these mechanisms in animal models may further our understanding of human autoimmune diseases, ultimately leading to the development of safer treatment regiments.

ABBREVIATIONS

APC, antigen-presenting cells;
DC, dendritic cells;
FTOC, fetal thymus organ culture;
NKT, natural killer T cells;
TCR, T cell receptor;
TLR, Toll-like receptors; Treg, regulatory T cells.

INTRODUCTION

The development of autoimmunity is a multi-factorial process that occurs when autoreactive lymphocytes are induced to activate their responses against self. Several pathways, both in the thymus and in the periphery, may lead to this phenomenon.

Impaired negative selection of thymocytes would cause infiltration of mature autoreactive T cells to the peripheral system, responding to an epitope of the pathogen, which is cross-reactive with self. Alternatively, self-determinants may be presented by activated antigen-presenting cells (APCs) leading to autoimmunity. In addition, failure of peripheral deletion mechanisms to eliminate self-reactive lymphocytes would result in their accumulation and subsequent activation, unless kept anergic by other mechanisms, breaching of which would provoke autoimmunity. Moreover, absence of regulatory cell populations maintaining tolerance would also limit protection against self-reactivity.

Many factors have been shown to mediate events leading to autoimmunity. Genetic predisposition to autoimmunity in susceptible individuals has been studied, showing associations with genes involved in apoptotic pathways and signaling [1]. Impaired clonal deletion of self-reactive lymphocytes during negative selection in the thymus contributes to autoimmunity [2]. Toll-like receptors (TLR) expressed on APCs are important in stimulating maturation of APC, regulation of autoantibody production and cytokine secretion [3]. Natural killer T cells (NKT) are thought to play an important role in the development of autoimmune disease, since low levels of NKT have been shown to associate with susceptibility to autoimmunity [4]. Regulatory T cells (Treg) $CD4^+CD25^+$ have been found essential for suppressing immune responses, with FOXP3 being identified as crucial for their function [5]. The role of cytokines and their receptor signaling in autoimmunity has been investigated, suggesting that they control activation of lymphocytes and survival [6].

Collectively, the induction and the development of autoimmunity depend on multiple mechanisms involving different gene products, signaling pathways, cell types and lymphoid tissues. In this review, we discuss the structure and function of the thymus as relates to the mechanisms of thymocyte development, selection and egress from the thymus, as well as the factors that mediate susceptibility to autoimmunity or the induction of tolerance.

EMBRYOGENESIS OF THE THYMUS

Thymus is a lymphoid organ that plays a central role of the thymus in allograft rejection [7-10], T cell maturation, differentiation and selection of the cellular repertoire [11, 12]. The embryogenesis of the thymus and other structures such as respiratory tract, thyroid and parathyroid glands, liver, pancreas and digestive tract are all related to the endoderm [13]. Considerable controversy exists in regard to the contribution of the third pharyngeal cleft in the organogenesis of the thymus, proposing that both the third pharyngeal cleft (ectoderm) and the third pharyngeal pouch (endoderm) are involved [14-19]. This model suggests that the epithelial component of the cortical compartment originates from ectodermal-derived stem cells while the medulla is derived from endodermal stem cells [15]. In support to this model, several studies have reported the interaction of ectoderm and endoderm structures as a key factor in the development of functional thymus, based on morphological studies in nude and wild type mice [16]. However, convincing functional and morphological evidence supports a single origin model [20, 21]. Recent studies by cell lineage-tracing analysis confirm that there is no evidence of the contribution of ectoderm to the thymic development [22].

The epidermal primordium of the thymus expands from the third pharyngeal pouch. The interaction between thymic epithelium and neural crest-derived mesenchyme from the third and fourth branchial arches generates a visible structure around day 11 in the mouse embryo (E11) [18, 19]. The contact of thymic epithelium with mesenchymal cells promotes epithelium proliferation. Experimental assays using microdissected thymic lobes with or without mesenchyme from BALB/c and C57BL/10 mouse embryos have shown that 12-day lobes cultured without mesenchyme exhibit poor lymphoid development, suggesting an essential role of the mesenchymal cells in the normal development of the thymus [23, 24]. The organization of the thymic epithelium is determined to support T cell development, such as specific antigenic, structural and spatial features promote an efficient organ function [25]. At this point of maturation, the structure of the thymic epithelium is conformed by the presence of thymic epithelial cells that express different patterns of molecules that mediates adhesion, migration and cell death [26, 27].

In the mouse between E10 and E12, important morphological changes in the stratified epithelium, with expression of MHC class II molecules and expression of Notch ligand, are key factors in the establishment of a microenvironment supporting T cell development [28]. Similar changes can be found in human embryos of 35 days of gestation, in 7-8 days chick embryos or 4-day Xenopus embryos. Several studies support the existence of a common stem cell progenitor for medullar and cortical epithelial cells. However, this model has to be confirmed by functional and clonal analysis to determine whether thymic epithelial stem cells can be differentiated from endodermal progenitor stem cells [29].

CELLULAR COMPOSITION OF THE THYMUS

The presence of hemopoietic progenitors in the early stages of thymic development (around E12) has been described [30]. In the thymus, the most primitive stem cells of T lineage are CD4[-], CD8[-], CD25[-], CD44[+], c-kit[high] (CD117) [31], which are capable of differentiating into mature T cells. However, using irradiated mouse models, it has been demonstrated that these early T cell lineage stem cells can also develop into B-lymphocytes, NK cells and dendritic cells (DC) [32, 33]. Their development requires additional signals derived from non-lymphoid cell lineages such as stromal cells, mesenchymal cells and thymic epithelial cells.

Thymic dendritic cells (TDC) drive the T cell repertoire generation in the thymus [34]. TDC act as antigen presenting cells and play a crucial role in the positive and negative selection occurring at the later stages of T cell development. TDC are located in the medulla but can also be found in the cortico-medullary junction [34-36]. Based on the surface markers and functional differences, three types of TDC have been characterized [37]. In mice, TDC express MHC class II, CD11[+], CD45[-] markers, with the high percentage of these cells also expressing CD8 while a small subgroup is lacking the expression of CD8. The major proportion of CD8[+] dendritic cells expresses CD8$\alpha\beta$ heterodimer [38].

Human thymus contains 2 distinct DC populations. One subset is CD11c[+], HLA-DR[+], CD45RA[low], CD83[+], CD4[+], CD11b[-], which constitutes 65 % of total DC in human thymus. These cells show well-defined functional activities such as IL-12p70 and TECK production, playing an important role in the induction of central tolerance [39]. Another subset of human TDC expresses the phenotype CD11c[+], HLA-DR[+], CD45RA[low], CD83[+], CD4[+] and CD11b[+][39]. These cells could act as antigen transporters and presenting cells of self-antigens to T lymphocytes [40]. Major thymic DC population is generated within the thymus, while minor thymic DC population derives from the blood [33, 37, 41-43].

Thymic plasmacytoid dendritic cells (pDC) represent about 35 % of DC in the thymus with a phenotype CD11c[medium] MHC II[low], CD45RA[high], CD45R[high] and CD4 and/or CD8 [44, 45]. Thymic pDC also express Ly6C[+] and a proportion express CD4 and/or CD8α,. high levels of TLR7 and 9, and low levels of TLR2 and 3 [45]. These cells might be involved in negative selection, however, they poorly function as antigen presenters unless activated by infectious agents. In mice (CD11c[+]MHC-II[low]CD45RA[+]CD45R[+]Ly6C[+]) and in humans (CD11c[-]HLA-DR[low] CD45RA[+]CD123[+]) thymic pDC produce high amounts of IFN-α, and some evidence points at its involvement in the production of regulatory T cells [46-49].

ORIGIN OF HEMOPOIETIC STEM CELLS IN THE THYMUS

During embryogenesis, thymic colonization begins with the infiltration of basophilic stem cells in mesenchymal and jugular vein in the vicinity of the thymus [50]. The extrathymic origin of these basophilic cells has been demonstrated by chick chimeras-based analysis [51]. In mammals, embryonic thymus is colonized by lymphoid progenitors after 10 days of embryonic development [52]. These thymocyte progenitors originate in the fetal liver [53, 54] or the yolk sac [52, 55], whereas after birth they come from the bone marrow (BM) [56]. Hemopoietic stem cells migrate to rudimentary thymus from embryonic blood vessels and accumulate in the spaces within thymic epithelial tissue [27, 57]. Repopulation and subsequent proliferation of these infiltrating progenitor stem cells promotes the expansion of the rudimentary thymus resulting in the development of clusters of lymphoid cells between epithelial cell reticular structures [58].

It has been shown that a single thymic stem cell progenitor can give rise to all T cell lineages within the thymus *in vivo* [59] and *in vitro* [60, 61]. Cellular interactions in the course of thymic development have been studied extensively by transplanting BM cells into irradiated recipients and analyzing T lymphocytes in the radiation chimeras [62, 63]. At the later stage, an *in vitro* model of thymocyte differentiation was developed in which lymphohemopoietic cells were seeded onto the lymphoid-depleted fetal thymuses (FT) [64]. Being the first *in vitro* system used in a number of studies of thymic repopulation and T cell development, it, however, bared some disadvantages as compared to the *in vivo* irradiation chimeras in which newly emigrating lymphoid progenitors interacted with the radio-resistant lymphocytes in the process of their maturation in the thymus. Subsequently, the *in vitro* system in which T cell progenitors from different sources were co-cultured with the irradiated fetal thymuses has been developed [65], enabling analysis of cellular and molecular interactions in the course of thymocyte reconstitution and maturation [66-71].

In birds, there is a controversy in regard to the origin of T progenitor stem cells [72]. Recent studies suggest that they differentiate from paraaortic mesoderm at the 3rd day of embryonic development, in contrast to the previous studies that support the notion that hemopoietic progenitors originate from yolk sac [52, 55].

Phenotypic analyses in BALBc mouse model have shown that the first wave of migrant stem cells entering the embryonic thymus on day 12 expresses CD45, c-kit, CD44, CD34, α–integrin, CD25⁻, CD62L and Thy-1.2 [73]. In *nude* mouse models, lymphoid stem cells are not capable to enter the epithelium from the prethymic mesenchyme due to mutation in *Foxn1* transcription factor [74].

The earliest thymocytes are generated from the bone marrow (BM) with the phenotype CD4⁻, CD8⁻, CD25⁻ and CD44⁺ and are denominated DN1 subset [31]. Interestingly, BM-derived cells such as the lineage-negative Sca-1⁺, c-Kit⁺, which are also named LSK, are highly pluripotential and, as recent studies have shown, are the main source of thymus immigrant cells [43]. DN1 population of early T cells progenitors is derived from the first immigrant cells in the thymus [31]. Other lymphoid stem cell populations also have a potential to differentiate into B and T cell lymphocyte lineages and also into certain myeloid lineages [43]. The role of transcription factors in T lineage differentiation process has been studied, being found essential for hemopoietic stem cells pluripotential development, maintenance and self-renewal. Some of these factors include Ikaros, PU.1, Runx1, c-Myb, Notch, Wnt/TCF and GATA-3 [75-80].

THE ROLE OF NOTCH IN T CELL DEVELOPMENT

Signaling through transmembrane receptor Notch is necessary during early T lineage development [81-83]. Lack of Notch leads to arrest in T cell but not B cell development [84]. Notch proteins are transcriptional activators expressed as heterodimeric transmembrane molecules. In mammals, Notch 1, 2, 3 and 4 molecules and five ligands named Jagged 1 and

2 and Delta-like 1, 3 and 4 have been described [81, 82]. The interaction of Notch with its ligands results in a proteolytic cleavage of Notch, leading to the release of the intracellular fragment of Notch from the cellular membrane and subsequent translocation to the nucleus [85, 86]. Next, the intracellular fragment of Notch binds to the transcription factor CSL, which promotes binding of the co-activator mastermind-like 1 (MAML1), generating a trans-activator complex that regulates the expression of genes involved in the development of T cells, such as *Hes1* and *Ptcra* [85]. Recent reports on the control of Notch signaling pathways using inhibitors of ligand-receptor interaction, e.g. gamma secretase inhibitors, to prevent the enzymatic cleavage of Notch and dominant-negative MAML-1 [87-89], support the potential of Notch pathways in the treatment of immune disorders [85, 90]. Other studies suggest that T-cell/B-cell lineage commitment occurs before the Notch signaling in the thymus [84].

STUDIES OF THYMIC FUNCTION

It appears that two factors are necessary for the normal development and continued function of the thymus; an intact reticulo-endothelial framework including DC and the supply of stem cells sensitive first to the local inductive and then to the expanding humoral function of the thymus. In this regard, there is a progressive decrease of restorative effectiveness of the thymus or thymus grafts when the treatment of neonatally-thymectomized mice is delayed [91]. The cells capable of responding to the expanding action of the thymus represent population that has received "thymic influence" before thymectomy was performed, while the humoral function of the thymus can expand solely by "post-thymic cells" in the lymphoid tissues [92]. In addition, using a 45-day old neonatally-thymectomized mouse model, the hemopioetic stem cells of adult and newborn origin were shown to act in cooperation with the thymus to restore its function [92].

GENERATION OF T CELL REPERTOIRE THROUGH THYMIC SELECTION: CELLULAR AND MOLECULAR EVENTS

T cells expressing a highly diverse αβ TCR repertoire develop in the thymus from hemopoietic stem cells [93-95]. On entering the thymus through the cortico-medullary junction, these cells (DN1) migrate to the subcapsular epithelium, upregulate CD25 (DN2) then downregulate CD44 (DN3), undergoing a complex differentiation process in the thymic cortex and then in the medulla, involving proliferation, expression of accessory molecules, rearrangement of TCR genes and selection of the TCR repertoire [96, 97]. For normal T cell development, signals from non-hemopoietic stromal cells are required which include various types of thymic epithelial cells (TECs). The thymic epithelium provides a broad spectrum of signals for thymocyte proliferation, differentiation and selection. Thymic nurse cells, expressing high levels of MHC class I and II molecules and also containing antigen processing machinery, are involved in thymocyte selection, mediated by peptide/MHC (pMHC) ligands. Self-peptides bound to MHC molecules control both positive and negative selection [98]. Thymocytes that carry TCRs having low-affinity interactions with MHC-bound self-peptides are positively selected, and are exported into the pool of mature peripheral lymphocytes. In contrast, thymocytes bearing those TCRs that recognize self-peptides with "high" affinity are eliminated primarily upon interaction with dendritic cells [97, 99]. However, some MHC molecules associated with autoimmunity may be able to present only a limited number of self-peptides, leading to MHC/TCR interactions, which are less peptide-dependent. Together with the impairment in the negative selection due to the lack of negatively selecting ligands, this condition may predispose to autoimmunity, as has been recently reported by Logunova et al. [100]. On the other hand, many T cell clones may escape negative selection due to the cryptic epitopes on self-proteins, which are not presented adequately [101].

The avidity of pMHC/TCR interactions plays a major role in T cell recognition [102]. Crystal structure analyses have revealed fine details about peptide conformation inside the peptide binding groove of MHC molecules and the amino acid residues interacting with the TCR Vα and Vβ domains including their CDR3 loops [103-106]. Peptide analogs of antigenic peptides with substitutes at amino acid residues, APL, have been shown to generate qualitatively different T cell responses compared with those produced by the antigenic peptides themselves [107]. A recent study by Hahn et al. [108] proposed a novel mechanism by which autoreactive T cells may escape negative selection. In this report, the structure of the trimolecular complex for a TCR from a patient with multiple sclerosis that causes autoimmunity in transgenic mice revealed unconventional topologies of peptide/MHC/TCR interactions. Rather than being centered on the peptide-MHC complex, this TCR contacted only the N-terminal peptide segment and made asymmetrical interactions with the MHC helices, reducing the interaction surface with peptide and altering the geometry for CD4 association.

During positive selection, low affinity ligands stimulate TCRs, promoting signaling via the α-chain connecting peptide motif (α-CPM) and ITAM residues in the TCR-CD3$\gamma\delta$ complex. This low affinity interaction induces partial phosphorylation of the linker for activation of T cells (LAT) transmembrane scaffolding protein, recruiting multiple signaling molecules important for T cell activation such as phospholipase C1, which leads to the generation of diacylglycerol and calcium influx for the activation of RasGRP and low levels of ERK and NFAT, respectively. Mice homozygous for a single tyrosine mutation in LAT exhibited an early block in T cell maturation [109].

Following positive selection, thymocytes migrate to the cortico-medullary junction where they interact with macrophages and DC that express high density of MHC/self peptide complexes. T cells that interact with peptide/MHC complexes with high affinity are negatively selected by apoptosis. The first experiments describing clonal deletion showed elimination of Vβ17α T cells in animals that expressed an endogenous superantigen and the I-E MHC molecule [110]. It has been shown that negative selection of thymocytes requires a second signal apart from the TCR-MHC [111]. For example, CD28 can provide a co-stimulatory signal required for negative selection [112]. A high-affinity TCR ligand along with co-stimulation results in fully phosphorylated LAT, recruitment of Grb2/SOS1, and strong, transient activation of ERK along with p38 and JNK activation [113, 114].

REGULATION OF THYMOCYTE EGRESS

Lymphocyte migration within the thymus and from the thymus to the periphery plays an important role in regulation of the immune responses. As thymocytes progress through the differentiation stages, they migrate from the cortico-medullary junction, the site of entry of T cell progenitors from the BM, to the subcapsular region of the thymus, then to the cortex and to the medulla [115, 116]. Finally, functionally mature thymocytes exit the thymus and repopulate the peripheral lymphoid tissues. The processes that regulate trafficking of lymphoid precursors to and within the thymus, and that mediate emigration of mature T cells from the thymus to the periphery remain poorly understood. Impairment of any of these migratory mechanisms may lead to escape of self-reactive T cells from the thymus, thus provoking autoimmunity. Several mediators, including the early activation marker CD69 [117], chemokine receptors [118], adhesion molecules [119], extracellular matrix proteins [120], neuroendocrine factors [121] and G-protein coupled receptors (GPCR) [122] have been shown to regulate thymocyte export. Cellular mechanisms involved in thymocyte egress are discussed below.

Chemokine Pathways

Chemokines are basic polypeptides of about 100 amino acids, usually containing four Cys residues linked by disulphide bonds, which are produced by certain thymic stroma cells and are abundantly expressed in the thymus. Specifically, thymic epithelial, medullary epithelial and dendritic cells have been shown to secrete various chemokines. Growing evidence suggests that chemokines and their receptors, expressed differentially on thymocytes during discrete maturational stages, control homing of T cell progenitors to the thymus, their intrathymic migration, and exit to the periphery [118]. Chemokines deliver signals for lymphocyte proliferation and survival, and regulate thymocyte trafficking by functioning in concert with other adhesion molecules such as selectins and integrins [119]. Chemokines stimulate responding cells by activating pertussis toxin-sensitive $G_i\alpha$ protein-coupled seven-transmembrane receptors (GPCR), leading to activation of intracellular secondary mediators which control directional cell migration. To date, 43 human chemokines have been identified, acting via binding to 19 different GPCR.

Some chemokine receptors are expressed on DP and SP thymocytes, e.g. CCR9, with its ligand CCL25 secreted by TEC and DC. Others, e.g. CCR5 and CCR8, expressed on mature SP thymocytes, have been suggested to play a role in mediating thymocyte emigration. In particular, CCR7 has been demonstrated to mediate homing of naïve T cells to peripheral lymphoid organs via ligands CCL19 and CCL21 [118, 123, 124].

Extracellular Matrix Proteins

Extracellular matrix (ECM) proteins laminin and fibronectin are produced by TECs, fibroblasts and MHC class II$^+$ macrophages in the thymus. Other ECM proteins including nidogen, associated with laminin, and galectins -1, -3, and -5 as well as glycosaminoglycans are produced by thymic epithelium. ECM proteins form molecular bridges between thymocytes and the thymic microenvironment, mediating adhesion of thymocytes via their ECM receptors VLA-4, -5 and -6, and their disassembly from the cell complexes. In the absence of ECM proteins, normal thymocyte development and migration are severely perturbed, both in *in vitro* cultures of TEC and in *in vivo* knockout mouse models, suggesting a crucial role of the ECM protein network in the thymic function [120].

S1P Pathway

Sphingosine 1-phosphate (S1P), a member of sphingolipid family, is an important signaling molecule present in high concentrations in body fluids. SIP binds to members of a family of G protein-coupled receptors ($S1P_{1-5}$/Edg) with up to nanomolar affinity, triggering diverse effects, including proliferation, survival, migration, morphogenesis, adhesion molecule expression, and cytoskeletal changes. S1P receptors are widely expressed during embryonic development and in the adult. The tissue distribution shows that lymphoid organs express high levels of $S1P_1$ and $S1P_4$. Thus, these receptors may be potential targets for pharmacological drug design aimed at effecting thymocyte migration. The expression of $S1P_1$ on T cells controls their exit from the thymus and entry into the blood, and, thus, has a central role in regulating the numbers of peripheral T-cells [125]. Interestingly, $S1P_1$ knockout mice show a block in the egress of mature T-cells into the periphery. The regulated expression of $S1P_1$ receptor levels, which is increased in mature SP thymocytes and peripheral T cells, may control responsiveness to the high levels of sphingosine 1-phosphate in the blood, which selectively induces mature T-cell migration to the periphery. Recently, $S1P_1$ receptors have been implicated in lymphocyte trafficking and homing based on studies using FTY720, a potent immunosuppressive agent, which is an agonist ligand for $S1P_{1,3,4,5}$ receptors blocking egress of T cells from the thymus. Studies of thymocyte egress mechanisms through the S1P receptor pathway may aid in facilitating emigration from the thymus to the periphery and provide additional means of enriching the mature T cell pool with desired specificities [126, 127]. Pathways of thymocyte development and selection are shown in Figure 1.

THE THYMUS AND AUTOIMMUNITY: PREVIOUS OBSERVATIONS IN THYMUS-DEFICIENT MICE

Studies of thymectomized mice have demonstrated dysfunctions of the immune system, revealing a loss of T-cell mediated immunity and a defect in the total number of lymphocytes [128, 129]. Immunodeficiency produced by thymectomy could be corrected by administration of syngenic and allogenic T cells with the subsequent development of immunological tolerance [130]. In the NOD mouse model of diabetes, a number of observations are compatible with the requirement for diminished regulatory T cell function for transfer of the disease. Gombert et al. [131] demonstrated that NOD mice had a deficit in NK T cells. These studies have been interpreted as demonstrating that a deficiency of NK T cells in NOD mice contributes to the pathogenesis of IDDM by permitting the development of pathogenic Th1 effector cells. Preliminary studies suggest that a similar defect may be seen in human diabetes, as diabetic siblings had lower frequencies of CD4⁻CD8⁻ NK T cells that expressed the Vα24JαQ TCR [132].

The athymic condition of the nude mouse was reported first by Pantelouris et al [133], and he later described two primitive structures in the thymic region totally deprived of lymphoid tissue [134]. The defect in the thymus architecture resulted in the repopulation failure of the normal BM stem cells, supporting a defect in the development of thymic epithelium [135].

THE ROLE OF AIRE PROTEIN IN PROTECTION AGAINST AUTOIMMUNITY

AIRE (autoimmune regulator) has been identified as an important mediator involved in central tolerance. In support to this notion, defective expression of AIRE causes a human autoimmune disease with multi-organ involvement [136]. In AIRE-deficient mouse models, the transcription factor AIRE regulates autoimmunity by mechanism in which expression of peripheral tissue-restricted antigens is upregulated in the thymus [137]. In this context, it has been suggested that in the absence of AIRE, the induction of central tolerance is incomplete, promoting an autoimmune response against self tissue-specific antigens leading to multi organ involvement. The highest levels of AIRE expression have been detected in the thymic medullary epithelial cells and in dendritic cells, which are though to have a role in negative selection of thymocytes [138]. In a recent study using the NOD diabetes mouse model, the role of proinsulin-2 expression in the thymus was described, suggesting that thymic expression of an islet antigen is required for establishing functional tolerance and for preventing type 1 diabetes [139]. In addition to the role of AIRE in up-regulation of self-protein expression in the thymus, AIRE might also be involved in positive selection of regulatory T cells [140, 141], as discussed below. A very recent study by Anderson et al. [142] demonstrated that AIRE enhances the antigen-presentation capability of medullary epithelial cells, leading to negative selection of T effector cells, rather than functioning as a positive selection mediator of regulatory T cells. Thus, it looks like the role of AIRE in central tolerance has to be further investigated as related to autoimmunity.

REGULATORY T CELLS AND AUTOIMMUNITY

Recent work has revealed the vital role of regulatory T cells (Treg) in protection from autoimmune diseases. Several Treg populations have been described, including CD4⁺, CD8⁺ and NKT cells. CD4⁺ Tregs were discovered by Sakaguchi et al. [143, 144], as a small subset expressing IL-2R α-chain (CD25), which, however, might have been described earlier as T suppressor cells [145]. The tissue distribution of Treg is diverse; these have been detected in lymphoid tissues such as thymus, lymph nodes, spleen and peripheral blood [146]. However, Tregs have been also described in healthy and diseased peripheral tissues such as synovia [147], tumors [148, 149], allografts [150], skin [151], lungs [152], pancreas [153], and gut [154].

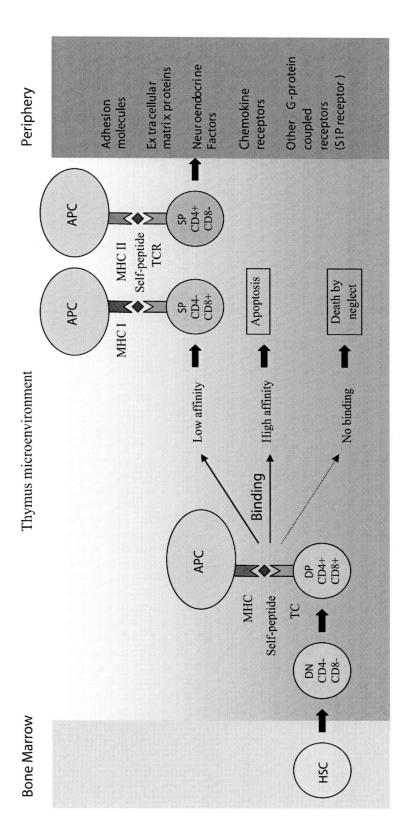

Figure 1. Pathways of thymocyte development and egress to the periphery. Hemopoietic stem cells (HSC) originating in the BM or embryonic FL repopulate the thymus and undergo differentiation form CD4⁻CD8⁻ (DN) cells to αβTCR⁺CD4⁺CD8⁺ (DP). The interaction with self-peptides presented by class I and II MHC molecules expressed on thymic APC leads to positive or negative selection, depending on the affinity of these interactions. Those thymocytes whose TCRs interact with high affinity to pMHC undergo apoptosis, while those bound to pMHC with low affinity mature to become MHC class I restricted CD8⁺ SP or class II-restricted CD4⁺ SP cells. These mature thymocytes then emigrate to the peripheral lymphoid organs aided by different regulators of egress mechanisms (Modified from Fridkis-Hareli, M; Reinherz, EL. Med. Immunol., 2004, 3, 2-12).

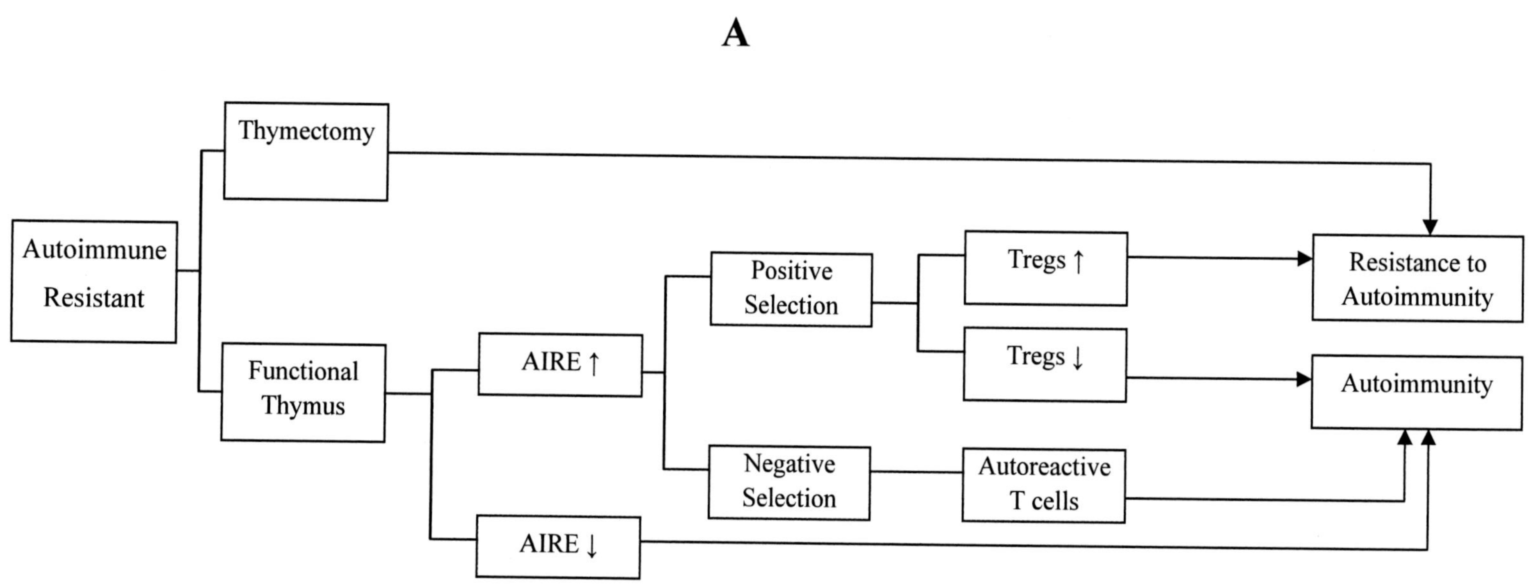

A

Figure 2. Continued on next page.

B

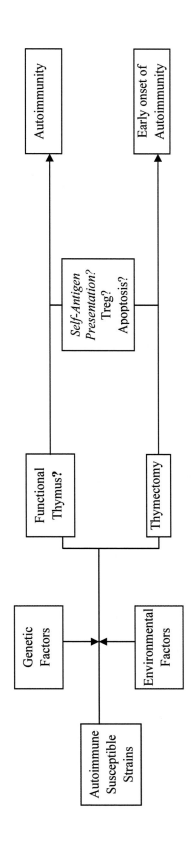

Figure 2. Effects of thymic function on the susceptibility to autoimmunity. Various factors contribute to the onset of autoimmunity. A) In mouse strains resistant to autoimmunity (C3H, CBA, C57Bl), thymectomy does not lead to the induction of disease [174, 177]. Within the functional thymus, interactions of maturing thymocytes with self-APC lead to either positive selection, which would also produce Tregs controlling autoreactivity, or negative selection eliminating self-reactive T cells [178]. The expression of AIRE protein is critical for proper antigen presentation [136, 137]. B) In mouse strains susceptible to autoimmunity, both genetic and environmental factors influence the outcome of immune responsiveness. In the presence of functional thymus, autoimmunity might develop as a result of impairment in regulatory mechanisms involving negative selection, antigen presentation or Treg function. On the other hand, thymectomy would lead to the early onset of autoimmunity, as affected by the lack of central tolerance regulation.

T cells with regulatory activity are released to the periphery through the thymic selection process as functionally and phenotypically mature population capable of preventing autoimmunity. High reactivity of $CD4^+CD25^+$ Treg, together with the high level of expression of various accessory molecules, guarantee their efficient activation upon encounter with a broad variety of self peptide/MHC complexes in peripheral tissues, promoting the control of self-reactive T cells. High affinity or agonistic interactions with self-antigen are required for differentiation, however, these interactions at the high affinity levels result in clonal deletion. Several populations of Treg have been described with $CD4^+CD25^+$ being most extensively studied [155]. However, $CD25^-$ T cells have also been shown to control autoimmune disease [156-158]. In contrast, experimental assays demonstrated that transfer of $CD4^+CD25^-$ cells from normal mice with BALB/c background to athymic nude (*nu/nu*) mice resulted in an autoimmune syndrome [159]. Among subpopulations of Treg, $CD45RB^{lo}$ and CD62L have been implicated in protection [160]. Other markers, e.g. FoxP3 (a transcription factor expressed in Treg [161, 162] and integrins ($\alpha_4\beta_7$ and $\alpha_4\beta_1$) [163] have been identified, suggesting that Treg might have both migratory and suppressive properties. Surface molecules (CTLA-4 and GITR) and cytokines (TGF-β) play an important role in Treg development and function [164]. In addition to $CD4^+$ Tregs, the role of $CD8^+$ T cells in immune regulation has been investigated. Thus, a population of $CD8^+$ suppressor T cells restricted to murine MHC molecule Qa-1 has been shown to inhibit autoreactive $CD4^+$ T cells [165-167]. In another study by Kumar [168], $CD8^+$ Treg responses against peptides derived from autoreactive TCR Vβ8.2 chain led to protection of Lewis rats and mice from developing experimental allergic encephalo-myelitis. Furthermore, it has also been shown that a distinct population of antigen-specific $CD8^+CD28^-$ cells can suppress immune responses by upregulation of inhibitory receptors ILT3 and ILT4 on the DC and their subsequent tolerization [169, 170]. Approaches using Treg populations in T cell vaccination and their regulatory mechanisms have been a subject of extensive discussions [171]. In addition to $CD4^+$ and $CD8^+$ Treg populations, NKT cells restricted to the nonclassical MHC class I molecule CD1d have been shown to function as suppressors of pathogen-activated autoreactive T cells [172].

Thus, accumulated evidence on the role of Treg in suppressing self-reactivity suggests that treatment of human autoimmune conditions with Treg will become increasingly important for development of novel therapeutic approaches. Mechanisms of enhancement of Treg generation, as well as their maintenance at the levels, which ensure suppression of self-responses will need to be elucidated in the near future.

THE ROLE OF THE THYMUS IN AUTOIMMUNITY: PERSPECTIVES FOR FUTURE RESEARCH

The claim that negative selection in the thymus has been resolved [173] should be questioned since it has not been solved in regards to induction of autoimmunity. Although the requirement of the thymus for T cell differentiation from stem cells is well established, its role in repertoire selection in relation to autoimmunity is not complete. In negative selection two signals are required, TCR and co-stimulation, mediated by bone marrow derived circulating antigen presenting cells and thymic medullary epithelium. In this regard, mice and humans with mutations in AIRE exhibit autoimmune phenomena. AIRE-/- mice express fewer tissue specific antigens in the thymus and fail to negatively select tissue-specific thymocytes efficiently. It is unknown whether this is due to expression of antigen or problem with antigen presentation. This is not the case for positive selection when the cortical epithelial cells are the mediators; thymocytes expressing TCRs that bind to thymic self-MHC peptide complexes with intermediate/low affinity are selected to mature bearing MHC restriction specificity. Negative selection pathway appears to involve different molecular processes at different stages in development. In this context, it is necessary to understand the role of AIRE or other molecules in negative selection for autoreactive cells as compared to the repertoire of regulatory T cells with CD25+ CD4 phenotype. For example, the thymus of autoimmune-susceptible strains should be used to establish the role of epithelial or DC in the generation of autoreactive T cells and/or Tregs (as reviewed above).

A possible hypothesis to explain the acceleration of autoimmune diseases in neonatally thymectomized autoimmune susceptible strains of mice [174], including NOD mice [175] and athymic mice [176] could be that their immunological defects would be preferentially in the generation of Tregs. It is well known that in aged individuals a significant decline of the immune system function has been observed. A paradoxical issue is the increase of autoantibody production with the decline of immune system function [177, 178]. Several studies support the hypothesis that autoantibody production is a result of the decrease of T cell suppressor subset function since the same autoimmune phenomena occur at earlier onset following neonatal thymectomy [174] For example, NZB mice are susceptible to autoimmune diseases and autoantibody production probably due to a breakdown in the suppressor cells (has to be investigated with markers for Tregs) that occur with aging of these mice [145]. The diagram presenting the effects of the thymus function on the susceptibility to autoimmunity is depicted in Figure 2.

STEM CELLS IN THE TREATMENT OF AUTOIMMUNITY

In the previous chapters of this review we have described central and peripheral mechanisms by which stem cells may lead to autoimmunity. Indeed, the susceptibility to autoimmune diseases resides in hemopoietic stem cells, as confirmed in many animal models of autoimmune diseases by transfer of hemopoietic stem cells from affected to normal mice [179]. Vice versa, resistance to developing autoimmunity could also be transferred by hemopoietic stem cells, as shown by transplantation from normal to autoimmune-prone mice [180]. Although rodent models of autoimmunity are fundamentally different from human diseases due to complexity of genetic factors and the mechanisms involved in regeneration of an immune system following lymphoid depletion therapy, the possibility of therapeutic approaches using stem cell transplantation has been investigated for treatment of severe autoimmune conditions which resist other therapies [181]. Various protocols have been developed including immunosuppression and chemotherapy followed by autologous as well as allogeneic hemopoietic stem cell transplantation, leading to initiation of multiple clinical trials [182]. The mechanisms involved in elimination of autoreactive T and B cells have been extensively investigated, suggesting that multiple pathways operate including depletion by immunosuppressive treatment (total body irradiation, cyclophosphamide, antibodies), destruction of autoimmune host cells by alloreactive donor T cells, thymic deletion, peripheral anergy, tolerization by regulatory T cells, and tolerization of autoreactive B cells. Although the data look promising, the risk of developing graft-versus-host disease and the lack of information on the efficacy of stem cell transplantation hinder its wide use in the treatment of autoimmune diseases. Understanding of the tolerization processes will lead to the development of less toxic regiments, and bring hope for patients with severe autoimmune diseases.

CONCLUDING REMARKS

Hemopoietic stem cell differentiation in the thymus results in generation of T cell repertoire capable of fighting infections and preventing responses to self-antigens. Molecular and cellular mechanisms leading to maturation of stem cells have been thoroughly investigated in the past decade. Breaching of any of these pathways may induce self-reactivity and a subsequent onset of autoimmunity. Experimental evidence suggests that regulation of negative selection, antigen presentation by DC and production and induction of Treg are crucial checkpoints in the maintenance of tolerance. Since thymus plays a central role in maturation of T cells, we have undertaken an approach of covering topics on thymopoiesis and selection processes, with the emphasis on molecular and cellular interactions, which might lead to out-brake of autoimmunity. As these mechanisms are elucidated, the contribution of each of the factors involved in responses against self will be clarified. We suggest that the studies of thymus development in relation to the negative and positive selection should be performed as comparative analysis of genetically susceptible and autoimmune strains of mice. These studies need to include comparative analyses of stem cell lineages originating in the embryonic tissues of the thymus. We anticipate that the autoimmune susceptible strains will have stem cell defects that produce abnormal molecular and cellular pathways of central and peripheral tolerance, including, but are not limited to, antigen presentation by DC, expression of AIRE protein and function of Tregs. We believe that investigation of thymus function in deficiencies induced by a) molecular manipulations, b) thymus in mice resistant to autoimmunity and c) mice with inborn thymic defects (autoimmune-susceptible strains) will answer unknown questions of selection by the thymus.

ACKNOWLEDGEMENTS

This work was supported by NIH grants HL29583 and HL59838 (to E.J.Y). J.Z. was supported in part by grants from the Instituto Nacional de Enfermedades Respiratorias, Mexico and by Fundación México en Harvard A.C.

REFERENCES

[1] Raman, K; Mohan, C. 2003. Genetic underpinnings of autoimmunity- lessons from studies in arthritis, diabetes, lupus and multiple sclerosis. *Curr. Opin. Immunol.*, 2003, 15, 651-659.

[2] Ohashi, PS. Negative selection and autoimmunity. Curr. *Opin. Immunol.*, 2003, 15, 668-676.

[3] Pasare, C; Medzhitov, R. Toll-like receptors: balancing host resistance with immune tolerance. *Curr. Opin. Immunol.*, 2003, 15, 677-682.

[4] Hammond, KJL; Kronenberg, M. Natural killer T cells: natural or unnatural regulators of autoimmunity? *Curr. Opin. Immunol.*, 2003, 15, 683-689.

[5] Gavin, M; Rudensky, A. Control of immune homeostasis by naturally arising regulatory CD4$^+$ T cells. *Curr. Opin. Immunol.*, 2003, 15, 690-693.

[6] Yadav, D; Sarvetnick, N. Cytokines and autoimmunity: redundancy defines their complex nature. *Curr. Opin. Immunol.*, 2003, 15, 697-703.

[7] Miller, J.F.A.P. Immunological function of the thymus. Lancet, 1961, 2, 748–749.

[8] Martinez, C; Kersey, J; Papermaster, BW; Good, RA. Skin homograft survival in thymectomized mice. *Proc. Soc. Exp. Biol. Med.,* 1962, 109, 193-196.

[9] Papermaster, BW; Good, RA. Relative contributions of the thymus and the bursa of Fabricius to the maturation of the lymphoreticur system and immunological potential in the chicken. *Nature,* 1962, 196, 838-840.

[10] Good, RA; Dalmasso, AP; Martinez, C; Archer, OK; Pierce, JC; Papermaster, BW. The role of the thymus in development of immunologic capacity in rabbits and mice. *J. Exp. Med.*, 1962, 116, 733-796.

[11] Dalmasso, AP; Martinez, C; Sjodin, K; Good, RA. Studies on the role of the thymus in immunobiology; reconstitution of immunologic capacity in mice thymectomized at birth. *J. Exp. Med.*, 1963,118, 1089-1109.

[12] Dalmasso, AP; Martinez, C; Good, RA. Failure of spleen cells from thymectomized mice to induce graft vs. host reactions. *Proc. Soc. Exp. Biol. Med.*, 1962, 110, 205-208.

[13] LeLievre, CS; LeDouarin, NM. Mesenchymal derivatives of the neural crest: analysis of chimaeric quail and chick embryos. *J. Embryol. Exp. Morph.*, 1975, 34, 125-154.

[14] Jiang, X; Rowitch, DH; Soriano, P; McMahon, AP; Sucov, HM. Fate of the mammalian cardiac neural crest. *Development*, 2000, 127, 1607-1616.

[15] Cordier, AC; Haumont, SM. Development of thymus, parathyroids and ultimo-branchial bodies in NMRI and nude mice. *Am. J. Anat.*, 1980, 157, 227–263.

[16] Cordier, AC; Heremans, JF. Nude mouse embryo: ectodermal nature of the primordial thymic defect. Scand. *J. Immunol.*, 1975, 4, 193-196.

[17] Janeway, CA; Travers, P; Walport, M; Sclomchik, M. Immunobiology 5: The immune system in health and disease. *New York: Garland Publishing and Current Biology,* 2001.

[18] Manley, NR. Thymus organogenesis and molecular mechanisms of thymic epithelial cell differentiation. *Semin. Immunol.*, 2000, 12, 421–428.

[19] Manley, NR; Blackburn, CC. A developmental look at thymus organogenesis: where do the non-hematopoetic cells in the thymus come from? *Curr. Opin. Immunol.*, 2003, 15, 225–232.

[20] Le Douarin, NM; Jotereau, FV. Tracing of cells of the avian thymus through embryonic life in interspecific chimeras. *J. Exp. Med.*, 1975, 142, 17–40.

[21] Moore-Scott, BA; Gordon, J; Blackburn, CC; Condie, BG; Manley, NR. A new serum-free *in vitro* culture technique for mid gestation mouse embryos. *Genesis*, 2003, 35, 164–168.

[22] Gordon, J. *et al.* Functional evidence for a single endodermal origin for the thymic epithelium. *Nature Immunol,* 2005 (in press).

[23] Suniara, RK; Jenkinson, EJ; Owen, JJ. An essential role for thymic mesenchyme in early T cell development. J. Exp. Med., 2000, 191, 1051-1056.

[24] Jenkinson, WE; Jenkinson, EJ; Anderson, G. Differential requirement for mesenchyme in the proliferation and maturation of thymic epithelial progenitors. *J. Exp. Med.*, 2003, 198, 325-32.

[25] Boyd, RL. *et al.* The thymic microenvironment. *Immunol. Today*, 1993, 14, 445–459.

[26] Manley, NR. Thymus organogenesis and molecular mechanisms of thymic epithelial cell differentiation. *Semin. Immunol.*, 2000, 12, 421-428.

[27] Anderson, G; Jenkinson, EJ. Lymphostromal interactions in thymic development and function. *Nat. Rev. Immunol.*, 2001, 1, 31-40.

[28] Parreira, L; Neves, H; Simoes, S. Notch and lymphopoiesis: a view from the microenvironment. *Semin. Immunol.*, 2003, 15, 81-89.

[29] Bennett, AR. *et al.* Identification and characterization of thymic epithelial progenitor cells. *Immunity*, 2002, 16, 803–814.

[30] Suniara, RK; Jenkinson, EJ; Owen, JJ. Studies on the phenotype of migrant thymic stem cells. *Eur. J. Immunol.*, 1999, 29, 75-80.

[31] Porrit, HE; Rumfeld, LL; Tabrizifard, S; Schmitt, TM; Zuniga-Pflucker, JC; Petrie HT. Heterogeneity among DN1 prothymocytes reveals multiple progenitors with different capacities to generate T cell and non T cell lineages. *Immunity*, 2004, 20, 735-745.

[32] Matsusaki Y. et al. Characterization of c-kit positive intrathymic stem cells that are restricted to lymphoid differentiation. *J. Exp. Med.*, 1993, 178, 1283-1292.

[33] Ardavin, C; Wu, L; Li, CL; Shortman, K. Thymic dendritic cells and T cells develop simultaneously within the thymus from a common precursor population. *Nature*, 1993, 362, 761–763.

[34] Dakie, A, Shao, QX; D'Amico, A; O'Keeffe, M; Chen, WF; Shortman, K; et al. Development of the dendritic cell system during mouse ontogeny. *J. Immunol.*, 2004, 172, 1018-27.

[35] Bendriss-Vermare, N; et al. Human thymus contains IFN-alpha-producing CD11c(-), myeloid CD11c(+) and mature interdigitating dendritic cells. *J. Clin. Invest.*, 2001, 107, 835-844.

[36] Shortman, K; Wu, L. Thymic dendritic cells. In: Lotze MT, Thomson AW, editors. Dendritic Cells: Biology and Clinical Applications. *Academic Press Ltd.*; 1998. p.15-28.

[37] Wu, L; Shortman, K. Heterogeneity of thymic dendritic cells. *Semin. Immunol.*, 2005, 17, 304-312.

[38] Vremec, D; Pooley, J; Hochrein, H; Wu, L; Shortman, K. CD4 and CD8 expression by dendritic cell subtypes in mouse thymus and spleen. *J. Immunol.*, 2000, 164, 2978-2986.

[39] Vandenabeele, S; Hochrein, H; Mavaddat, N; Winkel, K; Shortman, K. Human thymus contains 2 distinct dendritic cell populations. *Blood,* 2001, 97, 1733 - 1741.

[40] Goldschneider, I; Donskoy, E. Two developmentally distinct populations of dendritic cells inhabit the adult mouse thymus: demonstration by differential importation of hematogenous precursors under steady state conditions. *J. Immunol.,* 2003, 170, 3514–3521.

[41] Okada, T; Lian, ZXNM; Ansari, AA; Ikehara, S; Gershwin, ME. Murine thymic plasmacytoid dendritic cells. *Eur. J. Immunol.,* 2003, 33, 1012–1019.

[42] Shortman K, Liu Y-J. Mouse and human dendritic cell subtypes. *Nat. Rev. Immunol.* 2000, 2, 153-63.

[43] Wu, L; Scollay, R; Egerton, M; Pearse, M; Spangrude, GJ; Shortman, K. CD4 expressed on earliest T-lineage precursor cells in the adult murine thymus. *Nature,* 1991, 349, 71–74.

[44] Wu, L; Li, CL; Shortman, K. Thymic dendritic cell precursors: relationship to the T lymphocyte lineage and phenotype of the dendritic cell progeny. *J. Exp. Med.,* 1996, 184, 903–911.

[45] Saunders, D; Lucas, K; Ismaili, J; Wu, L; Maraskovsky, E; Dunn, A; et al. Dendritic cell development in culture from thymic precursor cells in the absence of granulocyte/macrophage colony-stimulating factor. *J. Exp. Med.,* 1996, 184, 2185–2196.

[46] O'Keeffe, M; Hochrein, H; Vremec, D; Caminschi, I; Miller, JL; Andres, EM; et al. Mouse plasmacytoid cells: long-lived cells, heterogeneous in surface phenotype and function, that differentiate into CD8+ dendritic cells only after microbial stimulus. *J. Exp. Med.,* 2002, 196, 1307-1319.

[47] Hochrein H, Shortman K, Vremec D, Scott B, Hertzog P, O'keffe M. Differential production of IL-12, IFN-alpha, and IFN-gamma by mouse dendritic cell subsets. *J. Immunol.* 2001, 166, 5448-55.

[48] Moseman, EA; Liang, X; Dawson, AJ; Panoskaltsis-Mortari, A; Krieg, AM; Liu,YJ; et al. Human plasmacytoid dendritic cells activated by CpG oligodeoxinucleotides induce the generation of CD4+CD25+ regulatory T cells. *J. Immunol.,* 2004, 173, 4433-4442.

[49] Martin, P; Del Hoyo, GM; Anjuere, F; Arias, CF; Vargas, HH; Fernandez, LA; et al. Characterization of a new subpopulation of mouse CD8alpha+B2220+ dendritic cells endowed with type 1 interferon production capacity and tolerogenic potential. *Blood,* 2002, 100, 383-390.

[50] Dunon, D; Imhof, BA. T cell migration during ontogeny and T cell repertoire generation. *Curr. Top. Microbiol. Immunol.,* 1996, 212, 79-93.

[51] Coltey, M; Bucy, RP; Chen, CH; Cihak, J; Lo¨sch, U; Char, D; Le Douarin, NM; Cooper, MD. Analysis of the first two waves of thymus homing stem cells and their T cell progeny in chick-quail chimeras. *J. Exp. Med.,* 1989, 170, 543-557.

[52] Fontaine-Perus, JC; Calman, FM; Kaplan, C; Le Douarin, NM. Seeding of the 10-day mouse embryo thymic rudiment by lymphocyte precursors in vitro. *J. Immunol.,* 1981, 126, 2310-2316.

[53] Umiel, T; Globerson, A; Auerbach, R. Role of the thymus in the development of immunocompetence of embryonic liver cells in vitro. *Proc. Soc. Exp. Biol. Med.,* 1968, 129, 598-600.

[54] Stutman, O. Intrathymic and extrathymic T cell maturation. *Immunol. Rev.*, 1978, 42, 138-184.

[55] Moore, MA; Owen, JJ. Experimental studies on the development of the thymus. *J. Exp. Med.*, 1967, 126, 715-726.

[56] Fowlkes, BJ; Edison, L; Mathieson, BJ; Chused, TM. Early T lymphocytes:differentiation in vivo of adult intrathymic precursor cells. *J. Exp. Med.*, 1985, 162, 802-822.

[57] Anderson, G, Moore NC, Owen JJ; Jenkinson, EJ. Cellular interactions in thymocyte development. *Annu. Rev. Immunol.* 1996, 14, 73-99.

[58] Gill, G; Malin, M; Sutherland, J; Gray, D; Hollander, G; Boyd, R. Thymic generation and regeneration. *Immunol. Rev.*, 2003, 195, 28-50.

[59] Ezine, S; Weissman, IL; Rouse, RV. Bone marrow cells give rise to distinct cell clones within the thymus. *Nature*, 1984, 309, 629-631.

[60] Kingston, R; Jenkinson, EJ; Owen, JJ. A single stem cell can recolonize an embryonic thymus, producing phenotypically distinct T-cell populations. *Nature*, 1985, 317, 811-813.

[61] Williams, GT; Kingston, R; Owen, MJ; Jenkinson, EJ; Owen, JJ. A single micromanipulated cell gives rise to multiple T-cell receptor gene rearrangements in the thymus in vitro. *Nature*, 1986, 324, 63-64.

[62] Wallis, VJ; Leuchars, E; Chawlinski, S; Davis, AJS. On the sparse seeding of bone marrow and thymus in radiation chimaeras. *Transplantation*, 1975, 19, 2-11.

[63] Boersma, WJA; Kokenberg, E; van der Westen, G; Haaijman, JJ. Postirradiation thymocyte regeneration after bone marrow transplantation. III. Intrathymic differentiation and development of thymocyte subpopulations. *Eur. J. Immunol.*, 1982, 12, 615-619.

[64] Jenkinson, EJ; Franchi, LL; Kingston, R; Owen, JJ. Effect of deoxyguanosine on lymphopoiesis in the developing thymus rudiment in vitro: application in the production of chimeric thymus rudiments. *Eur. J. Immunol.*, 1982, 12, 583-587.

[65] Fridkis-Hareli, M; Sharp, A; Abel, L; Globerson, A. Thymocyte development in an in vitro constructed chimera of irradiated fetal thymus and lymphohemopoietic cels. *Thymus*, 1991, 18, 225-235.

[66] Fridkis-Hareli, M; Abel, L; Globerson, A. Patterns of dual lymphocyte development in co-cultures of foetal thymus and lymphohaemopoietic cells from young and old mice. *Immunology*, 1992, 77, 185-188.

[67] Fridkis-Hareli, M; Abel, L; Eisenbach, L; Globerson, A. Differentiation patterns of CD4/CD8 thymocyte subsets in cocultures of fetal thymus and lymphohemopoietic cells from c-fos transgenic and normal mice. *Cell. Immunol.*, 1992, 141, 279-292.

[68] Fridkis-Hareli, M; Eren, R; Sharp, A; Abel, L; Kukulansky, T; Globerson, A. MHC recognition in colonization of the thymus by bone marrow cells. *Cell. Immunol.*, 1993, 149, 91-98.

[69] Fridkis-Hareli, M; Abel, L; Globerson, A. In vitro analysis of thymic microenvironmental effects on bone marrow cells of severe combined immunodeficient (SCID) mice. *Cell. Immunol.*, 1993, 147, 237-246.

[70] Fridkis-Hareli, M; Abel, L; Globerson, A. Developmental pathways of cortical and medullary thymocytes in aging. *Aging: Immunol. Infect. Dis.*, 1993, 4, 245-250.

[71] Fridkis-Hareli, M; Mehr, R; Abel, L; Globerson, A. Developmental interactions of CD4 T cells and thymocytes: age-related differential effects. *Mech. Ageing Dev.,* 1994, 173, 169-178.

[72] Moore, MAS. The role of cell migration in the ontogeny of the lymphoid system. *Stem Cells Dev.,* 2004, 13, 1-21.

[73] Mori, S; Shortman, K; Wu, L. Characterization of thymus-seeding precursor cells from mouse bone marrow. *Blood,* 2001, 98, 696-704.

[74] Nehls, M; Kyewski, B; Messerle, M; Waldschutz, R; Schuddekopf, K; Smith, AJ; Bohem T. Two genetically separable steps in the differentiation of thymic epithelium. *Science,* 1996, 272, 886-889.

[75] Nichogiannopoulou, A; Trevisan, M; Neben, S; Friedrich, C; Georgopoulos, K. Defects in hemopoietic stem cell activity in *Ikaros* mutant mice. *J. Exp.Med.,* 1999, 190, 1201–1214.

[76] Mukouyama, Y; Chiba, N; Mucenski, ML; Satake, M; Miyajima, A; et al. Hematopoietic cells in cultures of the murine embryonic aorta-gonadmesonephros region are induced by c-Myβ. *Curr. Biol.,* 1999, 9, 833–836.

[77] Fisher, RC; Lovelock, JD; Scott, EW. A critical role for PU.1 in homing and long-term engraftment by hematopoietic stem cells in the bone marrow. *Blood,* 1999, 94, 1283–1290.

[78] North, TE; de Bruijn, MF; Stacy, T; Talebian, L; Lind, E; et al. Runx1 expression marks long-term repopulating hematopoietic stem cells in the midgestation mouse embryo. *Immunity,* 2002, 16, 661–672.

[79] Varnum-Finney, B; Xu, L; Brashem-Stein, C; Nourigat, C; Flowers, D; et al. Pluripotent, cytokine-dependent, hematopoietic stem cells are immortalized by constitutive Notch1 signaling. *Nat. Med.,* 2000, 6, 1278–81.

[80] Rothernberg, EV; Taghon, T. Molecular genetics of T cell development. *Annu. Rev .Immunol.,* 2005, 23, 601-649.

[81] Maillard, I; Fang, T; Pear, WS. Regulation of lymphoid development, differentiation, and function by the Notch pathway. *Annu. Rev. Immunol.,* 2005, 23, 945-974.

[82] Rothenberg, EV, Taghon, T. Molecular genetics of T cell development. *Annu Rev Immunol.,* 2005, 23, 601-649.

[83] Tan, JB; Visan, I; Yuan, JS; Guidos, CJ. Requerimento for Notch1 signals at sequential early stages of intrathymic T cell development. *Nat. Immunol.,* 2005, 6, 671-679.

[84] Harman, BC; Jenkinson, WE; Parnell ,SM; Rossi, SW; Jenkinson, EJ; Anderson, G. T/B lineage choice occurs prior to intrathymic Notch signaling. *Blood,* 2005, 106, 886-892.

[85] von Boehmer, H. Notch in lymphopoiesis and T cell polarization. *Nat Immunol.,* 2005, 6, 641-642.

[86] Nam, Y; Aster, JC; Blacklow, SC. Notch signaling as a therapeutic target. *Curr. Opin. Chem. Biol.,* 2002, 6, 501-509.

[87] Sambandam, A; Maillard, I; Zediak, VP; Xu, L; Gerstein, RM; Aster, JC; Pear, WS; Bhandoola, A. Notch signaling controls the generation and differentiation of early T lineage progenitors. *Nat. Immunol.,* 2005, Jul;6, 663-670.

[88] Tan, JB; Visan, I; Yuan, JS; Guidos ,CJ. Requirement for Notch1 signals at sequential early stages of intrathymic T cell development. *Nat. Immunol.,* 2005, 6, 671-679.

[89]   Minter, LM; Turley, DM; Das, P; Shin, HM;, Joshi, I; Lawlor, RG; Cho, OH; Palaga, T; Gottipati, S; Telfer, JC; Kostura, L; Fauq, AH; Simpson, K; Such, KA; Miele, L; Golde, TE; Miller, SD; Osborne, BA. Inhibitors of gamma-secretase block in vivo and in vitro T helper type 1 polarization by preventing Notch upregulation of Tbx21. *Nat Immunol.*, 2005, 6, 680-688.

[90]   Briend, E; Young, LL; McKenzie, GJ; Tugal, T; Ragno, S; Champion, BR. Modulation of the notch pathway for immunotherapy. *Curr. Opin. Mol. Ther.*, 2005, 7, 56-61.

[91]   Stutman, O; Yunis, EJ; Good, RA. Carcinogen-induced tumors of the thymus: IV. Humoral influences of normal thymus and functional thymomas and influence of postthymectomy period on restoration. *J. Exp. Med.*, 1969, 130, 809-819.

[92]   Stutman, O; Yunis, EJ; Good, RA. Studies on thymus function: II. Cooperative effect of newborn and embryonic hemopoietic liver cells with thymus function *J. Exp. Med.*, 1970, 132, 601-612.

[93]   Page, DM; Alexander, J; Snoke, K; Apella, E; Sette, A; Hedrick, SM; Grey, HM. Negative selection of CD4+CD8+ thymocytes by T-cell receptor peptide antagonists. *Proc. Natl. Acad. Sci. USA*, 1994, 91, 4057–4061.

[94]   Spain, LM; Jorgensen, JL; Davis, MM; Berg, LJ. A peptide antigen antagonist prevents the differentiation of T cell receptor transgenic thymocytes. *J. Immunol.*, 1994, 152, 1709–1717.

[95]   Ghendler, Y; Teng, MK; Liu, JH; Witte, T; Liu, J; Kim, KS; Kern, P; Chang, HC; Wang, JH; Reinherz, EL. Differential thymic selection outcomes stimulated by focal structural alteration in peptide/major histocompatibility complex ligands. *Proc. Natl. Acad. Sci. USA.*, 1998, 95, 10061–10066.

[96]   Pircher, HP; Burki, R; Lang, R; Hengartner, H; Zinkernagel, RM. Tolerance induction in double-specific T cell receptor transgenic mice varies with antigen. *Nature*, 1989, 342, 559–561.

[97]   Puglielli, MT; Zajac, AJ; van der Most, RG; Dzuris, JL; Sette, A; Altman, JD; Ahmed, R. In vivo selection of a lymphocytic choriomeningitis virus variant that affects recognition of the gp33-41 epitope by Hb but not H-2Kb. *J. Virol.*, 2001, 75, 5099–5107.

[98]   Nguyen, LT; Bachmann, MF; Ohashi, PS. Contribution of LCMV transgenic models to understanding T lymphocyte development, activation, tolerance, and autoimmunity. *Curr. Top. Microbiol. Immunol.*, 2002, 263, 119–143.

[99]   Williams, O; Tarazona, R; Wack, A; Harker, N; Roderick, K; Kioussis, D. Interactions with multiple peptide ligands determine the fate of developing thymocytes. *Proc. Natl. Acad. Sci. USA.*, 1998, 95, 5706–5711.

[100] Logunova, NN; Viret, C; Pobezinsky, LA; Miller, SA; Kazansky, DB; Sundberg, JP; Chervonsky, AV. Restricted MHC-peptide repertoire predisposes to autoimmunity. *J. Exp. Med.*, 2005, 202, 73-84.

[101] van den Elzen, P; Menezes, JS; Ametani, A; Maverakis, E; Madakamutil, L; Tang, XL; Kumar, V; Sercarz, EE. Limited clonality in autoimmunity:drivers and regulators. *Autoimmune Rev.*, 2004, 3, 524-529.

[102] Ashton-Rickardt, PG; Bandeira, A; Delaney, JR; Van Kaer, L; Pircher, HP; Zinkernagel, RM; Tonegawa, S. Evidence for a differential avidity model of T cell selection in the thymus. *Cell*, 1994, 76, 651–663.

[103] Smyth, LA; Williams, O; Huby, RD; Norton, T; Acuto, O; Ley, SC; Kioussis, D. Altered peptide ligands induce quantatively but not qualitatively different intracellular signals in primary thymocytes. *Proc. Natl. Acad. Sci. USA.*, 1998, 95, 8193–8198.

[104] Mamalaki, C; Norton, T; Tanaka, Y; Townsend, AR; Chandler, P; Simpson, E; Kioussis, D. Thymic depletion and peripheral activation of class I major histocompatibility complex-restricted T cells by soluble peptide in T-cell receptor transgenic mice. *Proc. Natl. Acad. Sci.USA.*, 1992, 89, 11342–11346.

[105] Tissot, AC; Ciatto, C; Mittl, PR; Grutter, MG; Pluckthun, A. Viral escape at the molecular level explained by quantitative T-cell receptor/peptide/MHC interactions and the crystal structure of a peptide/MHC complex. *J. Mol. Biol.*, 2000, 302, 873–885.

[106] Achour, A; Michaelsson, J; Harris, RA; Odeberg, J;, Grufman, P; Sandberg, JK; Levitsky, V; Karre, K; Sandalova, T; Schneider, G. A structural basis for LCMV immune invasion: subversion of H-2Db and H-2Kb presentation of gp33 revealed by comparative crystal structure analyses. *Immunity*, 2002, 17, 757–768.

[107] Fridkis-Hareli, M; Reche, P; Reinherz, EL. Peptide variants of viral CTL epitopes mediate positive selection and emigration of Ag-specific thymocytes in vivo. *J. Immunol.*, 2004, 173, 1140–1150.

[108] Hahn, M; Nicholson, MJ; Pyrdol, J; Wucherpfennig, KW. Unconventional topology of self peptide-major histocompatibility complex binding by a human autoimmune T cell receptor. *Nat. Immunol.*, 2005, 5, 490-496.

[109] Hildebrand, JA. A LAT mutation that inhibits T cell development yet induces lymphoproliferation. *Science,* 2002, 296, 2040-2043.

[110] Kappler, J; Roehm, N; Marrack, P. T cell tolerance by clonal elimination in the thymus. *Cell*, 1987, 49, 273–280.

[111] Amsen, D; Kruisbeek, AM. Thymocyte selection: not by TCR alone. *Immunol. Rev.*, 1998, 165, 209–229.

[112] Punt, JA; Osborne, BA; Takahama, Y; Sharrow, SO; Singer, A. Negative selection of CD4CCD8C thymocytes by T cell receptor-induced apoptosis requires a costimulatory signal that can be provided by CD28. *J. Exp. Med.*, 1994, 179, 709–713.

[113] Mariathasan, S; Zakarian, A; Bouchard, D; Michie, AM; Zuniga-Pflucker, JC; Ohashi, PS. Duration and strength of extracellular signal-regulated kinase signals are altered during positive versus negative thymocyte selection. *J. Immunol.*, 2001, 167, 4966–4973.

[114] Kuo, CT; Leiden, JM. Transcriptional regulation of T lymphocyte development and function. *Annu. Rev. Immunol.,* 1999, 17, 149–187.

[115] Halin C, Mora JR, Sumen C; von Adrian UH. In vivo imaging of lymphocyte trafficking. *Annu. Rev. Cell. Dev. Biol.* 2005. In press.

[116] Bousso P. Real time imaging of T cell development. *Curr. Opin. Immunol.*, 2004, 16, 400-5.

[117] Feng, C; Woodside, KJ; Vance, BA; El-Khoury, D; Canelles, M; Lee, J; Gress, R; Fowlkes, BJ; Shores, EW; Love, PE. A potential role for CD69 in thymocyte emigration. *Int Immunol.*, 2002, 14, 535–544.

[118] Norment, AM; Bevan, MJ. Role of chemokines in thymocyte development. *Semin Immunol.*, 2000, 12, 445–455.

[119] Patel, DD; Haynes, BF. Cell adhesion molecules involved in intrathymic T cell development. *Semin Immunol.*, 1993, 5, 282–292.

[120] Savino, W; Ayres-Martins, S; Neves-dos-Santos, S; Smaniotto, S; Ocampo, JSP; Mendes-da-Cruz, DA; Terra-Granado, E; Kusmenok, O; Villa-Verde, DMS. Thymocyte migration: an affair of multiple cellular interactions? *Braz. J. Med. Biol. Res.*, 2003, 36, 1015–1025.

[121] Savino, W; Dardenne, M. Neuroendocrine control of thymus physiology. *Endocrine Rev.*, 2000, 21, 412–443.

[122] Matloubian, M; Lo, CG; Cinamon, G;, Lesneski, MJ; Xu, Y; Brinkmann, V; Allende, ML; Proia, RL; Cyster, JG. Lymphocyte egress from thymus and peripheral lymphoid organs is dependent on S1P receptor 1. *Nature*, 2004, 427, 355–360.

[123] Cyster, JG. Lymphoid organ development and cell migration. *Immunol. Rev.*, 2003, 195, 5–14.

[124] Rot, A; von Adrian, UH. Chemokines in innate and adaptive host defense. *Annu. Rev. Immunol.*, 2004, 22, 891–928.

[125] Allende, ML; Dreier, JL; Mandala, S; Proia, RL. Expression of the sphingosine 1-phosphate receptor S1P1, on T-cells controls thymic emigration. *J. Biol. Chem.*, 2004, 279, 15396–15401.

[126] Rosen, H; Sanna, G; Alfonso, C. Egress: a receptor-regulated step in lymphocyte trafficking. *Immunol. Rev.*, 2003, 195, 160–177.

[127] Spiegel, S; Milstien, S. Sphingosine-1-phosphate: an enigmatic signaling lipid. *Nat. Rev. Mol. Cell. Biol.*, 2003, 4, 397–407.

[128] Yunis, EJ; Hilgard, HR; Sjodin, K; Martinez, C; Good, RA. Immunological reconstitution of thymectomized mice by injections of isolated thymocytes. *Nature*, 1964, 201, 784-786.

[129] Hilgard, HR; Yunis, EJ; Sjodin, K; Martinez, C; Good, RA. Reversal of wasting in thymectomized mice by the injection of syngeneic spleen or thymus cell suspensions. *Nature,* 1964, 202, 668-670.

[130] Yunis, EJ; Martinez, C; Smith, J; Good, RA. Facilitation of host lymphoid tissue development in neonatally thymectomized mice by injection of allogeneic dispersed thymus cells. *Nature*, 1964, 204, 850-853.

[131] Gombert, JM; Herbelin, A; Tancrede-Bohin, E; Dy, M; Carnaud, C; Bach, JF. Early quantitative and functional deficiency of NK1+-like thymocytes in the NOD mouse. *Eur. J. Immunol.*, 1996, 26, 2989-2998.

[132] Kukreja, A; Cost, G; Marker, J; Zhang, C; Sun, Z; Lin-Su, K; Ten, S; Sanz, M; Exley, M; Wilson, B; Porcelli, S; Maclaren, N. Multiple immuno-regulatory defects in type-1 diabetes. *J. Clin. Invest.*, 2002, 109, 131-140.

[133] Pantelouris, EM. Absence of thymus in a mouse mutant. *Nature*, 1968, 217, 370-371.

[134] Pantelouris, EM; Hair, J. Thymus dysgenesis in nude (nu/nu) mice. *J. Embryol. Exp. Morphol.*, 1970, 24, 615-623.

[135] Cordier, AC; Heremans, JF. Nude mouse embryo: ectodermal nature of the primordial thymic defect. Scand. *J. Immunol.*, 1975, 4, 193-196.

[136] Liston, A; Lesage, S; Wilson, J; Peltonen, L; Goodnow, CC. Aire regulates negative selection of organ-specific T cells. *Nat. Immunol.*, 2003, 4, 350-354.

[137] Anderson, MS; Venanzi, ES; Klein, L; Chen, Z; Berzins, SP; Turley, SJ; von Boehmer, H; Bronson, R; Dierich, A; Benoist, C; Mathis, D. Projection of an immunological self shadow within the thymus by the AIRE protein. *Science*, 2002, 298, 1395-1401.

[138] Gotter, J; Brors, B; Hargenhahn, M; Kyewski, B. Medullary epithelial cells of the human thymus express a highly diverse selection of tissue-specific genes co-localized in chromosomal clusters. *J. Exp. Med.*, 2004, 199, 155-166.

[139] Thebault-Baumont, K; Dubois-Laforgue, D; Krief, P; Briand, JP; Halbout, P; Vallon-Geoffroy, K; Morin, J; Laloux, V; Lehuen, A; Carel, JC; et al.: Acceleration of type 1 diabetes mellitus in proinsulin 2-deficient NOD mice. *J. Clin. Invest.*, 2003, 111, 851-857.

[140] Jordan, MS; Boesteanu, A; Reed, AJ; Petrone, AL; Holenbeck, AE; Lerman, MA; Naji, A; Caton, AJ. Thymic selection of $CD4^+CD25^+$ regulatory T cells induced by an agonist self-peptide. *Nat. Immunol.*, 2001, 2, 301-306.

[141] Apostolou, I; Sarukhan, A; Klein, L; von Boehmer, H. Origin of regulatory T cells with known specificity for antigen. *Nat. Immunol.* 2002, 3, 756-763.

[142] Anderson, MS; Venanzi, ES; Chen, Z; Berzins, SP; Benoist, C; Mathis, D. The cellular mechanism of Aire control of T cell tolerance. *Immunity*, 2005, 2, 227-239.

[143] Sakaguchi, S; Sakaguchi, N; Asano, M; Itoh, M; Toda, M. Immunologic self-tolerance maintained by activated T cells expressing IL-2 receptor alpha-chains (CD25). Breakdown of a single mechanism of self-tolerance causes various autoimmune diseases. *J. Immunol.,* 1995, 155, 1151-1164.

[144] Asano, M; Toda, M; Sakaguchi, N; Sakaguchi, S. Autoimmune disease as a consequence of developmental abnormality of a T cell subpopulation. *J. Exp. Med.*, 1996, 184, 387-396.

[145] Gershon, RK; Metzler, CM. Suppressor Cells in aging. In: *Comprehensive Immunology*, Eds. Makinodan, T; Yunis, EJ, pp. 103-110. *Plenum Medical Book Company*, New York, 1976.

[146] Sakaguchi, S. Naturally arising $CD4^+$ regulatory T cells for immunologic self-tolerance and negative control of immune responses. *Annu. Rev. Immunol.*, 2004, 22, 531-562.

[147] Cao, D; Malmstrom, V; Baecher-Allan, C; Hafler, D; Klareskog, L; Trollmo, C. Isolation and functional characterization of regulatory $CD25^{bright}CD4^+$ T cells from the target organ of patients with rheumatoid arthritis. *Eur. J. Immunol.*, 2003, 33, 215-223.

[148] Woo, EY; Yeh, H; Chu, CS; Schlienger, K; Carroll, RG; Riley, JL; Kaiser, LR; June, CH. Cutting edge: Regulatory T cells from lung cancer patients directly inhibit autologous T cell proliferation. *J. Immunol.,* 2002, 168, 4272-4276.

[149] Curiel, TJ; Coukos, G; Zou, L; Alvarez, X; Cheng, P;Mottram, P; Evdemon-Hogan, M; Conejo-Garcia, JR; Zhang, L; Burow, M; et al. Specific recruitment of regulatory T cells in ovarian carcinoma fosters immune privilege and predicts reduced survival. *Nat. Med.*, 2004, 10, 942-949.

[150] Graca, L; Cobbold, SP; Waldmann, H. Identification of regulatory T cells in tolerated allografts. *J. Exp. Med.*, 2002, 195, 1641-1646.

[151] Belkaid, Y; Piccirillo, CA; Mendez, S; Shevach, EM; Sacks, DL. $CD4^+CD25^+$ regulatory T cells control Leishmania major persistence and immunity. *Nature*, 2002, 420, 502-507.

[152] Hori, S; Carvalho, TL; Demengeot, J. $CD25^+CD4^+$ regulatory T cells suppress $CD4^+$ T cell-mediated pulmonary hyperinflammation driven by Pneumocystis carinii in immunodeficient mice. *Eur. J. Immunol.*, 2002, 32, 1282-1291.

[153] Green, EA; Choi, Y; Flavell, RA. Pancreatic lymph node-derived CD4$^+$CD25$^+$ Treg cells: highly potent regulators of diabetes that require TRANCE-RANK signals. *Immunity.*, 2002, 16, 183-191.

[154] Mottet, C; Uhlig, HH; Powrie, F. Cutting Edge: Cure of colitis by CD4$^+$CD25$^+$ regulatory T cells. *J. Immunol.*, 2003, 170, 3939-3943.

[155] Fehervari, Z; Sakaguchi, S. Development and function of CD4+CD25+ regulatory T cells. *Curr. Opin. Immunol.*, 2004, 16, 203-208.

[156] Olivares-Villagomez, D; Wensky, AK; Wang, Y; Lafaille, JJ. Repertoire requirements of CD4+ T cells that prevent spontaneous autoimmune encephalomyelitis. *J. Immunol.*, 2000, 164, 5499-5507.

[157] Gonzalez, A; Andre-Schmutz, I; Carnaud, C; Mathis, D, Benoist ,C. Damage control, rather than unresponsiveness, effected by protective DX5+ T cells in autoimmune diabetes. *Nat. Immunol.*, 2001, 2, 1117-1125.

[158] Stephens, LA; Mason, D. CD25 is a marker for CD4+ thymocytes that prevent autoimmune diabetes in rats, but peripheral T cells with this function are found in both CD25+ and CD25- subpopulations. *J. Immunol.*, 2000, 165, 3105-3110.

[159] Suri-Payer E; Amar, Z; Thornton, AM; Shevach, EM. CD4+CD25+ T cells inhibit both the induction and effector function of autoreactive T cells and represent a unique lineage of immunoregulatory cells. *J. Immunol.*, 1998, 184, 1212-1218.

[160] Alyanakian, MA; You, S; Damotte, D; Gouarin, C; Esling, A; Garcia, C; Havouis, S;Chatenoud, L; Bach, JF. Diversity of regulatory CD4+ T cells controlling distinct organ-specific autoimmune diseases. *Proc. Natl. Acad. Sci. USA*, 2003, 100, 15806-15811.

[161] Hori, S; Nomura, T; Sakaguchi, S. Control of regulatory T cell development by the transcription factor Foxp3. *Science*, 2003, 299, 1057-1061.

[162] Fontenot, JD; Gavin, M; Rudensky, A. FoxP3 programs the development and function of CD4+CD25+ regulatory T cells. *Nat. Immunol.*, 2003, 4, 330-336.

[163] Stassen, M; Fondel, S; Bopp, T; Richter, C; Muller, C; Kubach, J; Becker, C; Knop, J; Enk, AH; Schmitt, S et al. Human CD25+ regulatory T cells: two subsets defined by the integrins alpha 4 beta 7 or alpha 4 beta 1 confer distinct suppressive properties upon CD4+ T helper cells. *Eur. J. Immunol.*, 2004, 34, 1303-1311.

[164] O'Garra, A; Vieira, P. Regulatory T cells and mechanisms of immune system control. *Nat. Med.*, 2004, 10, 801-805.

[165] Hu D, Ikizawa K, Lu L, Sanchirico ME, Shinohara ML, Cantor H. Analysis of regulatory CD8 T cells in Qa-1-deficient mice. *Nat Immunol* 2004; 5:469-71

[166] Sarantopoulos, S; Lu, L; Cantor, H. Qa-1 restriction of CD8$^+$ suppressor T cells. *J. Clin. Invest.*, 2004, 114, 1218-1221.

[167] Jiang, H; Chess, L. An integrated view of suppressor T cell subsets in immunoregulation. *J. Clin. Invest.*, 2004, 114, 1198-1208.

[168] Kumar, V. Homeostatic control of immunity by TCR peptide–specific Tregs. *J. Clin. Invest.*, 2004, 114, 1222-1226.

[169] Chang, CC; et al. Tolerization of dendritic cells by T(S) cells: the crucial role of inhibitory receptors ILT3 and ILT4. *Nat. Immunol.*, 2002, 3, 237-243.

[170] Najafian, N; et al. Regulatory functions of CD8+CD28- T cells in an autoimmune disease model. *J. Clin. Invest.*, 2003, 112, 1037-1048.

[171] Cohen, IR; Quintana, FJ; Mimran, A. Tregs in T cell vaccination: exploring the regulation of regulation. *J. Clin. Invest.*, 2004, 114, 1227-1232.

[172] Godfrey, DI; Kronenberg, M. Going both ways: immune regulation via CD1d-dependent NKT cells. *J. Clin. Invest.*, 2004, 114, 1379-1388.

[173] Sprent, J. Proving negative selection in the thymus. *J. Immunol.*, 2005, 174, 3841-3842.

[174] Yunis, EJ; Fernandez, G; Teague, PO; Stutman, O; Good, RA. The thymus, autoimmunity and the involution of the lymphoid system. In: *Tolerance, Autoimunity and Aging*. Ed. Gitman, L., Thomas, CC. pp. 62-119. New York, 1972.

[175] Anderson, MS; Bluestone, JA. The NOD mouse: a model of immune dysregulation. *Annu. Rev. Immunol.*, 2005, 23, 447-485.

[176] Jutila, JW. Congenitally athymic (nude) mice and their application to the study of immunity and aging. In *Comprehensive Immunology*, Eds. Makinodan, T; Yunis, EJ. pp.171-182. Plenum Medical Book Company, New York, 1976.

[177] Yunis, EJ; Hong, R; Grewe, MA; Martinez, C; Cornelius, E; Good, RA. Postthymectomy wasting associated with autoimmune phenomena. *J. Exp. Med.*, 1967, 125, 947-966.

[178] Yunis, EJ; Fernandez, G; Stutman, O. Susceptibility to involution of the thymus-dependent lymphoid system and autoimmunity. *J. Clin. Pathol.*, 1971, 56, 280-292.

[179] Ikehara, S. et al. Organ-specific and systemic autoimmune diseases originate from defects in haemopoietic stem cells. *Proc. Natl. Acad. Sci. USA*, 1990, 87, 8341-8344.

[180] Ikehara, S. Bone marrow transplantation for autoimmune diseases. *Acta Haematol.*, 1998, 99, 116-132.

[181] Sykes, M; Nikolic, B. Treatment of severe autoimmune disease by stem-cell transplantation. *Nature*, 2005, 435, 620-627.

[182] Hough, RE; Snowden, JA; Wulffraat, NM. Haemopoietic stem cell transplantation in autoimmune diseases: a European perspective. *Br. J. Haematol.*, 2005, 128, 432-459.

In: Progress in Stem Cell Research
Editor: Prasad S. Koka, pp. 119-131

ISBN: 978-1-60456-065-7
© 2008 Nova Science Publishers, Inc.

Chapter 7

CONTROL OF TISSUE REGENERATION THROUGH OXYGEN CONCENTRATIONS

*Jessica A. Shafer[b], Alan R. Davis[a,b,c] and Elizabeth A. Olmsted-Davis[a,b,c]**

[a]Center for Cell and Gene Therapy
[b]Departments of Pediatrics
[c]Orthopedic Surgery, Baylor College of Medicine, Houston, TX 77030

ABSTRACT

For centuries oxygen has been thought to be the key to all life. Without it, eukaryotic organisms including cells cannot survive. Oxidative stress, reactive oxygen and antioxidants have become household terms, yet it has only been recently that researchers have started to unravel the essential complex regulatory role oxygen plays in stem cell maintenance, proliferation, migration, and engraftment for tissue regeneration. Both adult and embryonic stem cells have now been shown to be housed in "niches" which possess 1-5% oxygen levels, considerably lower than 21% ambient oxygen. The term hypoxia is used to describe these lower oxygen levels but recent critics suggest this may be more accurately described as normoxia. Much evidence has come to light that cells possess several key factors that function as oxygen sensors and that oxygen status within target tissues may play a key role in stem cell engraftment and differentiation during tissue repair. One of the key factors involved is hypoxia inducible factor (HIF). This factor can both enhance cellular differentiation, as well as rapidly change local oxygen levels through stimulation of angiogenesis and reduction of cellular oxygen requirements, by switching the cell from aerobic to anaerobic respiration. Thus during tissue injury, hypoxic areas within the damaged region can induce expression of factors essential for the recruitment and engraftment of stem cells for regeneration. Further, stem cells when exposed to higher oxygen in the blood stream during mobilization, switch from anaerobic respiration in their hypoxic niche, to aerobic metabolism during proliferation. During this period of high energy production and cellular proliferation, reactive oxygen is generated, which in concert with other factors alters gene expression towards terminal

---

* Correspondence: Elizabeth A Olmsted-Davis, One Baylor Plaza, BCMN 505, Houston TX 77030, USA. Telephone: 713-798-1253; Fax: 713-798-1230; E-mail: edavis@bcm.tmc.edu

differentiation. Thus oxygen tension may be an essential component for the regeneration of tissue.

INTRODUCTION

Physiologically, oxygen is a vital necessity for the survival of cells. It is becoming increasingly evident that cells require oxygen for biological processes beyond survival. A significant body of evidence suggests that physiological gradients of oxygen are critical to regulate cellular recruitment, differentiation and physiological homeostasis. This complicates interpretation of many *in vitro* studies, because for decades they have been performed in ambient oxygen conditions. Such conditions may not actually represent normoxia or normal oxygen concentration experienced by cells within the human body [1,2]. In stem cell biology, hypoxic conditions may more accurately reflect the normal physiology. In fact, the oxygen environment in the developing embryo itself is hypoxic.[3] Embryos that are unable to sense and respond to hypoxia because they lack functional HIF-1 α undergo developmental arrest and death by day E11[4]. Recent experiments have also demonstrated that embryonic stem cells (ES) *in vitro* spontaneously differentiate in oxygen levels above 3-5% [1]. The results suggest that the low oxygen tension is essential for maintaining pluripotency. Using HIF-1 β null mutants that were unable to respond to a low oxygen, Adelman *et al* demonstrated the proliferation of an embryonic multi-lineage hematopoietic progenitor required hypoxia [5]. The authors found that "physiologic hypoxia" in the embryo is essential for proliferation and survival of these hematopoietic precursors during development. Ivanovic *et al* showed similar findings for hematopoietic progenitors isolated from cord blood [6]. Others have demonstrated the necessity of hypoxia for differentiation of specific structures in cardiovascular development [7], suggesting that oxygen tension plays a very specific role in coordinating the development of the embryo.

Physiologic hypoxia also applies to adult stem cell populations that occupy specific hypoxic niches within the adult organism. In the adult brain, normoxia is actually 1-5% O_2. Thus neural stem cells have been shown to require low oxygen for growth and survival [2]. Muscle satellite and mesenchymal stem cells have also been found to have greater proliferation in culture when grown in low oxygen [8]. This review will focus primarily on the influences of oxygen on adult stem cell populations.

Changes in oxygen tension influence proliferation, engraftment, and differentiation of adult stem cells through key genes that are under the control of hypoxia responsive elements [9]. Here we present an overview of the molecular mechanism utilized by these cells to sense and respond to oxygen levels in the local environment. These responses include regulating cellular energy metabolism and expression of factors essential for migration and homing to target tissues.

HOW CELLS CAN RESPOND TO THE LOCAL OXYGEN ENVIRONMENT

In 1861, Louis Pasteur demonstrated that oxygen inhibits fermentation and that glucose consumption is inversely proportional to oxygen availability, i.e. anaerobic metabolism is favored in low oxygen. This was the first evidence that the glycolytic pathway is positively regulated by hypoxia. Pasteur received significant recognition for this stunning observation that has since become universally known as the 'Pasteur Effect.' Since his original finding the up-regulation of glycolysis to permit the production of energy under reduced oxygen tension remains one of the hallmarks of the hypoxic response. Webster [10] established that expression of many glycolytic enzymes are induced under hypoxic conditions. It was further established by Iyer *et al* [4] that this induction is mediated by HIF-1 α.

A key regulator of glycolytic flux is fructose-2,6-bisphosphate, and its steady state concentration is regulated by the action of isozymes which are the product of four different genes (pfkfb1-4). Hypoxia can induce the expression of pfkfb3 in cells [11]. Extensive analysis of the 5' pfkfb3 promoter sequence revealed the presence of putative consensus binding sites for various transcription factors, one of which was a hypoxia response element (HRE) [11]. Promoter deletion analysis as well as putative HREs sequences (wild type and mutated) fused to a c-fos minimal promoter unit constructs demonstrate a region adjacent to the start site that was essential for oxygen regulation. In addition, experiments using mouse embryo fibroblasts from a mouse lacking the hypoxia inducible transcription factor HIF-1α demonstrated that HIF-1 protein is critically needed for the hypoxia trans-activation of this gene. A pfkfb3-promoter-reporter construct failed to be activated in these mutant fibroblasts thus providing a molecular mechanism by which local oxygen concentrations can regulate glycolysis. The glycolytic enzyme triosephosphate isomerase (TPI), which catalyses the reversible conversion of dihydroxyacetone phosphate into glyceraldehyde-3-phosphate, has also been found to be regulated by HIF [12]. The physiological importance of the induction of TPI in conditions of hypoxia is likely to increase the flow of triosephosphates through the glycolytic cascade. These papers illustrate the role of HIF-1 in the promotion of glycolysis and therefore an increase of anaerobic energy generation over aerobic processes.

HIF is the major transcription factor utilized by the cell to adapt to changes in local oxygen conditions. In high or ambient oxygen conditions this transcription factor is hydroxylated on proline residues by the prolyl hydroxylase, Elgn 1 (also known as PHD2). In its hydroxylated form, HIFα is recognized by the von Hipple Lindau (VHL) complex and targeted for ubiquitin-proteasome-mediated degradation [13]. This pathway is shown in Figure 1. Proteasomes are highly ordered complexes of multicatalytic proteinases that are distributed throughout eukaryotic cells at high concentrations to cleave peptides in an ATP/ubiquitin-dependent process.

HIF-1α is stabilized in low oxygen tension and translocates to the nucleus where it binds to its partner HIF-1β. This complex can then associates with HREs in various genes to coordinately regulate gene expression. Many genes key in adult stem cell mobilization, survival, proliferation, and differentiation are under the control of hypoxia responsive elements. These include SDF-1, VEGF, and erythropoietin.

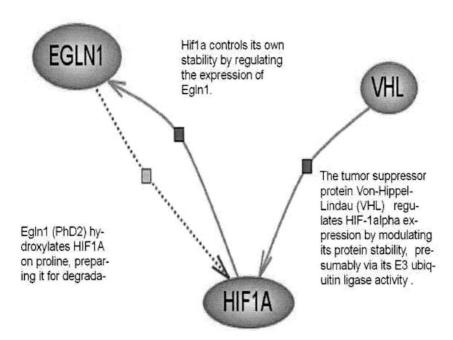

Figure 1. The hypoxia inducible factor (HIF) pathway. Under high pO_2 HIF is hydroxylated on proline which targets it for degradation, whereas in low pO_2 this factor migrates to the nucleus where it coordinately regulates gene expression

STEM CELL PROLIFERATION AND MOBILIZATION

Stem cell mobilization and proliferation for the regeneration of injured tissue most likely requires a complex inductive response including the release of growth factors, cytokines, and chemokines from the injured tissues. However, oxygen concentrations also play a key role in regulation of this process. Most cells must mobilize into areas of higher oxygen concentrations for conversion to aerobic respiration in order to produce the amount of ATP required for cellular replication [9]. Many researchers suggest that cell populations able to replicate in less ideal circumstances with low oxygen concentrations are the earliest stem cells with the highest degree of pluiripotency. Evidence for this comes from the embryo where cells proliferate under hypoxic conditions.

However, Danet *et al* [14] showed opposing effects of oxygen on the proliferative state of the adult hemapoietic stem cell. When HSCs were isolated based on the markers CD34[+], lin[-] and then placed under hypoxic conditions, more cells remained in quiescence in compararision to normoxic conditions. However, when CD34[+], CD38[-], lin[-] cells were isolated, this select population had a higher percentage of cells undergoing proliferation in hypoxic conditions when compared to oxygen rich conditions. [14] The authors speculated that this population may be an earlier progenitor that proliferates in low oxygen, an environment that would resemble the normal conditions within the bone marrow "niche". However, these progenitors may not be capable of maintaining a pluripotent phenotype when exposed to higher oxygen, thus limiting their potential to repopulate. Interestingly, the cells were unfortunately exposed to high O_2 during purification, which significantly effects interpretation of these results. Much evidence is accumulating to suggest cells grown in normoxic conditions generate reactive oxygen species that are capable of inducing terminal differentiation in progenitors. This topic is covered in more detail in the following sections.

The tissue repair model developed by Tepper et al [15] and described in more detail below, showed that human CXCR4 +, CD31+ donor bone marrow derived endothelial progenitor cells were shown to be proliferating within the ischemic tissue flap. However, since marrow derived cells must migrate through vessels that contain a high O_2 tension to arrive at the site of injury, the authors cannot rule out that the cells were not proliferating in response to O_2 exposure in the vessels.

Venezia et al [16] recently analyzed the stages of hematopoietic stem cell (HSC) mobilization and proliferation using microarray analysis. The authors reported the specific elevation of the genes in the electron transport chain during the transition of the cells from the quiescence niche to the proliferative zone. In most cell populations hypoxia is a signal for growth arrest. One mechanism may be through hypoxia inducible factor (HIF) which has been shown to mediate cell cycle arrest by increasing expression of cyclin dependant kinase inhibitors p27, and p21.[15] Using two different cell types Goda et al [17] showed the lack of G1 growth arrest in the presence of hypoxia in HIF-1α null cells as compared to wild type cells. Recently, Emerling et al [18] described that the proline hydroxylase responsible for induction of HIF degradation is inhibited by p38α mitogen activated protein kinase (MAPK). p38α MAPK is activated by reactive oxygen species generated during hypoxia; the end result being stabilization of HIF. In fact, mice deficient in p38α MAPK demonstrate a phenotype resembling Hif-1β$^{-/-}$ embryos. [26] Pumiglia et al. demonstrated that over- expression of p38α MAPK in endothelial cells resulted in decreased cell proliferation, whereas inhibition of this kinase caused a decrease in DNA synthesis. [19]. Seary et al also demonstrated that p38α MAP kinase was responsible for the observed growth arrest responses in vascular smooth muscle cells in response to TGF-β [19]. This data taken together suggests that cellular growth and proliferation could be attenuated in the presence of low oxygen via reactive oxygen species through the induction of the mitogen activated protein kinase p38α.

CELLULAR HOMING TO INJURED TISSUE IN RESPONSE TO OXYGEN

Transplantation models were the first to shed light on our understanding of the role of oxygen in homing and survival of adult stem cells. The "niche" for hematopoietic stem cell within the bone marrow was first described as being a hypoxic environment in 1979 when direct oxygen concentration was measured in the femurs of canines [1]. Not long after this, Pennathur-Das and Levitt [20] demonstrated the importance of mimicking physiological hypoxic conditions in vitro when they described the augmentation of erythropoiesis at 5% oxygen rather than 21%.

Scortenagna et al [21] was one of the first to demonstrate a role for oxygen in HSC homing and survival. The authors showed that HSCs isolated from a normal donor were incapable of repopulating a recipient mouse that was deficient in hypoxia inducible factor-2α. However, HSCs isolated from the HIF-2α$^{-/-}$ mice could rescue a lethally ablated wild type recipient suggesting that the defect was not within the stem cells capacity to expand and repopulate, but rather in the environment of the niche.

Aiuti *et al* further advanced our understanding of the role of oxygen tension and HSC homing by the isolation of stromal derived factor-1 (SDF-1) from the media of bone marrow stromal cells (22). They found that SDF-1 is a strong chemoattractant of $CD34^+$ hematopoietic stem cells. Later, Peled *et al* described homing of HSCs to the bone marrow niche required SDF-1 and its receptor CXCR-4 [23]. Studies using blocking antibodies to either SDF-1 or CXCR-4 showed the disruption in HSC homing as well as their repopulation of bone marrow.

The connection between the SDF-1/CXCR4 pathway and hypoxia was recently reported by Cerdeina *et al* [24]. The authors described a model of tissue injury in which a dermal muscle flap was made in a mouse that had definable areas of oxygen concentrations. This type of injury established an oxygen gradient, with low pO_2 at the distal "flap", and a relatively high pO_2 adjacent to uninjured tissue. . The authors demonstrated a correlating gradient of SDF-1 mRNA expression within the tissue with the most hypoxic regions having the highest concentration of the mRNA. A hypoxia inducible element was identified in the SDF-1 promoter, and HIF-1α was shown to enhance gene expression. Using this tissue injury model the authors demonstrated the preferential homing of $CXCR4^+$, $CD31^+$ progenitors to the more ischemic regions of the tissues. These areas had the highest level of SDF-1 and were found to possess the lowest oxygen environment. Further, this homing could be attenuated with addition of a blocking antibody to SDF-1. In follow up experiments Tepper *et al* [15] found that these $CXCR4^+$, $CD31^+$ progenitors were recruited from bone marrow. In these experiments, recipient mice were repopulated with donor bone marrow possessing a detectable tag and then used for this tisssue injury model.

SDF-1 mediated stem cell trafficking from their niche to distal sites has emerged as a common mechanism in tissue repair and growth. Studies using a model of neurogenesis confirm this theory. During development of the cerebellum, the granule cells form a layer known as the external granular layer. Klein *et al* [25] found SDF-1 expression in the outer covering of the cerebellum in a region known as the pia mater. When these granule cells were isolated they were shown to express CXCR4 and migrate towards SDF-1.

Further evidence that this pathway can recruit distant stem cells to areas of injury was described by Imitola *et al* [26] using a hypoxic-ischemic cerebral injury model, in which implanted donor neural stem cells migrated to the area of injury. Neural stem cells (NSCs) migrate through the parenchyma along nonsterotypical routes in a precise directed manner across great distances to injury sites in the CNS. The authors showed an increase of SDF-1 expression at the site of ischemia which correlated with areas of neural stem cell engraftment. Neuronal cells were found to migrate towards the ischemic cortex in experiments in which either the ischemic or un-injured cortex were cultured in the presence of CXCR4 neurospheres. This response could be abrogated by addition of antibodies against CXCR4 suggesting that the migration is specific to the SDF-1-CXCR4 pathway.

Ratajczak *et al* were able to selectively isolate tentative stem cells from whole bone by exploiting SDF-1's ability to function as a chemo attractant [27] [28]. Upon further purification, murine cells that are $CXCR4^+$, lin⁻, Sca^+ and $CD45^-$ or the human counterpart described to be $CXCR4^+$, lin⁻, $CD34^+$, $AC133^+$, and $CD45^-$ were found to be important for tissue regeneration. Interestingly, this bone marrow derived population is not an HSC since the cells were found to be negative for CD45, a surface marker specific to hematopoietic cells. These cells also express stem cell markers such as nanog and oct-4. When compared to the HSC by reverse transcription polymerase chain reaction these tissue committed stem cells (TCSC) were found to express mRNA of early markers of muscle, nerve and liver differentiated cells. The authors suggest that this may be the population of stem cells in bone marrow that is poised to migrate to the site of injury within various tissues. The data collectively demonstrates the major role oxygen tension changes play in initiated stem cell recruitment and tissue repair.

CELLULAR DIFFERENTIATION IN RESPONSE TO OXYGEN

Changes in oxygen tension within the microenvironment can influence the terminal differentiation of progenitor cells by selectively up-regulating genes associated with specific phenotypes. One of the best studied examples of this phenomenon is found at the growth plate in bone. Cartilage differentiation depends on reduction in oxygen tension to hypoxic conditions. *In vitro* studies using mesenchymal stem cells showed an increase in chondrogenesis when cells were grown at 5% oxygen as compared to 20% oxygen when cells [29] [30]. Robins *et al* [31] found increased expression of some chondrocytic markers such as SOX9, aggrecan and collagen type II, in stromal cells grown in 1% oxygen. Robins *et al* [31] identified a tentative HIF responsive element in the promoter of SOX9 suggesting that HIF was aiding in the induction of the chondrocytic differentiation.

Zhu *et al* showed similar differentiation potential for HIF using neural stem cells [2]. Neural stem cells in culture have a higher differentiation towards the dopaminergic phenotype when cultured at low oxygen as compared to high. The authors showed that the induction of erythropoietin by HIF α in the presence of low oxygen was responsible for directing the stem cells towards dopaminergic fate.

Low oxygen environment has also been shown to prevent differentiation into some phenotypes. Adipocytic differentiation in presence of inductive media has been shown to be inhibited at low oxygen. Yun *et al* [32] reported that preadipocytes grown in inductive media in the presence of low oxygen failed to undergo differentiation; however in parallel studies using cells isolated from the HIF-1α knock out mouse, adipocyte differentiation progressed similarly to when they are grown in ambient oxygen [32]. The authors demonstrated that HIF-1 induced DEC1/Stra13 which, when over-expressed in these cells, was found to inhibit their differentiation even in ambient oxygen concentrations through repression of the peroxisome proliferator activator gamma (PPARγ) promoter.

Smad3 is a positive effector of the transforming growth factor β (TGFβ) superfamily and is responsible for coordinately regulating gene transcription in response to these growth factors [33] The TGFβ superfamily of factors has been shown to be intricately involved in terminal differentiation of several cell types [34]. Both smad 3 and 4 and HIF-1 α have been shown to independently induce TGF β expression. But when co expressed there is synergistic expression, this has been shown for TGF β and other genes that have hypoxia response elements. [35] [36] Interestingly, Smad3 has also been shown to be regulated by p38 MAP kinase pathway which coordinates the transition from proliferation to differentiation [37]. The results suggest a role for both HIF-1 α and in reactive oxygen species in inducing terminal differentiation

Several studies suggest a role for reactive oxygen in the differentiation of stem cell/progenitors. Reactive oxygen is a byproduct of oxidative phosphorylation and may be a tentative mechanism through which cells transition from proliferating stem/progenitors to terminally differentiated cells. Experiments utilizing two varying types of stem cell populations, muscle satellite cells and embryonic neural progenitors, both responded to elevated oxidative phosphorylation by arrest of proliferation and induction of terminal differentiation [38,39]. In both cases, this transition was marked by the build up of reactive oxygen. Sattler et al, [40] demonstrated that several hematopoietic growth factors including steel factor, granulocyte colony stimulating factor, interleukin-3, and thrombopoietin function in part through creation of reactive oxygen. Exposure of cells to hydrogen peroxide, a byproduct of reactive oxygen, revealed cellular changes in phosphorylation state including the GM-CSF-receptor, stat 5 and other signaling molecules that suggest a method for reactive oxygen to induce differentiation of hematopoietic stem cells [40].

CONCLUSIONS

Changes in local oxygen concentrations are critical to the multiple transitions stem cells undergo from quiescence to proliferative, mobilized cells that undergo terminal differentiation. Stem cells maintain themselves in anaerobic metabolism whose low energy production is well adapted to the low energy demand of this G0-G1 resting cell type. Furthermore, the hypoxic environment also limits the production of reactive oxygen species. The preponderance of evidence suggests that for stem cells to maintain pluiripotency they must be protected from oxidative stress that occurs during cyclical exposure to high and low oxygen concentrations. Oxidative stress is a byproduct of oxidative phosphorylation. Often robust oxidative phosphorylation in response to elevated pO_2 will consume oxygen at a rate faster than the movement of the electron for production of ATP, and hence hydrogen peroxide or reactive oxygen, to a small extent can be produced in place of the water.

One of the mechanism stem cells use to protect themselves from oxidative stress has recently been described by Ito et al [41], who demonstrated the essential role for the protein ataxia telangiextasia mutated (ATM) in bone marrow repopulation. They showed that the self renewal potential of pluripotent cells was dependent on ATM-mediated inhibition of oxidative stress.[23] Transplantation competition assays were performed by injection of both HSC isolated from wild type and ATM[-/-] mice. After 4 weeks the number of donor-derived cells from either the wild type or ATM[-/-] mice was similar, showing that homing and engraftment were intact. However, after 16 weeks the bone marrow of the transplanted mice contained only type donor-derived cells and lacked ATM[-/-] cells. The ability of these ATM[-/-] bone marrow cells to repopulate was salvaged when both the transplant donor and recipient mice were treated with an anti- oxidative agent to reduce reactive oxygen species. The data from these knock out mice, suggests that ATM may be an essential component for the maintenance of stem cells in its hypoxic environment "niche".

Interestingly, there is recent evidence that one of the hallmarks of an adult HSC, expression of the ABCG2 transporter, also is critical to stem cell adapting to a low oxygen environment and its expression is upregulated by HIF-1 α. One of the known properties of this protein is to remove toxic substrates that can otherwise accumulate in cells.

Krishnamurthy *et al* showed that heme and byproducts of heme biosynthesis that accumulate in conditions of low oxygen tension are transported out of the cell by ABCG2. This is critical since accumulation leads to production of reactive oxygen species and interrupts mitochondrial functions. [42] Oxidative stress, reactive oxygen species, and changes in metabolism and mitochondrial functions are critical in changes mediated by oxygen such as differentiation and proliferation. Furthermore, many are now linking senescence of stem cell populations with down regulation of oxidative phosphorylation and glycoylsis suggesting that as cells age, these changing cycles of oxygen may eventually lead to senescence of the cells [43] [44]. It is clear that we have started to unravel the role of oxygen in the regulation of the adult stem cell from quiescence and pluripotency to homing, proliferation and terminal differentiation. There remain many questions that will continue to foster further investigations.

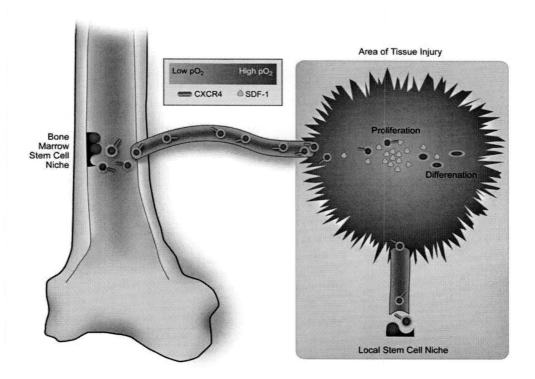

Figure 2. Control of tissue regeneration within an organism through changes in local oxygen concentrations. Stem cells migrate from their niche in either bone marrow or tissues (low pO_2) through the blood stream (high pO_2) to the injury site within tissues (low pO_2

In Figure 2 we summarize our concept of control of tissue regeneration through oxygen concentrations. We suggest that during tissue regeneration a hypoxic area is created at a distal site. This causes stromal cells in the area of low pO_2 to release SDF-1 and perhaps similar factors in response to HIF-1. The gradient of SDF-1 then activates migration of stem cells bearing CXCR4 either locally or within the bone marrow. As these cells enter the circulation, an area of high pO_2, downregulation of HIF1 and the effect of other signaling pathways cause the stem cells to shift to a proliferative mode. However, when the stem cells arrive at their destination they again experience an area of low pO_2, HIF1 is stabilized and the cells shift to a more quiescent mode, in this case, differentiation.

REFERENCES

[1]   Ezashi T, Das P, Roberts RM 2005 Low O2 tensions and the prevention of differentiation of hES cells. *Proc Natl Acad Sci U S A* 102(13):4783-8.

[2]   Zhu LL, Wu LY, Yew DT, Fan M 2005 Effects of hypoxia on the proliferation and differentiation of NSCs. *Mol Neurobiol* 31(1-3):231-42.

[3]   Fischer B, Bavister BD 1993 Oxygen tension in the oviduct and uterus of rhesus monkeys, hamsters and rabbits. *J Reprod Fertil* 99(2):673-9.

[4]   Iyer NV, Kotch LE, Agani F, Leung SW, Laughner E, Wenger RH, Gassmann M, Gearhart JD, Lawler AM, Yu AY, Semenza GL 1998 Cellular and developmental control of O2 homeostasis by hypoxia-inducible factor 1 alpha. *Genes Dev* 12(2):149-62.

[5]   Adelman DM, Maltepe E, Simon MC 1999 Multilineage embryonic hematopoiesis requires hypoxic ARNT activity. *Genes Dev* 13(19):2478-83.

[6]   Ivanovic Z, Hermitte F, de la Grange PB, Dazey B, Belloc F, Lacombe F, Vezon G, Praloran V 2004 Simultaneous maintenance of human cord blood SCID-repopulating cells and expansion of committed progenitors at low O2 concentration (3%). *Stem Cells* 22(5):716-24.

[7]   Ramirez-Bergeron DL, Runge A, Dahl KD, Fehling HJ, Keller G, Simon MC 2004 Hypoxia affects mesoderm and enhances hemangioblast specification during early development. *Development* 131(18):4623-34.

[8]   Swartz HM, Dunn JF 2003 Measurements of oxygen in tissues: overview and perspectives on methods. *Adv Exp Med Biol* 530:1-12.

[9]   Piccoli C, Ria R, Scrima R, Cela O, D'Aprile A, Boffoli D, Falzetti F, Tabilio A, Capitanio N 2005 Characterization of mitochondrial and extra-mitochondrial oxygen consuming reactions in human hematopoietic stem cells. Novel evidence of the occurrence of NAD(P)H oxidase activity. *J Biol Chem* 280(28):26467-76.

[10]   Webster KA 2003 Evolution of the coordinate regulation *of glycolytic enzyme genes by hypoxia.* J Exp Biol 206(Pt 17):2911-22.

[11]   Obach M, Navarro-Sabate A, Caro J, Kong X, Duran J, Gomez M, Perales JC, Ventura F, Rosa JL, Bartrons R 2004 6-Phosphofructo-2-kinase (pfkfb3) gene promoter contains hypoxia-inducible factor-1 binding sites necessary for transactivation in response to hypoxia. *J Biol Chem* 279(51):53562-70.

[12]   Gess B, Hofbauer KH, Deutzmann R, Kurtz A 2004 Hypoxia up-regulates triosephosphate isomerase expression via a HIF-dependent pathway. *Pflugers Arch* 448(2):175-80.

[13]   Maxwell PH, Pugh CW, Ratcliffe PJ 2001 Insights into the role of the von Hippel-Lindau gene product. A key player in hypoxic regulation. *Exp Nephrol* 9(4):235-40.

[14]   Danet GH, Pan Y, Luongo JL, Bonnet DA, Simon MC 2003 Expansion of human SCID-repopulating cells under hypoxic conditions. *J Clin Invest* 112(1):126-35.

[15] Tepper OM, Capla JM, Galiano RD, Ceradini DJ, Callaghan MJ, Kleinman ME, Gurtner GC 2005 Adult vasculogenesis occurs through in situ recruitment, proliferation, and tubulization of circulating bone marrow-derived cells. *Blood* 105(3):1068-77.

[16] Venezia TA, Merchant AA, Ramos CA, Whitehouse NL, Young AS, Shaw CA, Goodell MA 2004 Molecular signatures of proliferation and quiescence in hematopoietic stem cells. *PLoS Biol* 2(10):e301.

[17] Goda N, Ryan HE, Khadivi B, McNulty W, Rickert RC, Johnson RS 2003 Hypoxia-inducible factor 1alpha is essential for cell cycle arrest during hypoxia. *Mol Cell Biol* 23(1):359-69.

[18] Emerling BM, Platanias LC, Black E, Nebreda AR, Davis RJ, Chandel NS 2005 Mitochondrial reactive oxygen species activation of p38 mitogen-activated protein kinase is required for hypoxia signaling. *Mol Cell Biol* 25(12):4853-62.

[19] McMullen ME, Bryant PW, Glembotski CC, Vincent PA, Pumiglia KM 2005 Activation of p38 has opposing effects on the proliferation and migration of endothelial cells. *J Biol Chem* 280(22):20995-1003.

[20] Pennathur-Das R, Levitt L 1987 Augmentation of in vitro human marrow erythropoiesis under physiological oxygen tensions is mediated by monocytes and T lymphocytes. *Blood* 69(3):899-907.

[21] Scortegagna M, Ding K, Zhang Q, Oktay Y, Bennett MJ, Bennett M, Shelton JM, Richardson JA, Moe O, Garcia JA 2005 HIF-2alpha regulates murine hematopoietic development in an erythropoietin-dependent manner. *Blood* 105(8):3133-40.

[22] Aiuti A, Webb IJ, Bleul C, Springer T, Gutierrez-Ramos JC 1997 The chemokine SDF-1 is a chemoattractant for human CD34+ hematopoietic progenitor cells and provides a new mechanism to explain the mobilization of CD34+ progenitors to peripheral blood. *J Exp Med* 185(1):111-20.

[23] Peled A, Petit I, Kollet O, Magid M, Ponomaryov T, Byk T, Nagler A, Ben-Hur H, Many A, Shultz L, Lider O, Alon R, Zipori D, Lapidot T 1999 Dependence of human stem cell engraftment and repopulation of NOD/SCID mice on CXCR4. *Science* 283(5403):845-8.

[24] Ceradini DJ, Kulkarni AR, Callaghan MJ, Tepper OM, Bastidas N, Kleinman ME, Capla JM, Galiano RD, Levine JP, Gurtner GC 2004 Progenitor cell trafficking is regulated by hypoxic gradients through HIF-1 induction of SDF-1. *Nat Med* 10(8):858-64.

[25] Klein RS, Rubin JB, Gibson HD, DeHaan EN, Alvarez-Hernandez X, Segal RA, Luster AD 2001 SDF-1 alpha induces chemotaxis and enhances Sonic hedgehog-induced proliferation of cerebellar granule cells. *Development* 128(11):1971-81.

[26] Imitola J, Raddassi K, Park KI, Mueller FJ, Nieto M, Teng YD, Frenkel D, Li J, Sidman RL, Walsh CA, Snyder EY, Khoury SJ 2004 Directed migration of neural stem cells to sites of CNS injury by the stromal cell-derived factor 1alpha/CXC chemokine receptor 4 pathway. *Proc Natl Acad Sci U S A* 101(52):18117-22.

[27] Ratajczak MZ, Kucia M, Reca R, Majka M, Janowska-Wieczorek A, Ratajczak J 2004 Stem cell plasticity revisited: CXCR4-positive cells expressing mRNA for early muscle, liver and neural cells 'hide out' in the bone marrow. *Leukemia* 18(1):29-40.

[28] Kucia M, Ratajczak J, Ratajczak MZ 2005 Are bone marrow stem cells plastic or heterogenous--that is the question. *Exp Hematol* 33(6):613-23.

[29] Lennon DP, Edmison JM, Caplan AI 2001 Cultivation of rat marrow-derived mesenchymal stem cells in reduced oxygen tension: effects on in vitro and in vivo osteochondrogenesis. *J Cell Physiol* 187(3):345-55.

[30] Jaiswal RK, Jaiswal N, Bruder SP, Mbalaviele G, Marshak DR, Pittenger MF 2000 Adult human mesenchymal stem cell differentiation to the osteogenic or adipogenic lineage is regulated by mitogen-activated protein kinase. *J Biol Chem* 275(13):9645-52.

[31] Robins JC, Akeno N, Mukherjee A, Dalal RR, Aronow BJ, Koopman P, Clemens TL 2005 Hypoxia induces chondrocyte-specific gene expression in mesenchymal cells in association with transcriptional activation of Sox9. *Bone* 37(3):313-22.

[32] Yun Z, Maecker HL, Johnson RS, Giaccia AJ 2002 Inhibition of PPAR gamma 2 gene expression by the HIF-1-regulated gene DEC1/Stra13: a mechanism for regulation of adipogenesis by hypoxia. *Dev Cell* 2(3):331-41.

[33] Mogford JE, Roy NK, Cross KJ, Mustoe TA 2003 Use of hypoxia-inducible factor signal transduction pathway to measure O2 levels and modulate growth factor pathways. *Wound Repair Regen* 11(6):496-503.

[34] Agrotis A, Kalinina N, Bobik A 2005 Transforming growth factor-beta, cell signaling and cardiovascular disorders. *Curr Vasc Pharmacol* 3(1):55-61.

[35] Sanchez-Elsner T, Botella LM, Velasco B, Corbi A, Attisano L, Bernabeu C 2001 Synergistic cooperation between hypoxia and transforming growth factor-beta pathways on human vascular endothelial growth factor gene expression. *J Biol Chem* 276(42):38527-35.

[36] Zhang H, Akman HO, Smith EL, Zhao J, Murphy-Ullrich JE, Batuman OA 2003 Cellular response to hypoxia involves signaling via Smad proteins. *Blood* 101(6):2253-60.

[37] Seay U, Sedding D, Krick S, Hecker M, Seeger W, Eickelberg O 2005 TGF-{beta}-dependent Growth Inhibition in Primary Vascular Smooth Muscle Cells is p38-dependent. *J Pharmacol Exp Ther*.

[38] Tsatmali M, Walcott EC, Crossin KL 2005 Newborn neurons acquire high levels of reactive oxygen species and increased mitochondrial proteins upon differentiation from progenitors. *Brain Res* 1040(1-2):137-50.

[39] Duguez S, Sabido O, Freyssenet D 2004 Mitochondrial-dependent regulation of myoblast proliferation. *Exp Cell Res* 299(1):27-35.

[40] Sattler M, Winkler T, Verma S, Byrne CH, Shrikhande G, Salgia R, Griffin JD 1999 Hematopoietic growth factors signal through the formation of reactive oxygen species. *Blood* 93(9):2928-35.

[41] Ito K, Hirao A, Arai F, Matsuoka S, Takubo K, Hamaguchi I, Nomiyama K, Hosokawa K, Sakurada K, Nakagata N, Ikeda Y, Mak TW, Suda T 2004 Regulation of oxidative stress by ATM is required for self-renewal of haematopoietic stem cells. *Nature* 431(7011):997-1002.

[42] Krishnamurthy P, Ross DD, Nakanishi T, Bailey-Dell K, Zhou S, Mercer KE, Sarkadi B, Sorrentino BP, Schuetz JD 2004 The stem cell marker Bcrp/ABCG2 enhances hypoxic cell survival through interactions with heme. *J Biol Chem* 279(23):24218-25.

[43] Zhang X, Li J, Sejas DP, Pang Q 2005 Hypoxia-reoxygenation induces premature senescence in FA bone marrow hematopoietic cells. *Blood* 106(1):75-85.

[44] Bortoli S, Renault V, Eveno E, Auffray C, Butler-Browne G, Pietu G 2003 Gene expression profiling of human satellite cells during muscular aging using cDNA arrays. *Gene* 321:145-54.

In: Progress in Stem Cell Research
Editor: Prasad S. Koka, pp. 133-147

ISBN: 978-1-60456-065-7
© 2008 Nova Science Publishers, Inc.

Chapter 8

CONTROL OF THYMOCYTE PROLIFERATION AND THYMUS ORGAN SIZE BY CDK INHIBITORS P18^{INK4C} AND P27^{KIP1}

Grigoriy I. Kovalev[1], Tamara D. Simon [2], V. McNeil Coffield [3], Yue Xiong [4], David S. Franklin [5] and Lishan Su [1]

[1] Lineberger Comprehensive Cancer Center, Department of Microbiology and Immunology, The University of North Carolina at Chapel Hill, Chapel Hill, NC 27599;
[2] Lineberger Comprehensive Cancer Center, The University of North Carolina at Chapel Hill, Chapel Hill, NC 27599
[3] Lineberger Comprehensive Cancer Center, Department of Microbiology and Immunology, Curriculum in Genetics and Molecular Biology, School of Medicine, The University of North Carolina at Chapel Hill, Chapel Hill, NC 27599
[4] Lineberger Comprehensive Cancer Center, Department of Biochemistry and Biophysics, The University of North Carolina at Chapel Hill, Chapel Hill, NC 27599
[5] Department of Biological Science, Purdue University, West Lafayette, IN 47907

ABSTRACT

The cyclin-dependent kinase (CDK) inhibitors p18^{INK4c} and p27^{KIP1} are both highly expressed in the thymus and loss of p18 or p27 results in enlarged thymus in mice. To investigate the regulation of thymopoiesis by these two CDK inhibitors, we analyzed the thymocytes and thymus organs of $p18^{-/-}$, $p27^{-/-}$, and $p18^{-/-}/p27^{-/-}$ mutant mice. The $p18^{-/-}$ or $p27^{-/-}$ thymus organ was larger than the wild-type thymus, and $p18^{-/-}/p27^{-/-}$ thymus organ was further enlarged than either $p18^{-/-}$ or $p27^{-/-}$ thymus. The hematopoietic progenitor cells in the bone marrow and the major thymocyte subpopulations including pro-T and pre-T precursors remained normal in proportion and cell size. The sensitivity of thymocytes to dexamethasone, γ-radiation, and CD3/CD28 stimulation was not altered in single or double knockout (KO) mice. However, significantly increased numbers of cycling thymocytes were detected in either $p18^{-/-}$ or $p27^{-/-}$ mice, and an even higher percent of cycling thymocytes were detected in $p18^{-/-}/p27^{-/-}$ mice. We found that p18 was preferentially associated with CDK6 in thymocytes and absence of p27 did not change this association, while p27 preferentially bound CDK4 and CDK2 and their association was not changed in the absence of p18. We conclude that by regulating different CDKs, p18 and p27 independently and cooperatively control thymocyte proliferation and thymus organ size.

INTRODUCTION

The mechanisms that maintain the defined size of animals and their organs are poorly understood [1,2]. It has long been reported that the thymus organ in mice has intrathymic regulatory signals that determine its size. For example, transplantation of multiple fetal thymus lobes into mice generates multiple thymus organs each with similar size to a normal adult thymus, suggesting that thymocyte number and thymus size are controlled by factors within the thymus [3,4]. The number of cells in the thymus is determined by several factors, including ability of progenitor cells to proliferate and differentiate, and differentiated cells to proliferate and to survive. In response to extracellular "size control" signals (lack of growth factors or accumulation of inhibitors) in a full size thymus, intracellular "stop" molecules are proposed to halt proliferation of progenitors and/or thymocytes. Alternatively, the putative size control signals may induce death of thymocytes to keep the appropriate thymus organ size. Neither the size control signals nor the intracellular stop molecules in the thymus are clearly defined.

The central cell cycle control machinery has been well-characterized. Activation of cyclin-dependent kinases (CDK) 4 and 6 with D-type cyclins, in conjunction with subsequent activation of CDK2-cyclin E, results in phosphorylation and functional inactivation of retinoblastoma products (pRb) and progression through the G1 phase of the cell cycle [5-8]. Mammalian CDKs are also negatively regulated by seven CDK inhibitors consisting of two distinct gene families that differ in both structure and mechanism of action. Members of the INK4 family (p16^{INK4a}, p15^{INK4b}, p18^{INK4c}, and p19^{INK4d}) specifically inactivate CDK4 and CDK6 activity by forming a binary INK4-CDK4/6 complex [9], while members of the CIP/KIP family (p21$^{CIP1/WAF1}$, p27^{KIP1}, and p57^{KIP2}) inhibit activity of multiple CDKs by forming a ternary complex with cyclin and CDK. Hence, CDK inhibitors, especially the INK4 family proteins which specifically inhibit the G0/G1 regulatory CDKs (CDK4/6), could serve as intracellular "stop" molecules for the convergence of cell proliferation control signals from different stimulatory and inhibitory pathways. Indeed, it has been suggested that CDK inhibitors such as p18 and p27 may serve as intracellular stopping mechanisms [2] in response to regulatory signals during oligodendrocyte differentiation [10].

Relatively little is known about how the G0/G1 cell cycle regulatory molecules function during T cell development in the thymus. Of the four INK4 CDK inhibitors, p16^{INK4a} and p15^{INK4b} are not expressed at significant levels in lymphoid organs [11]. Importantly, loss-of-function mutations in either $p15$ [12] or $p16$ [13] in mice do not significantly affect T cell development in the thymus. On the other hand, p18^{INK4c} and p19^{INK4d} genes are both highly expressed in lymphoid organs/cells [11,14-19]. However, in $p18^{-/-}$ mice, but not in $p19^{-/-}$ mice, the thymus organ is increased in size and cellularity [20]. In addition, mouse T cells with defective $p18$, but not $p19$, showed enhanced proliferation in response to TCR stimulation [12,21,22]. Therefore, different family member of INK4 family proteins may have distinct activities even when expressed in the same cells. Among the CIP/KIP family CKIs, p21 [23] and p57 [24] are not detectably expressed in lymphoid organs, while p27 is preferentially expressed [25,26]. Hyperplasia in the thymus with increased proliferating thymocytes is reported in *p27* mutant mice, and TCR/IL2 stimulation of *p27*-deficient thymocytes leads to a higher rate of proliferation *in vitro* [27]. However, although T cell activation with mitogens and IL2 leads to a decrease of steady state p27 level in mature T cells [28,29], *p27*-deficient peripheral T cells from the spleen or lymph node (LN) show normal proliferation in response to either CD3/CD28 [21,30] or CD3/IL2 stimulation [31]. Thus, p18 and p27 are both involved in the negative modulation of thymocyte proliferation in the thymus, although only p18 seems to be also involved in modulating proliferation of peripheral T cells.

Mice with defective p18 or p27 functions exhibit remarkably similar phenotypes, including the development of gigantism, thymus hyperplasia, and wide spread organomegaly [12,20]. Relative to body size increase, the thymus organ in *p18* or *p27* mutant mice is preferentially enlarged. We report here that p18 and p27 cooperatively, as well as independently, modulate thymocyte proliferation and thymus organ size. Ablation of both *p18* and *p27* leads to a synergistic increase of thymus size due to dramatically increased number of thymocytes without any abnormalities in thymocyte development. The sensitivity to apoptosis induction remains normal in mutant thymocytes. However, loss of *p18* or *p27* led to increased proliferation of thymocytes, and *p18*−/−/*p27*−/− mice have even more thymocytes proliferating than either *p18* or *p27* single mutant mice. In thymocytes, p18 was preferentially associated with CDK6 whereas p27 was bound predominantly to CDK4 and CDK2. We conclude that p18 and p27 cooperatively and independently regulate thymocyte proliferation and cell number in the thymus by down regulating activity of CDK6 and CDK4/CDK2, respectively.

MATERIALS AND METHODS

Mice and Histopathology

WT, *p18*−/−, *p27*−/− and *p18*−/−/*p27*−/− mice were bred and maintained as described [20,21] . Littermates or age-matched mice (1 to 3 months of age) were used in each experiment.

Paraffin embedded section, hematoxylin and eosin (HE) and proliferating cell nuclear antigen (PCNA) staining were performed according to standard protocols.

Antibodies and FACS Assays

Monoclonal antibodies used for immunofluorescence staining include: hamster anti-mouse CD3 (500-A2), rat anti-mouse CD4 (CT-CD4), rat anti-mouse CD8α (CT-CD8a), rat anti-mouse CD25 (PC61 5.3) and rat anti-mouse CD44 (IM7.8.1) rat anti-mouse CD2 (RM.2-5), CD5 (53-7.3), CD45R/B220 (RA3-6B2), TER-119/Erythroid cells (Ly-76), Gr-1 (RB6-8C5), CD11b/Mac-1 (M1/70), CD117/c-Kit (2B8), Ly-6A/E/Sca-1 (E13-161.7) (Caltag

Laboratories, Burlingame, CA or BD Biosciences Pharmingen, San Jose, CA). Thymocyte and bone marrow cells were stained and analyzed on an FACSCAN flow cytometer (BD Biosciences, Mountain View, CA) as descried [21]. Nonviable cells were excluded by propidium iodide (PI) staining and light scatter profiles. The FACS data were analyzed with the Summit data analysis software (Cytomation, Fort Collins, CO).

Western and IP-Western Blot Assays

Antisera for p18, p27, CDK2, CDK4, CDK6 have been previously described [20,32]. Immuno-precipitation (IP) and immunoblotting procedures were performed as described previously [32,33] . Thymocytes from a number of age-matched wild type, *p18*$^{-/-}$, *p27*$^{-/-}$ and *p18*$^{-/-}$/*p27*$^{-/-}$ mice were pooled, lysed and protein concentrations were determined by Bradford assay. The cell extract was immunoprecipitated with anti-p18, anti-p27, anti-CDK2, -CDK4 and -CDK6 antibodies and the precipitate was immunoblotted with antisera for p18, p27, CDK2, CDK4, and CDK6.

Apoptosis

Thymocytes were irradiated at 300R single dose, or incubated in the presence of 100nM dexamethasone or activated with anti-CD3 with/without anti-CD28 mAb in R10 media (RPMI 1640 with 10% FCS) at 2×10^6/ml at 37^0C for 24 hours. Non-stimulated thymocytes were used as controls. After treatment, cells were washed and labeled with 1 µg/ml of propidium iodine (PI) in PBS/2%FBS. Dead cells (PI positive) were detected by flowcytometry. The percent dead cells of control samples were substracted from that of challenged samples to calculate specific apoptosis.

Cell Cycle Analysis

Standard staining of thymocytes by propidium iodide for DNA content was done similarly as described [34]. Briefly, thymocytes were fixed in 100% ethanol overnight at 20^0C, treated with 1 mg/ml of RNaseA and 30 µg/ml of PI in PBS/0.5% Triton X-100 for 15 min at 37^0C, and followed by FACS. Data was analyzed by DNA content frequency histogram deconvolution software (ModFit).

RESULTS

p18 and p27 Synergistically Control Thymus Organ Size and Thymocyte Number

Deletion of *p18* or *p27* lead to thymus hyperplasia and increased thymus organ size. The increased size of the *p18*$^{-/-}$ or *p27*$^{-/-}$ single mutant mice was similar to previously reported

[20,27,30,31]. The inactivation of both *p18* and *p27* genes lead to much more enlarged thymus (Fig. 1A). The number of thymocytes was significantly increased in thymuses of *p18⁻/⁻/p27⁻/⁻* mice compared with *p18⁻/⁻* and *p27⁻/⁻* mice. Consistent with previous reports, *p18⁻/⁻* thymus contained 1.7 fold increased number of thymocytes and *p27⁻/⁻* mutant with 4.5 fold increase than the wild-type thymus. However, thymus cellularity in *p18⁻/⁻/p27⁻/⁻* mice was increased 18 times (Fig. 1B).

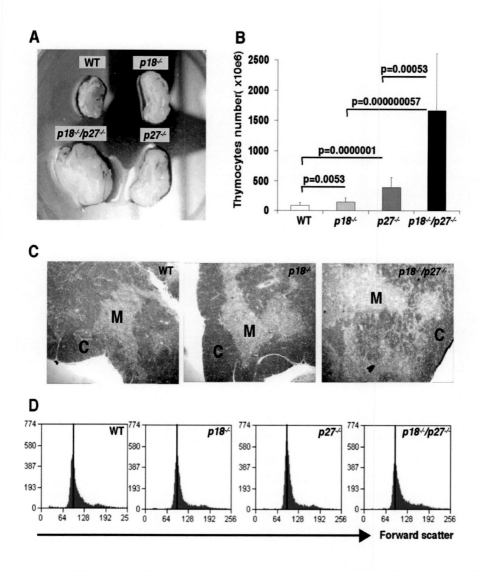

Figure 1. Synergistic control of thymus organ size and thymocyte number by p18 and p27. A. Enlarged thymus in KO mice. Representative thymus organs for WT, *p18⁻/⁻*, *p27⁻/⁻* and *p18⁻/⁻/p27⁻/⁻* are shown. B. Cooperative control of thymocyte numbers by p18 and p27 proteins. Average cell number in the thymus of WT (n=16), *p18⁻/⁻* (n=20), *p27⁻/⁻* (n=11) and *p18⁻/⁻/p27⁻/⁻* (n=10) mice is shown. Standard deviation (SD) is shown as error bars. p values between samples are shown. C. Normal thymic structures in *p18⁻/⁻* and *p18⁻/⁻/p27⁻/⁻* double null mice. A representative HE section of thymus from WT, *p18⁻/⁻*, and *p18⁻/⁻/p27⁻/⁻* mice is shown to illustrate the cortex (C) and medulla (M). D. Normal cell size of mutant thymocytes. Relative size of thymocytes is shown by their forward scatter profiles.

When the histology of the thymus organs was examined, normal thymic structures with clearly defined cortex and medulla regions were observed in the $p18^{-/-}$ and $p27^{-/-}$ single or $p18^{-/-}/p27^{-/-}$ double mutant organs (Fig. 1C). To test if loss of p18 and p27 affects the size of thymocytes, the cell size of thymocytes was assessed by flowcytometry, and was not significantly changed in mutant mice (Fig. 1D). These data suggest that p18 and p27, independently and cooperatively, controls thymus size by controlling thymocyte cell numbers.

Normal Thymocyte Development in $p18^{-/-}$, $p27^{-/-}$ or $p18^{-/-}/p27^{-/-}$

When the hematopoietic stem/progenitor or T progenitor cells in the bone marrow or thymus organs are analyzed, no significant increase in the relative contents of the stem or progenitor cells are observed (Table 1). To determine whether the thymus hyperplasia is associated with altered thymocyte maturation, we examined the maturation markers of thymocytes in mutant mice at each stage of their development. CD4/CD8 staining revealed normal development of DN (CD4-CD8-), DP (CD4+CD8+) and mature SP (CD4+ or CD8+) populations in all mutant mice (Fig. 2A). Further analysis of early developmental stages of pro-T (DN1 and DN2) and pre-T (DN3 and DN4) progenitors also did not show any change (Fig 2B). The immature single positive (CD8+CD3-CD4-) population was also not altered (Fig 2C). Hence, loss of p18 and/or p27, while stimulating thymocyte proliferation, does not affect thymocyte development.

Table 1. Hematopoietic stem/progenitor cell contents in mutant mice

Genotype	Bone Marrow		Thymus	
	Total Cell# (x10^6)	HSPC[a] (%)	Total Cell# (x10^6)	ITPC[b] (%)
WT	66.6±9.6	0.074±0.032	88.8±47.2	3.4±1.8
p18$^{-/-}$	73.9±24.8	0.069±0.039	149.8±70.0*	1.7±0.4
p27$^{-/-}$	66.7±18.3	0.104±0.055	401.6±158.1*	2.5±1.0
p18$^{-/-}$/p27$^{-/-}$	79.8±23.0	0.112±0.059	1669.6±939.6*	2.2±0.9

a: Lin-Sca1+kit+ hematopoietic progenitor cells (HSPC).
b: CD3-CD4-CD8- intrathymic thymocyte progenitor cells (ITPC).
*: p<0.01 relative to wild type mice.

Apoptosis Response of Thymocytes is Normal in $p18^{-/-}$, $p27^{-/-}$ and $p18^{-/-}/p27^{-/-}$

Lack or reduction of apoptosis may contribute to the increase of number of thymocytes and thymus size. We investigated the sensitivity of WT or mutant thymocytes to cell death triggered by different stimuli. Induction of apoptosis of thymocytes by dexamethazone, γ-irradiation and anti-CD3/CD28 activation was not altered in any of the mutant mice (Fig. 3). Thus, the increase in thymocyte number in $p18^{-/-}$ and/or $p27^{-/-}$ mutant mice is not due to altered sensitivity to apoptosis induction.

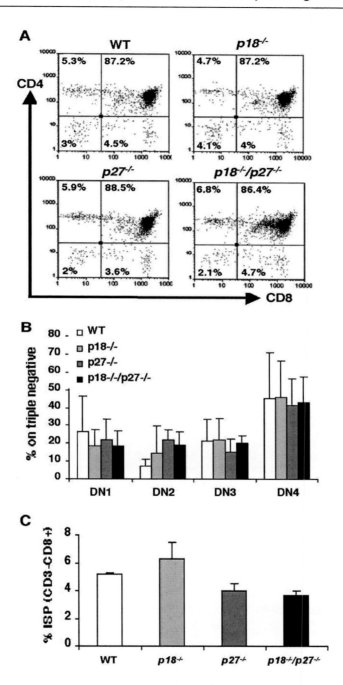

Figure 2. Normal thymocyte development in p18[-/-], p27[-/-] and p18[-/-]/p27[-/-] mice. A. FACS analysis of thymocytes stained with anti-CD4 and anti-CD8 is shown from one representative experiment. The experiment was done at least 3 times, with 6 mice per genotype. B. Subsets of double negative (DN) thymocytes (DN1 through DN4) are normal in mutant mice. Cells were stained with anti-CD3/CD4/CD8-TC, CD25-PE, CD44-FITC and DN populations (CD3-CD4-CD8- cells) were defined by expression of CD44 and CD25. The percentage of each DN populations is shown. SD is shown as error bars. C. Normal immature single positive (ISP) thymocytes in mutant mice. The average percentage of ISP (CD8+/CD4-/CD3-) and SD as error bars are shown.

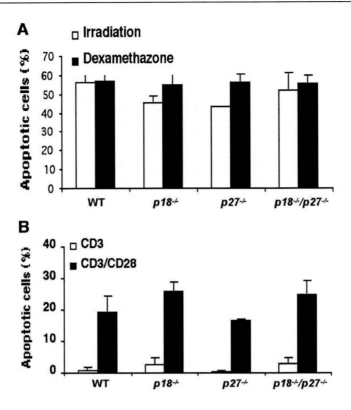

Figure 3. Thymocytes of *p18*^{-/-}, *p27*^{-/-} and *p18*^{-/-}/*p27*^{-/-} mice show normal response to apoptosis induction. A. Thymocytes were exposed to either γ-irradiation (open bars) or dexamethasone (close bars). Dead cells were detected by PI uptake. Percent apoptotic cells induced is the difference between exposed and non-exposed (control) samples. SD is shown as error bars. B. Anti-CD3/CD28 induced apoptosis. Thymocytes were challenged with anti-CD3 alone (open bars) or with anti-CD28 (close bars). Percentage of apoptotic cell is defined as above.

Thymocyte Hyper-Proliferation in *p18*^{-/-}, *p27*^{-/-} and *p18*^{-/-}/*p27*^{-/-}

Increased proliferation of thymocytes may contribute to the thymus hyperplasia in the mutant mice. Cell cycle analysis of thymocytes showed increased percentage of proliferating thymocytes in S and G2/M phases of cell cycle in *p18*^{-/-} and *p27*^{-/-} single KO cells compared with WT (12% and 10% vs. 6%, respectively), as previously reported [20,27]. Thymocytes from *p18*^{-/-}/*p27*^{-/-} mice showed an even higher fraction of cells in S/G2/M compared to *p18*^{-/-} or *p27*^{-/-} mice (25%, Fig. 4A). When the proliferating thymocytes were analyzed by immunohistochemical staining of thymus tissues with an anti-PCNA antibody, increased proliferation of thymocytes were detected in both the cortex and the medulla regions (Fig. 4B). Therefore, p18 and p27 cooperatively, as well as independently, modulate thymocyte proliferation to control thymocyte homeostasis and thymus organ size.

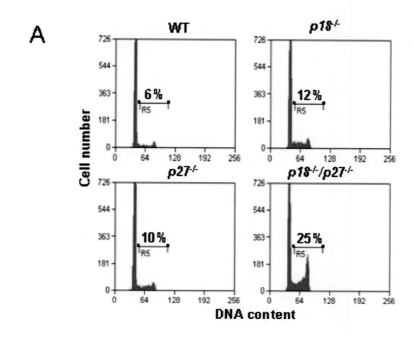

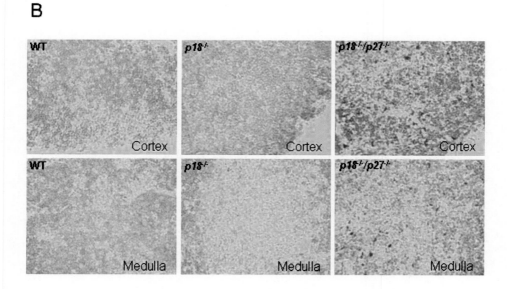

Figure 4. Increased proliferation of *p18⁻/⁻*, *p27⁻/⁻* and *p18⁻/⁻/p27⁻/⁻* thymocytes in vivo. A. Increased cells in S/G2/M phases of mutant thymocytes are shown. Cell cycle profiles are analyzed by PI uptake and percent thymocytes with >2N DNA contents are shown. Representative histograms from each genotype are shown. B. Increased thymocyte proliferation in both cortex and medulla region of the mutant thymus. Paraffin embedded thymus sections were stained with anti-PCNA antibody and counterstained with HE.

p18 and p27 Preferentially Target CDK6 and CDK4/CDK2, Respectively, in Thymocytes

In mature T cells, p18 is preferentially associated with CDK6, but not with CDK4, and loss of p18 leads to elevated level of CDK6 activity in mature T cells [21]. To determine the CDK association with p18 or p27 in thymocytes, we examined their association by co-precipitation with antibodies to p18, p27, CDK4 and CDK6. We found that p18 was preferentially associated with CDK6, but not with CDK4, and p27 was in association with CDK4 (and CDK2), but not detectably with CDK6 (Fig. 5). The level of p18, p27, CDK6 and CDK4/2, and their associations, were not altered by the loss of either p27 or p18. Thus, p18 and p27 appear to preferentially regulate CDK6 and CDK4/CDK2 in thymocytes, respectively, to modulate thymocyte proliferation.

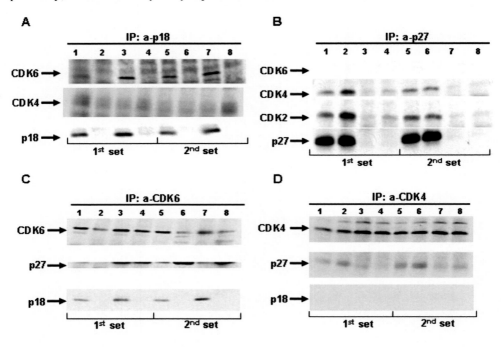

Figure 5. p18 and p27 target distinct CDKs in thymocytes. Cell extract was immunoprecipitated with anti-p18 (A), anti-p27 (B). anti-CDK6 (C) and anti-CDK4 (D) antibodies and blotted with the indicated antibodies. Two mice of each genotype were used. Lanes 1 & 5: WT, lanes 2 & 6: $p18^{-/-}$, lanes 3 & 7: $p27^{-/-}$, and lanes 4 & 8: $p18^{-/-}/p27^{-/-}$.

CONCLUSION

The control of animal body and organ size is an important question that has received relatively little attention until recent years. The size control of thymus organ has been reported to involve "signals" within the thymus organ [3,4]. The size control signals in the thymus organ are proposed to trigger intracellular stop machinery or suicide molecules to ensure that thymocytes are maintained at a constant number during development. The ability of CDK inhibitors p18 and p27 to arrest cell proliferation, and their preferential expression in thymocytes, suggest that they may serve as signal integrators or intracellular stop molecules to link the cell cycle machinery to organ size signals in the thymus. We report that $p18^{INK4c}$ and $p27^{KIP1}$ independently and cooperatively mediate signals that negatively modulate thymocyte proliferation and maintain thymus organ size. Loss of $p18^{INK4c}$ or $p27^{KIP1}$ each increased thymocyte number and thymus size. Simultaneous inactivation of both p18 and p27 led to much more dramatic phenotypes than either *p18* or *p27* single mutant. Thymus structures, thymocyte maturation and cell size appear to be normal in all mutant mice. The response of thymocytes to apoptosis induction by a number of stimuli was also not altered. Proliferation of thymocytes, on the other hands, was increased by the loss of p18 and/or p27. These results indicate that increased cell proliferation, not reduced cell death, contribute to hyper-cellularity and increased thymus organ size. Our biochemical analyses of the expression and complex formation of G1 regulatory proteins in thymocytes indicate that p18 and p27 preferentially target CDK6 and CDK4/2, respectively, to modulate thymocyte proliferation. Therefore, the thymus organ size sensor may function by signaling (directly or indirectly) to p18 and p27 to suppress thymocyte proliferation (Fig. 6). Identification of signals that regulate p18 or p27 expression in the thymus will shed light on understanding the mechanisms of thymocyte homeostasis and thymus organ size control.

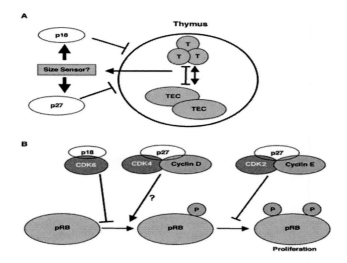

Figure 6. Control of thymus size and thymocyte proliferation by p18 and p27. A. p18 and p27 coordinate responses to two overlapping but different pathways to collaboratively control thymus organ size. The putative "size sensor" signals, produced from thymocytes (T) and/or thymic epithelial cells (TEK), regulate expression and/or activity of p18 and p27, directly or indirectly, when thymus size and thymocyte number reach the defined level. B. p18 preferentially targets CDK6 to block pRb inactivation and cell cycle progression. p27 targets CDK4/cyclinD and CDK2/CyclinE to affect early pRb inactivation and thymocyte proliferation.

Multiple members and two families of CDK inhibitors in mammalian cells are evolved to meet the complicated demands for integrating intricate and multifaceted cell growth signals, both intracellular and extracellular, into a central cell cycle control machinery. The expression of individual CDK inhibitor genes displays distinct temporary and spatial patterns during both *in vitro* cell differentiation and *in vivo* embryonic development, is maintained differentially in different adult and senescent tissues, and is regulated differently by different cell cycle checkpoint pathways. Multiple CDK inhibitors with apparently similar activity can also express in the same cell types. For example, p18[INK4c], p19[INK4d] and p27[KIP1] are all highly expressed in lymphoid organs and lymphocytes [11,14,16,17,25,26,29]. Yet, they are implicated in different functions or activities in the same cells due to their differential activity to interact with different CDKs. Furthermore, different physiologic functions of individual CDK inhibitor genes *in vivo* are suggested from the genetic analysis of mutant mice with targeted mutations in each of the seven CDK inhibitor genes. These mice display very different phenotypes, ranging from lack of any defects by the loss of *p15* or *p19* gene [12,22], compromised DNA damage response after inactivation of p21 gene [35], a modest increase of tumor development resulting from loss of *p16* [13,36], severe developmental defects by *p57* mutation [37], to hyperplastic cell proliferation and organomegaly in *p18* and *p27* mutant mice [12,20,27,30,31]. Interestingly, a recent report has shown that p18INK4c is involved in controlling the self-renewing divisions of hematopoietic stem cells [38]. Identification of the molecular pathways linking various cell growth or inhibition signals to the expression of individual CDK inhibitor genes, however, is still a major challenge to our understanding of cell cycle control *in vivo*. Investigation of such regulation pathways will provide mechanistic insight regarding regulation of cell proliferation, tumorigenesis and development, as exemplified by the p53-mediated activation of *p21* gene expression following DNA damage [39].

What cell types produce the "size sensors" that trigger intracellular stop signals, and how p18 and p27 modulate those cells, are amongst the most important questions regarding thymus organ size control. During thymus organogenesis and thymopoiesis, both positive signals and negative signals can be generated by thymocytes or stromal cells that modulate proliferation and differentiation of the other cell types (Fig. 6). Hyperproliferation of stromal cells other than thymocytes may affect production of the "size sensors" and lead to thymic hyperplasia. For example, over-expression of cyclin D1 and cyclin D2, but not cyclin D3, from an epithelial cell-specific promoter leads to increased thymus organ size in transgenic mice [40,41]. In addition, defective androgen receptors on thymic epithelial cells also lead to thymus enlargement [42]. However, it is not clear whether thymocytes from those transgenic or mutant mice show any hyperproliferation. It is likely that, in the *p18* and *p27* mutant mice, both mutant stromal and thymocytes contribute to the hyperplasia phenotype. It will require cell type specific gene inactivation to identify the necessary cell types that contribute to increased thymocyte proliferation and thymus size in the mutant mice.

Regulation of the cell size has been linked to animal and organ size control. Various genes have been recently identified to control the cell size through regulation of cell growth. For example, PTEN (phosphatase and tensin homologue deleted on chromosome 10), the insulin-phosphoinositide 3-kinase (PI3K)-Akt pathway, and the tuberous sclerosis complex (TSC) genes, Tsc1 and Tsc2, all participate in regulating cell size and organ size in animals [43-45]. In *p18* and *p27* mutant mice, while the cell numbers were increased, the cell size of thymocytes was normal (Fig. 1), indicating that the function of p18 and p27, and by extension the signals that regulate the expression of these two genes, is to regulate cell proliferation, not cell growth. Hence, organ size control may be achieved through regulation of both cell growth and cell proliferation.

ACKNOWLEDGMENTS

We thank Dr. N. Sharpless for critically reading the manuscript and helpful discussions; and Dr. Virginia Godfrey for histology, Jonathan Smith for technical support, members of the Su laboratory for discussions and the UNC DLAM and FACS core facilities for their help with animal cares and FACS analysis. The project was supported by grants from NIH (AI5380402, AI04840704 to L. S).

REFERENCES

[1]   Hafen, E; Stocker, H. How Are the Sizes of Cells, Organs, and Bodies Controlled? *PLoS Biol,* 2003 1, E86.

[2]   Conlon, I; Raff, M. Size control in animal development. *Cell,* 1999 96, 235-244.

[3]   Metcalf, D. The autonomous behavior of normal thymus grafts. *Aust J Expm Biol Med Sci,* 1963 41, 437-448.

[4]   Leuchars, E; Wallis, VJ; Doenhoff, MJ; Davies, AJ; Kruger, J. Studies of hyperthymic mice. I. The influence of multiple thymus grafts on the size of the peripheral T cell pool and immunological performance. *Immunology,* 1978 35, 801-809.

[5]   Hunter, T; Pines, J. Cyclins and cancer II: cyclin D and CDK inhibitors come of age. *Cell,* 1994 79, 573-582.

[6]   Morgan, DO. Principles of CDK regulation. *Nature,* 1995 374, 131-134.

[7]   Sherr, C. Mammalian G1 cyclins. *Cell,* 1993 73, 1059-1065.

[8]   Weinberg, RA. The retinoblastoma protein and cell cycle control. *Cell,* 1995 81, 323-330.

[9]   Sherr, CJ; Roberts, JM. Inhibitors of mammalian G1 cyclin-dependent kinases. *Genes and Dev,* 1995 9, 1149-1163.

[10]   Tokumoto, YM; Apperly, JA; Gao, FB; Raff, MC. Posttranscriptional regulation of p18 and p27 Cdk inhibitor proteins and the timing of oligodendrocyte differentiation. *Dev. Biol,* 2002 245, 224-234.

[11]   Zindy, F; Quelle, DE; Roussel, MF; Sherr, CJ. Expression of the p16INK4a tumor suppressor versus other INK4 family members during mouse development and aging. *Oncogene,* 1997 15, 203-211.

[12]   Latres, E; Malumbres, M; Sotillo, R; Martin, J; Ortega, S; Martin-Caballero, J; Flores, JM; Cordon-Cardo, C; Barbacid, M. Limited overlapping roles of P15(INK4b) and P18(INK4c) cell cycle inhibitors in proliferation and tumorigenesis. *Embo J,* 2000 19, 3496-3506.

[13]   Sharpless, NE; Bardeesy, N; Lee, KH; Carrasco, D; Castrillon, DH; Aguirre, AJ; Wu, EA; Horner, JW; DePinho, RA. Loss of p16Ink4a with retention of p19Arf predisposes mice to tumorigenesis. *Nature,* 2001 413, 86-91.

[14]   Chan, FKM; Zhang, L; Chen, L; Shapiro, DN; Winoto, A. Identification of human/mouse p19, a novel cdk4/cdk6 inhibitor with homology to p16^{ink4}. *Mol.Cell Biol,* 1995 15, 2682-2688.

[15]   Guan, KL; Jenkins, CW; Li, Y; Nichols, MA; Wu, X; O'Keefe, CL; Matera, AG; Xiong Y. Growth suppression by p18, a p16INK4/MTS1- and p14INK4B/MTS2-related

CDK6 inhibitor, correlates with wild-type pRb function. *Genes and Dev,* 1994 8, 2939-2952.

[16] Guan, KL; Jenkins, CW; Li, Y; O'Keefe, CL; Noh, S; Wu, X; Zariwala, M; Matera, AG; Xiong Y. Isolation and characterization of p19INK4d, a p16-related inhibitor specific to CDK6 and CDK4. *Molecular Biology of the Cell,* 1996 7, 57-70.

[17] Hirai, H; Roussel, MF; Kato, JY; Ashmun, RA; Sherr, CJ. Novel INK4 proteins, p19 and p18, are specific inhibitors of the cyclin D-dependent kinases CDK4 and CDK6. *Mol. Cell Biol,* 1995 15, 2672-2681.

[18] Ragione, FD; Russo, GL; Oliva, A; Mercurio, C; Mastropietro, S; Pietra, VD; Zappia, V. Biochemical characterization of p16INK4- and p18-containing complexes in human cell lines. *J. Biol. Chem,* 1996 271, 15942-15949.

[19] Drexler, HG. Review of alterations of the cyclin-dependent kinase inhibitor INK4 family genes p15, p16, p18 and p19 in human leukemia-lymphoma cells. *Leukemia,* 1998 12, 845-859.

[20] Franklin, DS; Godfrey, VL; Lee, H; Kovalev, GI; Schoonhoven, R; Chen-Kiang, S; Su, L; Xiong Y. CDK inhibitors p18(INK4c) and p27(Kip1) mediate two separate pathways to collaboratively suppress pituitary tumorigenesis. *Genes Dev,* 1998 12, 2899-2911.

[21] Kovalev, GI; Franklin, DS; Coffield, VM; Xiong, Y; Su L. An important role of CDK inhibitor p18(INK4c) in modulating antigen receptor-mediated T cell proliferation. *J Immunol,* 2001 167, 3285-3292.

[22] Zindy, F; van Deursen, J; Grosveld, G; Sherr, CJ; Roussel, MF. INK4d-deficient mice are fertile despite testicular atrophy. *Mol. Cell Biol,* 2000 20, 372-378.

[23] Parker, SB; Eichele, G; Zhang, P; Rawls, A; Sands, AT; Bradley, A; Olson, EN; Harper, JW; Elledge, SJ. p53-independent expression of p21^{Cip1} in muscle and other termnally differentiating cells. *Science,* 1995 267, 1024-1027.

[24] Matsuoka, S; Edwards, MC; Bai, C; Parker, S; Zhang, P; Baldini, A; Harper, JW; Elledge, SJ. p57^{Kip2}, a structurally distinct member of the p21CIP1 CDK inhibitor family, is a cadidate tumor suppressor gene. *Genes and Dev,* 1995 9, 650-662.

[25] Polyak, K; Lee, MH; Erdjument-Bromage, H; Koff, A; Roberts, JM; Tempst, P; Massague, J. Cloning of p27Kip1, a cyclin-dependent kinase inhibitor and a potential mediator of extracellular antimitogenic signals. *Cell,* 1994 78, 59-66.

[26] Toyoshima, H; Hunter, T. p27, a novel inhibitor of G1 cyclin-Cdk protein kinase activity, is related to p21. *Cell,* 1994 78, 67-74.

[27] Fero, ML; Rivkin, M; Tasch, M; Porter, P; Carow, CE; Firpo, E; Polyak, K; Tsai LH; Broudy, V; Perlmutter, RM; Kaushansky, K; Roberts, JM. A syndrome of multiorgan hyperplasia with features of gigantism, tumorigenesis, and female sterility in p27(Kip1)-deficient mice. *Cell,* 1996 85, 733-744.

[28] Nourse, J; Firpo, E; Flanagan, MW; Coats, S; Polyak, K; Lee, M-H; Massague, J; Crabtree, GR; Roberts, JM. Interleukin-2-mediated elimination of the p27^{Kip1} cyclin-dependent kinase inhibitor prevented by rapamycin. *Nature,* 1994 372, 570-573.

[29] Firpo, EJ; Koff, A; Solomon, MJ; Roberts, JM. Inactivation of a Cdk2 inhibitor during interleukin 2-induced proliferation of human T lymphocytes. *Mol.Cell Biol,* 1994 14, 4889-4901.

[30] Nakayama, K; Ishida, N; Shirane, M; Inomata, A; Inoue T; Shishido, N; Horii, I; Loh, DY. Mice lacking p27(Kip1) display increased body size, multiple organ hyperplasia, retinal dysplasia, and pituitary tumors. *Cell,* 1996 85, 707-720.

[31] Kiyokawa, H; Kineman, RD; Manova-Todorova, KO; Soares, VC; Hoffman, ES; Ono, M; Khanam, D; Hayday, AC; Frohman, LA; Koff, A. Enhanced growth of mice lacking the cyclin-dependent kinase inhibitor function of p27(Kip1). *Cell,* 1996 85, 721-732.

[32] Franklin, DS; Xiong, Y. Induction of p18INK4c and its predominant association with CDK4 and CDK6 during myogenic differentiation. Mol. Biol. Cell, 1996 7, 1587-1599.

[33] Jenkins CW, Xiong Y. Immunoprecipitation and immunoblotting in cell cycle studies. In: Pagano M, editor. *Cell Cycle: Material and methods.* New York: Springer-Verlag; 1995:250-263

[34] Crissman, HA; Oka, MS; Steinkamp, JA. Rapid staining methods for analysis of deoxyribonucleic acid and protein in mammalian cells. *J Histochem Cytochem,* 1976 24, 64-71.

[35] Deng, C; Zhang, P; Harper, JW; Elledge, SJ; Leder, P. Mice lacking p21$^{CIP1/WAF1}$ undergo normal development, but are defective in G1 checkpoint control. *Cell,* 1995 82, 675-684.

[36] Krimpenfort, P; Quon, KC; Mooi, WJ; Loonstra, A; Berns A. Loss of p16Ink4a confers susceptibility to metastatic melanoma in mice. *Nature,* 2001 413, 83-86.

[37] Zhang, P; Wong, C; DePinho, RA; Harper, JW; Elledge SJ. Cooperation between the Cdk inhibitors p27^{KIP1} and p57^{KIP2} in the control of tissue growth and development. *Genes and Dev,* 1998 12, 3162-3167.

[38] Yuan, Y; Shen, H; Franklin, DF; Scadden, DT; Cheng T. In vivo self-renewing divisions of haematopoietic stem cells are increased in the absence of the early G1-phase inhibitor, p18INK4C. *Nature Cell Biology,* 2004 6, 436 – 442.

[39] el-Deiry WS. p21/p53, cellular growth control and genomic integrity. *Curr Top Microbiol Immunol,* 1998 227, 121-137.

[40] Rodriguez-Puebla, ML; LaCava, M; Miliani De Marval, PL; Jorcano, JL; Richie, ER; Conti, CJ. Cyclin D2 overexpression in transgenic mice induces thymic and epidermal hyperplasia whereas cyclin D3 expression results only in epidermal hyperplasia. *Am J Pathol,* 2000 157, 1039-1050.

[41] Robles, AI; Larcher, F; Whalin, RB; Murillas, R; Richie, E; Gimenez-Conti, IB; Jorcano, JL; Conti, CJ. Expression of cyclin D1 in epithelial tissues of transgenic mice results in epidermal hyperproliferation and severe thymic hyperplasia. *Proc Natl Acad Sci U S A,* 1996 93, 7634-7638.

[42] Olsen, NJ; Olson, G; Viselli, SM; Gu, X; Kovacs, WJ. Androgen receptors in thymic epithelium modulate thymus size and thymocyte development. *Endocrinology,* 2001 142, 1278-1283.

[43] Potter, CJ; Pedraza, LG; Huang, H; Xu, T. The tuberous sclerosis complex (TSC) pathway and mechanism of size control. *Biochem Soc Trans,* 2003 31, 584-586.

[44] Backman, S; Stambolic, V; Mak, T. PTEN function in mammalian cell size regulation. *Curr Opin Neurobiol,* 2002 12, 516-522.

[45] Stocker, H; Hafen, E. Genetic control of cell size. *Curr Opin Genet Dev,* 2000 10, 529-535.

In: Progress in Stem Cell Research
Editor: Prasad S. Koka, pp. 149-169

ISBN: 978-1-60456-065-7
© 2008 Nova Science Publishers, Inc.

Chapter 9

HUMAN EMBRYONIC STEM CELL-DERIVED CARDIOMYOCYTES: THERAPEUTIC POTENTIALS AND LIMITATIONS

*Ronald A. Li[*1], Jennifer C. Moore[1],*
Yelena S. Tarasova[2] and Kenneth R. Boheler[2]

[1] Laboratory of Stem Cell Engineering and Bioelectricity, Stem Cell Institute,
University of California, Davis, CA.
[2] Laboratory of Cardiovascular Science, National Institute on Aging, NIH,
Baltimore, MD

ABSTRACT

Embryonic stem cell (ESC) lines, derived from the inner cell mass (ICM) of blastocyst-stage embryos, are pluripotent and have a virtually unlimited capacity for self-renewal and differentiation into derivatives of all three germ layers. Human ESCs (hESCs), in particular, are the subject of intensive investigation for potential applications in developmental biology and medicine. A promising aspect of hESCs is their ability to differentiate into cardiomyocytes (CMs), which generally lack the capacity to regenerate, and therefore their potential for cell-replacement heart therapies. Molecular, cellular and physiological analyses demonstrate that hESC-derived CMs are functionally viable and that they exhibit characteristics typical of heart cells in the early stages of cardiac development. This article reviews the current state of hESC-CM research, their therapeutic potentials and limitations.

Key Words: embryonic stem cells, human, cardiomyocytes, differentiation, pacemaker

---

[*] Corresponding authors: Ronald Li, Ph.D. Stem Cell Institute; University of California; Room 650, Shriners Hospital; 2425 Stockton Blvd; Sacramento , CA 95817; Lab: (916) 453-2278; email: ronaldli@uc davis.edu; Kenneth R. Boheler, Ph.D., NIH/NIA/GRC/LCS; 5600 Nathan Shock Drive, Baltimore, MD 21224, U.S.A. Tel: (1) 410-558-8095, Fax: (1) 410-558-8150, Email: bohelerk@grc.nia.nih.gov

Embryonic stem cells (ESCs), isolated from the inner cell mass of pre-implantation embryos, can be cultured indefinitely while maintaining important characteristics – a normal karyotype, self-renewal and pluripotency. Under appropriate conditions, ESCs can differentiate into the derivatives of all three embryonic germ layers (i.e. endoderm, mesoderm and ectoderm) in vitro and in vivo. Although pluripotent mammalian ESC lines were first derived from mouse blastocysts over 20 years ago [1, 2] (an achievement that revolutionized mouse genetics and led to the generation of the first animals with targeted gene mutations), the first successful isolation of human (h) ESCs by Thomson et al in 1998 [3] immediately sparked tremendous international scientific interest. Subsequently, several groups employed information originally learned from the in vitro differentiation of mESC lines to drive hESCs towards a cardiomyogenic fate raising the prospect of possible therapeutic uses of hESCs in cardiac diseases [4-7]. Since hESCs are immortal cell lines that have the potential to act as an unlimited *ex vivo* source of cells for cell-based therapies and transplantation, engineering hESCs and/or their tissue-specific derivatives could further provide a novel and flexible approach for achieving a range of different therapeutic goals for the treatment of human diseases (e.g. to modify cardiac excitability and to repair injured myocardium).

PLURIPOTENT EMBRYONIC STEM, GERM AND CARCINOMA CELLS

In addition to ESCs, two other types of pluripotent mammalian cell lines have been established. Prior to the derivation of mouse (m) ESC lines, embryonic carcinoma cell (ECC) lines were established from the undifferentiated components of germ cell tumors that arise spontaneously or experimentally by transfer of cells from the epiblast to extrauterine sites [7, 8]. Additionally, embryonic germ cell (EGC) lines have been isolated from primordial germ cells (PGCs) that are first detected in the epiblast and subsequently migrate within the developing genital ridges to populate the developing gonads [7] [9]. All of these embryo-derived stem cell lines have the capacity to differentiate in vitro into cells of all three germ layers, but the greatest developmental capacity is restricted to ES cell and some EG cell lines isolated from early PGCs that have undergone a limited degree of epigenetic modification (e.g., methylation).

Although human ECCs and EGCs can propagate indefinitely while maintaining their pluripotency in a manner similar to ESCs, they differ phenotypically and morphologically [9-11]. One such difference is the observation that while human EGCs are capable of differentiating into a variety of cell types, their pluripotency is not yet confirmed. For example, human myocardial cells have been derived from hESCs [12-18] but not from hEGCs [19]. This is probably because hEGCs represent partially differentiated cell lines that unlike hESCs are not truly pluripotent or which may have undergone extensive methylation events that reduce their differentiation potential [20, 21]. Alternatively, the cultivation conditions required to maintain these cells in vitro may be inhibitory to the generation of cardiac myocytes. It is therefore not yet clear whether the changes in differentiation potential arise from the intrinsic differences between human ESCs and EGCs (as a result of their different origins) or are merely due to their different culture and isolation conditions. The presence of severe karyotypic abnormalities (e.g. aneuploidy) as well as the tumorgenic nature of the ECCs precludes them from any future potential clinical applications although they have also been shown to differentiate into multiple cell types.

HEART DISEASE AND MOTIVATION FOR CELL-BASED THERAPY

The heart beats, with a regular rhythm, 2-3 billion times during the lifespan of an average person, pumping blood throughout the body. These pumping actions require the highly coordinated efforts of several different types of cardiomyocytes (CMs) such as atrial, ventricular and pacemaker cells. These specific cardiomyocyte types differ not only in their cellular morphologies but, more importantly, in their electrical properties, which in turn govern the excitability of the heart. Autonomous, rhythmic heartbeats are modulated by sympathetic and parasympathetic means according to everyday needs. These normal rhythms originate in the sino-atrial (SA) node of the heart, a region of specialized cardiac tissue consisting of only a few thousands pacemaker cells that generate spontaneous rhythmic action potentials (i.e. pacing) which subsequently propagate (i.e. conduction) to induce coordinated muscle contractions of the atria and ventricles for effective blood pumping. Since terminally-differentiated adult CMs generally lack the ability to regenerate [22], malfunctions or significant loss of CMs due to disease or aging can lead to lethal consequences such as heart failure and/or various lethal forms of arrhythmias (irregular heart rhythms).

Cardiac transplantation is currently the treatment of choice for end-stage heart failure, but this is hampered by a severe shortage of donor organs and by transplant rejection; and as the general population ages and heart disease becomes more prevalent, the shortage of donor organs will become even more pronounced. An alternative to heart transplantation is cell replacement therapy the aim of which is to replace, repair or enhance the biological function of damaged tissue or diseased organs [23-25]. Cell replacement therapy is potentially achievable by the transfer of isolated and defined cell populations to a target organ in sufficient numbers and quality for them to survive and restore function. Sources of cells or tissues are self (autologous), same species (allogeneic), different species (xenographic), primary or immortalized (cell lines) and embryonic and adult stem cell-derived donor cells. The ability to cultivate, multiply and manipulate these cell types has either limited or encouraged their use in specific treatment protocols [25]. Where possible, autologous cells are the cells of choice for treatment, but frequently as in the heart, these are unavailable.

Cell replacement therapy is a promising option for myocardial repair but this approach is also limited by the availability of transplantable human CMs (e.g. human fetal CMs). As a result, transplantation of tissues other than CMs, such as skeletal muscle myoblasts [26-30] and smooth muscle cells, have been developed as alternative therapies. However, even these suffer from the lack of transplantable cells and are further complicated by the fact that the transplanted cells are not genuine heart tissue, and hence, normal electrical coupling may not occur, leading to conduction blocks and/or arrhythmias. Although various lines of experimental evidence have suggested that mobilization of adult stem cells and resident cardiac stem cells can improve myocardial performance in mice [31-33], this concept has been challenged by experiments showing that the results might have been misinterpreted. Specifically, fusion of the adult or resident cardiac stem cells with existing heart tissue may have been observed, rather than direct conversion [34, 35]. Furthermore, the research findings in mice have thus far not been reproduced in primates [36], distancing these experiments from clinical trials. However, even if pluripotent adult stem cells exist, they represent only an extreme minority of the stem cell population (1 in a billion)[37] [38] and are extremely difficult to expand in vitro. Finally, although hematopoietic stem cells have been suggested as a possible source for transplantable cells, two recent studies indicate that these stem cells adopt only hematopoietic fates and do not transdifferentiate into cardiac cells [39, 40]. Thus, one goal of cardiac cellular transplantation has been to find a renewable source of cells that can be used in human hearts, and human ES cell derivatives may meet this demand [41].

The establishment of pluripotent hESC lines and their successful differentiation into genuine human CMs may represent a potential unlimited source of transplantable human cells. In addition to the possible therapies that could arise from hESC, they provide a unique opportunity to study the development of the human heart and the progression of certain pathophysiological phenomena, whose better understanding is also critical for developing more effective heart therapies. In fact, human cardiogenesis is very poorly understood as most of our existing knowledge comes from mouse studies despite the fact that significant differences between mouse and human cardiomyogenesis are known to exist.

CARDIAC DIFFERENTIATION - INSIGHTS FROM STUDIES WITH MOUSE ESCS

Previous studies using CMs derived from mESCs have provided significant insights into the development of mammalian hearts. In most cases, in vitro mESC differentiation requires the formation of 3-dimensional aggregates called embryoid bodies (EBs), which can then differentiate into a wide variety of specialized cell types including CMs (Fig. 1). Once differentiated, CMs can be readily identified by visual inspection as spontaneously-contracting outgrowths [4]. Many different aspects of the differentiation protocol such as EB size, media composition (e.g. the presence of fetal bovine serum, inducing agents and other growth and transcription factors, etc), the particular mESC lines being investigated, as well as the timing and duration of differentiation, all influence the cardiogenicity of mESCs [4, 42-47]. The developmental changes of mESC-derived CMs can be correlated with the length of time in culture, mimicking that seen in myocardial development *in vivo*: primordial pacemaker-like and SA nodal pacemaker (early), atrial and ventricular (intermediate and late) CMs appear and predominate at different stages during cardiac differentiation although a heterogeneous population of all three CM types is almost always seen in differentiated mouse EBs. Terminal differentiation and derivation of specific CM types (e.g. how to sustain the early nodal cells) is an area of tremendous interest that requires further investigation.

Morphologically, mouse ESC-derived nodal cells are non-striated, small and round whereas their atrial and ventricular counterparts show the organized myofibrillar and sarcomeric structures found in mature cardiac muscle cells [48]. Since nodal derivatives lack the contractile apparatus, they do not beat (unless coupled to muscle CMs) although they are electrically active. In contrast, mononucleated and rod-shaped striated atrial and ventricular derivatives are normally quiescent but are capable of beating upon stimulation by electrical signals generated from nodal cells or elsewhere. Electrophysiologically, mESC-derived CMs have signature action potential (AP) profiles typical of those found in postnatal cardiomyocytes (see reviews [45, 49, 50]). Functionally, mESC-derived CMs show pharmacological and physiological properties of specialized myocardial cells (e.g. rate-adaptation of APs, chronotropic responses to adrenergic stimulation, etc).

The reproducible induction of cardiomyogenesis observed in cultured EBs has been exploited to identify and test factors that might be capable of improving the differentiation process of ES cells to cardiomyocytes – a prerequisite for generating sufficient cells for replacement therapies in heart. These studies have generally relied on candidate signaling molecule experiments designed to assess the effects of a specific factor(s) on cardiomyogenesis in vitro and have led to the identification of a number of factors that promote mesoderm formation and/or cardiomyogenesis. For this reason, several families of peptide growth factors or cytokines, whether implicated in studies of embryonic heart formation or not, have been extensively studied for their effects on cardiomyogenesis and the induction of cardiac-restricted transcription factors and structural proteins.

Members of the TGF-ß superfamily (TGF-ß and BMP2) control several major cardiac specific transcription factors, including Nkx 2.5, through SMAD binding sites [51-53]. In the mouse, BMP2 is co-expressed spatially and temporally with GATA-4 and Nkx 2.5 in the pre-cardiac mesoderm, suggesting that BMP2 may control the expression of cardiac transcription factors [54, 55]. In turn, the addition of noggin, a BMP antagonist, to developing embryos inhibits differentiation of cardiac cells [54, 56]. In addition to controlling the transcription of Nkx2.5, transcription of Brachyury [57], a mesoderm-specific lineage marker that is vital for the formation and differentiation of posterior mesoderm and for axial development in all vertebrates, is also likely controlled either directly or indirectly by BMPs. Embryoid bodies stimulated with these growth factors show an increased potential for cardiac differentiation concomitant with a significant increase in beating areas and enhanced myofibrillogenesis [58-61].

Wnt signaling, another important pathway, in vertebrate cardiomyogenesis is more complex, but likely equally as important. The "canonical" wnts 1, 3A and 8, acting by inhibition of GSK3 (allowing nuclear localization of β-catenin), appear to inhibit cardiac differentiation, whereas the non-canonical wnt 11, involving protein kinase C, seems to enhance cardiac differentiation, at least in ECC cells (reviewed in [62]). Supporting this, inhibition of the canonical wnt signaling increases cardiac differentiation [63] and the conditional deletion of β-catenin from the definitive endoderm of the mouse results in the formation of multiple ectopic hearts [64]. The presence of crescent, dikkopf (dkk)-1 or other wnt antagonists induces cardiomyocyte differentiation in non-heart producing mesoderm. In the light of recent data showing that on the one hand wnts can act as growth factors for stem cells [65, 66] yet on the other can control differentiation in the positive or negative sense at later stages of development, it may be assumed that the response of an individual cell depends on the combination of co-factors (inhibitors and activators) also expressed at the time at which the signal is received. However, the role of the canonical wnts as a cardiac inhibitor has been questioned recently by studies showing that wnts 3A and 8, in addition to β-catenin are required for cardiomyocyte differentiation of P19Cl6 cells [67].

The cell surface κ opioid receptor also appears important for cardiac differentiation in mESC lines, as demonstrated by the fact that κ opioid receptor agonists elevate transcripts of the cardiac lineage promoting GATA-4 and Nkx-2.5 genes. As opioid receptor antagonists suppressed the nuclear increase of PKC-α, PKC-β1 and PKC- β2 isozymes, the number of beating clusters decreased in EBs. The expression of skeletal muscle and neuronal specific development did not appear, revealing the existence of an independent cardiogenic activation pathway. The promotion of GATA-4/ Nkx-2.5 expression and the consecutive PKC activation has been proved to be a main signal transduction step in cardiac differentiation of ES cells [68, 69]. Other studies involving the retinoblastoma protein (Rb) deficient ES cells recently identify LEK1 as a pivotal cardiogenic factor [70]. In Rb deficient cardiomyocytes, beating activity is delayed and the expression of GATA, MEF2 and Nkx-2.5 cardiogenic factors and myocardium specific genes are down regulated, suggesting a critical role of LEK1 protein in early stages of mesoderm derived cell lineage specification and differentiation. Restoring the structural interaction of Rb with LEK1 induced a transcriptional program priming ES cells toward a cardiac fate.

Some other substances have also been identified which promote or inhibit cardiomyogenesis in mESC in vitro, including leukemia inhibitory factor (LIF), retinoic acid (RA) and dimethylsulfoxide (DMSO). Nanomolar concentrations of RA significantly inhibit the development of beating clusters within EBs if administered during the first 5 days of EB formation; however, administration of RA between days 5 and 7 not only produces the opposite effects, it also causes an increase in the number of contracting EBs. Interestingly, RA mediated induction of cardiomyoblast differentiation preferentially leads to a ventricular cell type within EBs cultivated in high serum conditions [45, 71]. Paradoxically, depletion of RA in low serum conditions enhances cardiomyogenic differentiation, and CMs within EBs from late developmental stages are apparently insensitive to RA mediated differentiation effects [45]. Likewise, low doses of LIF in LIF-deficient and LIF receptor–deficient mES cells rescue the onset of cardiac differentiation; whereas higher doses attenuate CM differentiation. Finally, it has been shown that the treatment of EBs with DMSO can promote CM differentiation, or depending on the dose, skeletal muscle cells.

Several of the factors just described have been tested in hESC differentiation protocols to generate CMs. Remarkably, no significant improvement in cardiomyocyte differentiation has yet been observed with DMSO, RA or BMP-2 [12, 13, 15, 17]. It is currently unclear why these factors do not contribute to cardiomyogenesis in hES cells, but variations in concentration, timing and/or combinatorial effects with other factors may affect the outcome. It is also possible that different molecular pathways are involved due to intrinsic differences between the two species. More work therefore is required to understand the effects of signaling factors on cardiomyogenesis in differentiating hESC. It will ultimately be important to identify specific factors that control maturation, proliferation and electrical characteristics of these cells.

Finally, an alternative approach to the candidate molecule approach involves the use of systematic screens to identify compounds capable of promoting cardiomyogenesis. Takahashi et al, for example, screened and evaluated compounds that could directly promote cardiomyogenesis in cultured ES cells that carried a cardiac-restricted EGFP reporter transgene. Of the 880 compounds, only one, ascorbic acid, was observed to enhance EGFP expression in the mESC lines tested [72]. Similarly Wu et al screened a library of heterocyclic compounds designed around kinase-directed molecular scaffolds. These were tested in P19 embryonic carcinoma cell lines, and the findings led to the identification of cardiogenol A-D, which promoted elevated levels of cardiomyogenic differentiation in mESCs [73]. It is likely that this approach will be very important in the identification of novel inducers of cardiac mycoytes from hESCs.

SELECTION OF THE CARDIAC LINEAGE
FROM DIFFERENTIATED mESCs

Many specific growth conditions and genetic approaches have been employed to enrich mESC derived CMs. To isolate a pure population of mESC-derived CMs, Klug et al demonstrated that CMs could be genetically selected and isolated from other cells by conferring on an mESC line a neomycin resistance gene whose expression was driven by a cardiac-restricted promoter (e.g., α-myosin heavy chain (α-MHC)) [74]. After in vitro differentiation and selection with G418, 99.6% of the resistant cells were CMs. Subsequent to this study, fluorophores (such as green and cyan fluorescence proteins), LacZ, and other antibiotic resistance genes (e.g. hygromycin) have also been utilized along with different heart-specific promoters (e.g. cardiac α-actin and myosin light chain MLC) as markers for selecting the cardiac lineage. These strategies have made the selection of relatively pure populations of CMs from the heterogeneous cell populations in mouse EBs possible. Such genetic approaches, however, have not yet been applied to hESCs due to various technical difficulties such as those associated with gene delivery to the human cell lines (reviewed in [75]).

HUMAN VS. MOUSE ESCs: SIMILARITIES AND DIFFERENCES

As mentioned, much of what is currently known about cardiomyocyte differentiation in ESCs has been learned from studies in the mouse system. Despite the differences between the two species, this expertise has also been applied to hESC studies. During the differentiation of hESC into CMs, cardiac-specific proteins, receptors, and ion channels are expressed in a developmental continuum, which closely recapitulates the developmental pattern of early cardiogenesis in the embryo [4]. The differentiation of hESC-derived CMs have been brought about by different methods, including spontaneous differentiation, EB formation (Fig. 1) and co-culture with a mouse visceral endoderm-like cell-line (END-2) [12-15, 17]. However, in all of these methods, the efficiency of differentiation proved very low and insufficient to be considered adequate for treatments in patients at this time.

Like mESC derivatives, cardiomyocytes generated from hESCs exhibit spontaneous contractile activity, and molecular, phenotypic and electrophysiological studies have demonstrated that these cells are authentic cardiomyocytes [13, 17, 76]. Cardiomyocytes derived from hESCs have a typical beating rate comparable to that of the native human heart, and respond to a number of pharmacological agents involving adrenoreceptors or muscarinic receptors. For example, the beating rate and amplitude of contraction of hESC-derived CMs increase following the addition of isopreterenol, a β1 adrenergic receptor (β1-AR) agonist, while negative chronotropic responses have also been observed with carbachol, a muscarinic agonist [77]. Human ESC-derived CMs also undergo a degree of differentiation *in vitro*, characterized by maturation of the myofiber structure, expression of channels implicated in electrical excitation and contraction, and exit from the cell cycle [78]. Electrophysiologically, they display the three distinct types of rate-adaptive APs that are signatures of early-stage human nodal, atrial and ventricular CMs [14, 15]. Although some studies described up to 85% of the hESC-derived CMs to be ventricular-like [15], others report enhanced percentages of atrial and other non-ventricular-like cells [12, 14]. Given their therapeutic potentials, it is extremely desirable to derive and characterize chamber-specific hESC-CMs (e.g. SA nodal cells to correct excitability defects in sick sinus node syndromes, and ventricular cells for heart failure). Engineering hESCs to construct a library of "custom-tailored" CMs exhibiting a range of phenotypic behaviors may offer a novel and flexible approach for heart therapies.

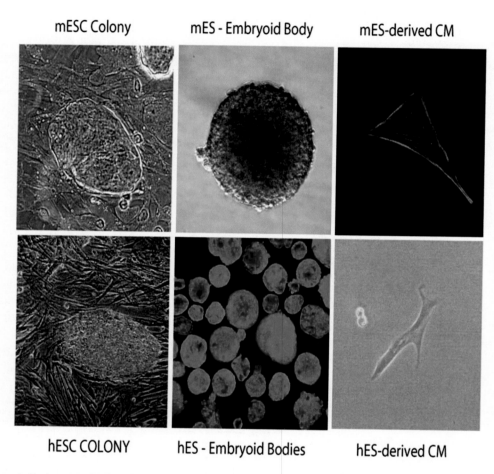

Figure 1. Embryonic Stem cells and differentiation to cardiomyocytes (CM). The top row shows examples of mouse embryonic stem (mES) cells. Typical images of (*Left*) mES cells grown as an undifferentiated colony on feeder layers composed of embryonic mouse fibroblasts; (*Center*) embryoid bodies, following aggregation of undifferentiated mES cells; and (*Right*) an isolated cardiomyocyte stained with α-actinin after isolation from a spontaneous beating area originating from the plated embryoid body. The formation of embryoid bodies as shown in the center panel initiates differentiation. The lower row shows examples of human embryonic stem cells. Typical images of (*Left*) a typical hESC colony cultivated on a layer of mouse fibroblast feeder cells; (*Center*) differentiating human embryoid bodies; and (Right) a human ES cell derived cardiomyocyte following isolation. Cells shown in the center panel have been genetically modified to constitutively express a green fluorescent protein (GFP) for cell-tracking after transplantation. Some images have been adapted from [4, 88, 96].

Although a series of extensive and elegant studies performed with mESCs has laid the platform for understanding cardiac differentiation, and mammalian embryogenesis in general, it is widely acknowledged by investigators in the field that human and mouse ESCs behave very differently [4]. Some of these differences are intrinsic to the two species, others are technical in nature. To name a few, 1) human and other primate ESCs are much more difficult to culture than murine ESCs: hESCs grow about 3 to 5 times slower and require much more stringent conditions than mESCs; 2) leukemia inhibitory factor (LIF) is sufficient to maintain mESCs, but not hESCs, in their undifferentiated state; 3) agents such as retinoic acid and DMSO that are known to promote cardiac differentiation of mESCs, do not enhance and even inhibit that of hESCs suggesting that different molecular pathways and/or some species-specific modulators are involved [13]; 4) conventional methods for genetic manipulation such as electroporation and plasmid transfection that are highly effective for mESCs prove to be highly inefficient or even ineffective for hESCs; 5) mouse and human development differ significantly in embryonic genomic expression and early structures such as placenta, extraembryonic membranes, embryonic disc, egg cylinder, etc [79-81]. Thus, findings from mESCs are not necessarily applicable in hESCs although they are clearly useful for making certain predictions when designing hESC experiments. Given these known differences, and the fact that humans are the ultimate target for therapeutic applications, further studies of hESCs and their derivatives are warranted even though the process of culturing and handling hESCs is much more costly, labor-intensive and technically challenging.

THERAPEUTIC POTENTIAL

Myocardial Infarction and Cell Replacement

Myocardial infarction remains the major worldwide cardiovascular disorder in humans [82]. Immediately after a heart attack, oxygen starvation of myocardial tissues leads to cell death, and in the absence of immediate thrombolytic treatment of the blocked coronary artery, the damage is often irreversible and the heart is permanently impaired. Longer term, the remaining cardiomyocytes hypertrophy in an attempt to meet the functional demands, while cardiac fibroblasts secrete collagen and other extracellular matrix proteins during scar formation, which may further impair ventricular function. Myocardial tissue recovery is particularly limited by its intrinsic inability to regenerate. Palliative interventions to treat damaged heart muscle include changes in life-style, medications that reduce functional requirements or limit certain aspects of remodelling, or surgical interventions that improve cardiac function. In severe cases, transplantation is the only option, and today's most urgent problem in transplantation is the lack of suitable donor organs and tissues.

As mentioned earlier, damaged myocardium could be treated by cell transplantation/replacement therapy (Fig. 2). Potential and actual sources of cells or tissues are self (autologous), same species (allogeneic), different species (xenographic), primary or immortalized cell lines, and embryonic or adult stem cell-derived donor cells. The ability to cultivate, multiply and manipulate these cell types has either limited or encouraged their use in specific treatment protocols [25]. With the cultivation of human ESCs that can generate authentic cardiomyocytes (as described above), the first steps towards gene replacement therapy to treat myocardial infarction have now been taken, and although it is premature to envision clinical trials, a number of pre-clinical trials in animal models (rodents and non-human primates) are envisioned or are on-going.

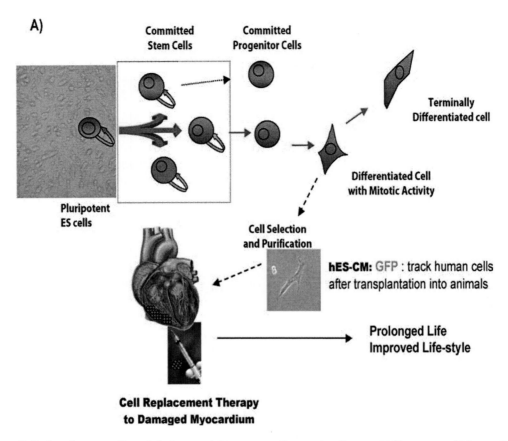

Figure 2. Embronic stem cells and their potential to treat cardiovascular disease. A) *Treatment of Myocardial Infarction*. Stages of differentiation from pluripotent stem cells to a terminal adult-like cell. In the case of heart, somatic stem and progenitor cells are committed very early during the differentiation of ES cells. One possible strategy to treat myocardial infarcts is to differentiate hES cells in vitro and isolate a pure population of human cardiac cells with mitotic activity. Selection of purified populations of cardiomyocytes can be achieved through either antibiotic selection of genetically modifed hES cells or FACS sorting of fluorescently marked hES cell derivatives, similar to those described in Fig 1. If the cells can be appropriately synchronized and purified, then cell replacement therapy in heart may be possible. The aim of such an approach is to find an alternative to organ transplantation to prolong life and to improve life-style – an important goal for an increasingly aged population increasingly that is at enhanced risk for cardiac-associated morbidity and mortality.

Currently, five goals must be achieved before human stem cells can be deemed successfully in cell replacement therapies for human myocardial infarction [41, 76]. It will be necessary to 1) purify specific cell lineages (e.g., ventricular or atrial), 2) demonstrate that differentiation of purified cardiomyocytes function in a normal physiological way in vivo, 3) demonstrate the efficacy of transplantation in rodent and large animal models of heart disease, 4) ensure against the formation of ESC-derived tumors, and 5) prevent immunological rejection [7]. Several strategies to address these issues have already been discussed in principle, but the latter is of particular importance. In transplantation scenarios, immunological rejection must be prevented. All stromal-derived and hematopoietic-derived (except RBCs) cells express either HLA class I and/or class II molecules that are recognized by specific lymphocytes. When these molecules are recognized as foreign, immunosuppressive therapy (i.e., cyclosporin A, Cytoxan) is required to ensure systemic tolerance to HLA molecules. Unfortunately, most of the immunosuppressive drugs currently used are associated with complications, including opportunistic infections, drug-related toxicities, skin malignancies and post-transplantation lymphoproliferative disorders. Only humans with similar HLA molecules can be donors for other hosts, requiring pre-screening to determine allogeneic compatibility. Currently all ESC lines contain HLA molecules that are identical to that of the donor and are not appropriate for therapies in most patients. As such, banks of ESCs with known HLA backgrounds would need to be established to ensure allogenic compatibility for potential patient use, but the isolation of many thousands of clonal derived ES cells with defined HLA molecules would represent an enormous amount of work, time and investment. Such a goal may even be unattainable, and under current law, could only be performed in the private sector.

Public funded research in the U.S. and many other countries currently does not permit derivation of new human ES cell lines; however, the generation of autologous donor cells through a process known as 'somatic nuclear transfer' (SNT) [83, 84] may overcome this limitation. Using this approach, somatic cell nuclei of a patient could be fused to enucleated human eggs, and subsequently cultivated in vitro to form blastocysts. These in vitro derived blastocysts could be employed to generate hESC lines, from which differentiated cell derivatives (i.e., cardiomyocytes) could be generated for transplantation purposes [83, 84]. This strategy was believed to be applicable to hESC based on proof-of-principle studies by a group from Korea [85, 86]; however, these papers have now been retracted and serious ethical concerns have been raised that are beyond the scope of this review. Regardless, hESC derivatives obtained through SNT should be immunologically compatible for transplantation purposes, because they contain (except in the mitochondrial genome) the exact same genetic information as that of the patient from which the nucleus was derived.

While it is clear that substantial testing must be performed in animal models (preferably in large animals such as swines or even non-human primates) to overcome these possible limitations to replacement therapy mentioned above, it remains unclear how efficient this approach will be in the treatment of myocardial infarction. The results of these basic research endeavors anticipate the eventual use of these cells in replacement therapies for myocardial infarction in humans, but as in all basic research, the results will also highlight limitations to their applications that have not yet been adequately considered, including the viability of in vitro derived cells in vivo and how best to limit the washout of these cells, time-dependent changes in phenotypic properties, etc, after targeted placement into damaged myocardium.

Cell-Based Pacemakers as an Alternative to Conventional Electronic Devices

Pacemaking activity, the generation of spontaneous cellular electrical rhythms, governs numerous biological processes from the autonomous beating of the heart to respiratory rhythms and sleep cycles. As mentioned, normal heartbeats originate in the sino-atrial (SA) node and as a result, malfunctions of pacemaker cells due to disease or aging lead to various forms of arrhythmias (e.g. bradycardias or abnormally low heart rates). While traditional treatments require pharmacological intervention and/or implantation of electronic pacemakers are effective they are also associated with significant risks (e.g. infection, hemorrhage, lung collapse and death) and expenses (>600,000 cardiac pacemakers are implanted annually worldwide; cost~\$40,000 per patient). Other disadvantages include limited battery life (replaced every 5-10 years), permanent implantation of catheters into the heart, and lack of autonomic neurohumorous responses, etc. Therefore, it is highly desirable to develop more effective and economical, and perhaps, biological alternatives.

Using a gene-based approach, Nuss and colleagues have demonstrated that "latent" pacemaker activity of normally-silent ventricular muscle myocytes can be unleashed to produce spontaneous firing activity by genetic inhibition of the inwardly rectifying K^+ channels (a.k.a. I_{K1}), encoded by the Kir2 gene family, which are normally absent in nodal cells but intensely expressed in ventricular cells [87]. However, the induced automaticity was ~3-fold slower than normal, and genetic suppression of I_{K1} does not provide a direct means to modulate the induced rhythm. Since the generation of pacemakers by gene therapy relies upon the conversion of pre-existing heart tissue, rather than the implantation of a new "surrogate node", damaged SA nodal cells, at least conceptually, can be better replaced or supplemented with cell-based pacemakers.

Recently, we have reported that electrically-active hESC-derived CMs can functionally integrate with, and actively pace 1) recipient monolayers of quiescent ventricular cells *in vitro* and 2) the silenced ventricular myocardium after *in vivo* transplantation (Fig. 3). Maximal therapeutic flexibility could further be achieved by *ex vivo* genetic manipulation of hESC-derived CMs [88] (e.g. a genuine pacemaker gene such as the hyperpolarization-activated cyclic nucleotide-modulated or HCN channel family) [89] to exhibit a desired firing frequency. Such an *ex vivo* approach is potentially advantageous over the in situ gene transfer approach by enabling the isolation of clonal genetically-modified cell lines or their cardiac derivatives whose transgene location has been characterized to minimize the risk of inappropriate gene insertion (and thus, the associated oncogenesis). These findings were in complete accordance with those reported by Field and colleagues (2003) which demonstrate that mouse embryonic cardiomyocytes transplanted into the left ventricle of syngeneic adult mice fully integrate into the host tissue matrix and form gap junction proteins [90], and further demonstrates that exogenous transplanted hESC derivatives can even electrically drive the surrounding myocardium. Furthermore, unlike electronic devices, hESC-derived pacemakers retain their responsiveness to β-adrenergic stimulation as well as such pharmacological agents as ion channel blockers (e.g. lidocaine and ZD7288). Qualitatively similar results have been obtained using different culture and animal models [12]. As an alternative to hESCs, Rosen and colleagues have exploited human mesenchymal stem cells as a gene delivery vehicle to facilitate and/or induce pacing [91]. Such efforts, and the differences between the two approaches, have been extensively reviewed and discussed elsewhere [92, 93].

Although initial hESC experiments are promising, a number of issues need to be addressed before they can be tested in humans clinically. For instance, time-dependent electrical remodeling of hESC-derived CMs (such as changes in ion channel expression) after engraftment could lead to arrhythmias. Additionally, the graft size, the long-term survival and functional efficacy of the grafted cells, transplantation site, purity of nodal cells in the graft, time course for maturation, etc, are other contributing factors that also need to be considered. Given that the native SA node is such a complex structure consisting of a gradient of nodal pacemaker cells with a range of phenotypic properties [94], it is likely that all of the above-mentioned factors will need to be carefully taken into consideration for future efforts to bioengineer a surrogate SA node.

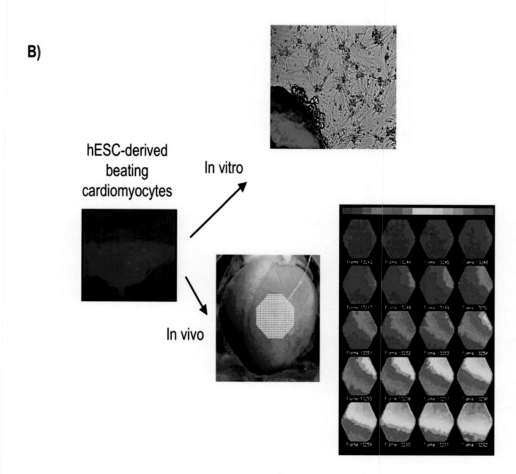

Figure 3. Embronic stem cells and their potential to treat cardiovascular disease. (B) *Cell-based Pacemaker cells*. A spontaneously beating hEB outgrowth, which stably expresses GFP, was micro-dissected and transplanted onto a *quiescent* (transparent) monolayer of neonatal rat ventricular cardiomyocytes (NRVM) in vitro. Multi-electrode array recordings indicate that electrically-active hESC-derived cardiomyocytes can behave as a surrogate pacemaker to actively pace the otherwise quiescent NRVMs, indicating functional integration between donor and recipient cells. Similar observation was made by ex vivo mapping of hearts that have been pre-transplanted with hESC-derived CMs in vivo. Circles represent the transplantation site, as identified by the GFP epifluorescence of hESC-derived CMs (the right atrium had been removed to eliminate contaminations due to intrinsic pacing, and to render the ventricle quiescent; see Xue et al for further experimental details). The area of earliest membrane depolarization always corresponds to the transplantation site. Adapted from [96,97].

Limitations

While several reviews have already described strategies with hESC derivatives for myocardial regeneration, prevention of immune rejection, and *in vivo* transplantation techniques, others have described technical advances related to cell selection strategies, upscaling methodologies, and improved cell viability. Although aspects of each of the above concerns have been improved, or in some cases "perfected", continued problems that stem from inefficient differentiation, tumorigenicity, immunogenicity, as well as complicated ethical issues surrounding the isolation of cells from in vitro fertilized human embryos still need to be addressed [7]. Importantly, the direct administration of ESCs can not be envisioned because of tumor formation, and a number of specific challenges remain before the therapeutic potential of ES cell derived cardiomyocytes can be materialized. These include the generation of sufficient numbers of the desired cell type (atrial-, ventricular- or pacemaker) probably by driven differentiation, how to best deliver the purified cells to appropriate sites, their maturation into adult phenotypes either in vitro or in vivo, and how to escape rejection by the host immune system. A number of solutions to these issues have been considered, including the creation of large stem cell banks that represent a wide array of histocompatibility backgrounds (see above), but detailed protocols will need to be tested to ensure that exogenously grown cells integrate into the areas of damage, that the cells couple correctly, and that conduction blocks and arrhythmias are absent. The latter two problems are particularly important and will require long-term follow ups to ensure that any short-term benefit is not mitigated by long-term consequences. Additionally, the limited number of hESC lines available for use in U.S. government supported research, poses a significant problem. Most of these lines currently have been passaged many times, such that there may be loss of imprinting and altered epigenetic states. Perhaps more insidious, these human cell lines may be contaminated with mouse proteins, and it has been reported that several of these lines have already accumulated a number of genetic mutations [95]. On the other hand, work limited to a few hESC lines has probably limited the passionate, and at times intense, debate over the use of hESCs. Alternatively, hESCs may be useful for somatic nuclear transfer - a procedure to create new stem cell lines that may be a "custom match" to a patient requiring transplantation therapy (for review see [7]). These approaches are not currently practical because of the relatively low number of clones generated; however, recent work portends the probable success of this methodology [78].

CONCLUSIONS

Currently no hESC-based therapies are on-going in the United States, although recent studies with hESCs have shown great promise and demonstrate the therapeutic potential of these approaches. Importantly, mouse and some human ES cells and their derivatives have been employed successfully in rodent models of diabetes, Parkinson's disease, myocardial infarction, spinal injury and severe immune disorder [5]. Although we cannot currently use ESC-based therapeutic strategies in humans, for the reasons described earlier, the recent technical achievements in cell and molecular biology will positively influence stem cell research. We predict that in the future these scientific endeavors will lead to the generation of functional tissue grafts for clinical applications, including the treatment of cardiac diseases.

ACKNOWLEDGEMENTS

This work was supported by grants from the National Institutes of Health (R01 HL72857 to R.A.L.) and the Intramural Research Program of the NIH, National Institute on Aging (to K.R.B.).

REFERENCES

[1] Evans, M. J. and Kaufman, M. H. Establishment in Culture of Pluripotential Cells from Mouse Embryos. *Nature*, 1981, 292, 154-156.

[2] Martin, G. R. Isolation of a Pluripotent Cell Line from Early Mouse Embryos Cultured in Medium Conditioned by Teratocarcinoma Stem Cells. *Proc.Natl.Acad.Sci.U.S.A.*, 1981, 78, 7634-7638.

[3] Thomson, J. A., Itskovitz-Eldor, J., Shapiro, S. S., Waknitz, M. A., Swiergiel, J. J., Marshall, V. S. and Jones, J. M. Embryonic Stem Cell Lines Derived from Human Blastocysts. *Science*, 1998, 282, 1145-1147.

[4] Boheler, K. R., Czyz, J., Tweedie, D., Yang, H. T., Anisimov, S. V. and Wobus, A. M. Differentiation of Pluripotent Embryonic Stem Cells into Cardiomyocytes. *Circ Res*, 2002, 91, 189-201.

[5] Gepstein, L. Derivation and Potential Applications of Human Embryonic Stem Cells. *Circ.Res.*, 2002, 91, 866-876.

[6] Kehat, I. and Gepstein, L. Human Embryonic Stem Cells for Myocardial Regeneration. *Heart Fail.Rev.*, 2003, 8, 229-236.

[7] Wobus, A. M. and Boheler, K. R. Embryonic Stem Cells: Prospects for Developmental Biology and Cell Therapy. *Physiol Rev*, 2005, 85, 635-678.

[8] McBurney, M. W. and Rogers, B. J. Isolation of Male Embryonal Carcinoma Cells and Their Chromosome Replication Patterns. *Developmental Biology*, 1982, 89, 503-508.

[9] Shamblott, M. J., Axelman, J., Wang, S., Bugg, E. M., Littlefield, J. W., Donovan, P. J., Blumenthal, P. D., Huggins, G. R. and Gearhart, J. D. Derivation of Pluripotent Stem Cells from Cultured Human Primordial Germ Cells. *Proc Natl Acad Sci U S A*, 1998, 95, 13726-13731.

[10] Andrews, P. W. Teratocarcinomas and Human Embryology: Pluripotent Human Ec Cell Lines. Review Article. *Apmis*, 1998, 106, 158-167; discussion 167-158.

[11] Przyborski, S. A., Christie, V. B., Hayman, M. W., Stewart, R. and Horrocks, G. M. Human Embryonal Carcinoma Stem Cells: Models of Embryonic Development in Humans. *Stem Cells Dev*, 2004, 13, 400-408.

[12] Kehat, I., Gepstein, A., Spira, A., Itskovitz-Eldor, J. and Gepstein, L. High-Resolution Electrophysiological Assessment of Human Embryonic Stem Cell-Derived Cardiomyocytes: A Novel in Vitro Model for the Study of Conduction. *Circ Res*, 2002, 91, 659-661.

[13] Xu, C., Police, S., Rao, N. and Carpenter, M. K. Characterization and Enrichment of Cardiomyocytes Derived from Human Embryonic Stem Cells. *Circ Res*, 2002, 91, 501-508.

[14] He, J. Q., Ma, Y., Lee, Y., Thomson, J. A. and Kamp, T. J. Human Embryonic Stem Cells Develop into Multiple Types of Cardiac Myocytes: Action Potential Characterization. *Circ Res*, 2003, 93, 32-39.

[15] Mummery, C., Ward-van Oostwaard, D., Doevendans, P., Spijker, R., van den Brink, S., Hassink, R., van der Heyden, M., Opthof, T., Pera, M., de la Riviere, A. B., Passier, R. and Tertoolen, L. Differentiation of Human Embryonic Stem Cells to Cardiomyocytes: Role of Coculture with Visceral Endoderm-Like Cells. *Circulation*, 2003, 107, 2733-2740.

[16] Schuldiner, M., Yanuka, O., Itskovitz-Eldor, J., Melton, D. A. and Benvenisty, N. Effects of Eight Growth Factors on the Differentiation of Cells Derived from Human Embryonic Stem Cells. *Proc Natl Acad Sci U S A*, 2000, 97, 11307-11312.

[17] Kehat, I., Kenyagin-Karsenti, D., Snir, M., Segev, H., Amit, M., Gepstein, A., Livne, E., Binah, O., Itskovitz-Eldor, J. and Gepstein, L. Human Embryonic Stem Cells Can Differentiate into Myocytes with Structural and Functional Properties of Cardiomyocytes. *J Clin Invest,* 2001, 108, 407-414.

[18] Itskovitz-Eldor, J., Schuldiner, M., Karsenti, D., Eden, A., Yanuka, O., Amit, M., Soreq, H. and Benvenisty, N. Differentiation of Human Embryonic Stem Cells into Embryoid Bodies Compromising the Three Embryonic Germ Layers. *Mol Med,* 2000, 6, 88-95.

[19] Shamblott, M. J., Axelman, J., Littlefield, J. W., Blumenthal, P. D., Huggins, G. R., Cui, Y., Cheng, L. and Gearhart, J. D. Human Embryonic Germ Cell Derivatives Express a Broad Range of Developmentally Distinct Markers and Proliferate Extensively in Vitro. *Proc Natl Acad Sci U S A*, 2001, 98, 113-118.

[20] Wei, G. and Mahowald, A. P. The Germline: Familiar and Newly Uncovered Properties. *Annu Rev Genet*, 1994, 28, 309-324.

[21] Morgan, H. D., Santos, F., Green, K., Dean, W. and Reik, W. Epigenetic Reprogramming in Mammals. *Hum Mol Genet,* 2005, 14 Spec No 1, R47-58.

[22] Soonpaa, M. H. and Field, L. J. Survey of Studies Examining Mammalian Cardiomyocyte DNA Synthesis. *Circ Res*, 1998, 83, 15-26.

[23] Koh, G. Y., Soonpaa, M. H., Klug, M. G. and Field, L. J. Strategies for Myocardial Repair. *J Interv Cardiol,* 1995, 8, 387-393.

[24] Soonpaa, M. H., Daud, A. I., Koh, G. Y., Klug, M. G., Kim, K. K., Wang, H. and Field, L. J. Potential Approaches for Myocardial Regeneration. *Ann N Y Acad Sci*, 1995, 752, 446-454.

[25] Gage, F. H. Cell Therapy. *Nature*, 1998, 392, 18-24.

[26] Murry, C. E., Wiseman, R. W., Schwartz, S. M. and Hauschka, S. D. Skeletal Myoblast Transplantation for Repair of Myocardial Necrosis. *J Clin Invest*, 1996, 98, 2512-2523.

[27] Taylor, D. A., Atkins, B. Z., Hungspreugs, P., Jones, T. R., Reedy, M. C., Hutcheson, K. A., Glower, D. D. and Kraus, W. E. Regenerating Functional Myocardium: Improved Performance after Skeletal Myoblast Transplantation. *Nat Med*, 1998, 4, 929-933.

[28] Koh, G. Y., Klug, M. G., Soonpaa, M. H. and Field, L. J. Differentiation and Long-Term Survival of C2c12 Myoblast Grafts in Heart. *J Clin Invest*, 1993, 92, 1548-1554.

[29] Menasche, P., Hagege, A. A., Scorsin, M., Pouzet, B., Desnos, M., Duboc, D., Schwartz, K., Vilquin, J. T. and Marolleau, J. P. Myoblast Transplantation for Heart Failure. *Lancet*, 2001, 357, 279-280.

[30] Menasche, P., Hagege, A. A., Vilquin, J. T., Desnos, M., Abergel, E., Pouzet, B., Bel, A., Sarateanu, S., Scorsin, M., Schwartz, K., Bruneval, P., Benbunan, M., Marolleau, J. P. and Duboc, D. Autologous Skeletal Myoblast Transplantation for Severe Postinfarction Left Ventricular Dysfunction. *J.Am.Coll.Cardiol.,* 2003, 41, 1078-1083.

[31] Orlic, D., Kajstura, J., Chimenti, S., Bodine, D. M., Leri, A. and Anversa, P. Transplanted Adult Bone Marrow Cells Repair Myocardial Infarcts in Mice. *Ann N Y Acad Sci,* 2001, 938, 221-229; discussion 229-230.

[32] Orlic, D., Kajstura, J., Chimenti, S., Bodine, D. M., Leri, A. and Anversa, P. Bone Marrow Stem Cells Regenerate Infarcted Myocardium. *Pediatr Transplant*, 2003, 7 Suppl 3, 86-88.

[33] Orlic, D., Kajstura, J., Chimenti, S., Limana, F., Jakoniuk, I., Quaini, F., Nadal-Ginard, B., Bodine, D. M., Leri, A. and Anversa, P. Mobilized Bone Marrow Cells Repair the Infarcted Heart, Improving Function and Survival. *Proc Natl Acad Sci U S A*, 2001, 98, 10344-10349.

[34] Terada, N., Hamazaki, T., Oka, M., Hoki, M., Mastalerz, D. M., Nakano, Y., Meyer, E. M., Morel, L., Petersen, B. E. and Scott, E. W. Bone Marrow Cells Adopt the Phenotype of Other Cells by Spontaneous Cell Fusion. *Nature*, 2002, 416, 542-545.

[35] Ying, Q. L., Nichols, J., Evans, E. P. and Smith, A. G. Changing Potency by Spontaneous Fusion. *Nature*, 2002, 416, 545-548.

[36] ORLIC, D. Adult Bone Marrow Stem Cells Regenerate Myocardium in Ischemic Heart Disease. *Ann NY Acad Sci*, 2003, 996, 152-157.

[37] Jiang, Y., Jahagirdar, B. N., Reinhardt, R. L., Schwartz, R. E., Keene, C. D., Ortiz-Gonzalez, X. R., Reyes, M., Lenvik, T., Lund, T., Blackstad, M., Du, J., Aldrich, S., Lisberg, A., Low, W. C., Largaespada, D. A. and Verfaillie, C. M. Pluripotency of Mesenchymal Stem Cells Derived from Adult Marrow. *Nature*, 2002, 418, 41-49.

[38] Verfaillie, C. M. Adult Stem Cells: Assessing the Case for Pluripotency. *Trends Cell Biol*, 2002, 12, 502-508.

[39] Balsam, L. B., Wagers, A. J., Christensen, J. L., Kofidis, T., Weissman, I. L. and Robbins, R. C. Haematopoietic Stem Cells Adopt Mature Haematopoietic Fates in Ischaemic Myocardium. *Nature*, 2004, 428, 668-673.

[40] Murry, C. E., Soonpaa, M. H., Reinecke, H., Nakajima, H., Nakajima, H. O., Rubart, M., Pasumarthi, K. B., Virag, J. I., Bartelmez, S. H., Poppa, V., Bradford, G., Dowell, J. D., Williams, D. A. and Field, L. J. Haematopoietic Stem Cells Do Not Transdifferentiate into Cardiac Myocytes in Myocardial Infarcts. *Nature*, 2004, 428, 664-668.

[41] Boheler, K. R. and Fiszman, M. Y. Can Exogenous Stem Cells Be Used in Transplantation? *Cells Tissues Organs*, 1999, 165, 237-245.

[42] Wobus, A. M., Wallukat, G. and Hescheler, J. Pluripotent Mouse Embryonic Stem Cells Are Able to Differentiate into Cardiomyocytes Expressing Chronotropic Responses to Adrenergic and Cholinergic Agents and Ca2+ Channel Blockers. *Differentiation*, 1991, 48, 173-182.

[43] Wobus, A. M., Kleppisch, T., Maltsev, V. and Hescheler, J. Cardiomyocyte-Like Cells Differentiated in Vitro from Embryonic Carcinoma Cells P19 Are Characterized by Functional Expression of Adrenoceptors and Ca2+ Channels. *In Vitro Cell Dev Biol Anim*, 1994, 30A, 425-434.

[44] Wobus, A. M., Rohwedel, J., Maltsev, V. and Hescheler, J. Development of Cardiomyocytes Expressing Cardiac-Specific Genes, Action Potentials, and Ionic Channels During Embryonic Stem Cell-Derived Cardiogenesis. *Ann N Y Acad Sci*, 1995, 752, 460-469.

[45] Wobus, A. M., Kaomei, G., Shan, J., Wellner, M. C., Rohwedel, J., Ji, G., Fleischmann, B., Katus, H. A., Hescheler, J. and Franz, W. M. Retinoic Acid Accelerates Embryonic Stem Cell-Derived Cardiac Differentiation and Enhances Development of Ventricular Cardiomyocytes. *J Mol Cell Cardiol*, 1997, 29, 1525-1539.

[46] Czyz, J. and Wobus, A. Embryonic Stem Cell Differentiation: The Role of Extracellular Factors. *Differentiation*, 2001, 68, 167-174.

[47] Wobus, A. M., Guan, K., Yang, H. T. and Boheler, K. R. Embryonic Stem Cells as a Model to Study Cardiac, Skeletal Muscle, and Vascular Smooth Muscle Cell Differentiation. *Methods Mol Biol*, 2002, 185, 127-156.

[48] Westfall, M. V., Pasyk, K. A., Yule, D. I., Samuelson, L. C. and Metzger, J. M. Ultrastructure and Cell-Cell Coupling of Cardiac Myocytes Differentiating in Embryonic Stem Cell Cultures. *Cell Motil Cytoskeleton*, 1997, 36, 43-54.

[49] Metzger, J. M., Samuelson, L. C., Rust, E. M. and Westfall, M. V. Embryonic Stem Cell Cardiogenesis: Applications for Cardiovascular Research. *Trends in Cardiovascular Medicine*, 1997, 7, 63-68.

[50] Hescheler, J., Fleischmann, B. K., Lentini, S., Maltsev, V. A., Rohwedel, J., Wobus, A. M. and Addicks, K. Embryonic Stem Cells: A Model to Study Structural and Functional Properties in Cardiomyogenesis. *Cardiovasc Res*, 1997, 36, 149-162.

[51] Liberatore, C. M., Searcy-Schrick, R. D., Vincent, E. B. and Yutzey, K. E. Nkx-2.5 Gene Induction in Mice Is Mediated by a Smad Consensus Regulatory Region. *Dev Biol*, 2002, 244, 243-256.

[52] Lien, C. L., McAnally, J., Richardson, J. A. and Olson, E. N. Cardiac-Specific Activity of an Nkx2-5 Enhancer Requires an Evolutionarily Conserved Smad Binding Site. *Dev.Biol.*, 2002, 244, 257-266.

[53] Brand, T. Heart Development: Molecular Insights into Cardiac Specification and Early Morphogenesis. *Dev.Biol.*, 2003, 258, 1-19.

[54] Schultheiss, T. M., Burch, J. B. and Lassar, A. B. A Role for Bone Morphogenetic Proteins in the Induction of Cardiac Myogenesis. *Genes Dev.*, 1997, 11, 451-462.

[55] Andree, B., Duprez, D., Vorbusch, B., Arnold, H. H. and Brand, T. Bmp-2 Induces Ectopic Expression of Cardiac Lineage Markers and Interferes with Somite Formation in Chicken Embryos. *Mech Dev,* 1998, 70, 119-131.

[56] Schlange, T., Andree, B., Arnold, H. H. and Brand, T. Bmp2 Is Required for Early Heart Development During a Distinct Time Period. *Mech Dev*, 2000, 91, 259-270.

[57] Behfar, A., Zingman, L. V., Hodgson, D. M., Rauzier, J. M., Kane, G. C., Terzic, A. and Puceat, M. Stem Cell Differentiation Requires a Paracrine Pathway in the Heart. *Faseb J,* 2002, 16, 1558-1566.

[58] Johansson, B. M. and Wiles, M. V. Evidence for Involvement of Activin a and Bone Morphogenetic Protein 4 in Mammalian Mesoderm and Hematopoietic Development. *Mol Cell Biol*, 1995, 15, 141-151.

[59] Zaffran, S. and Frasch, M. Early Signals in Cardiac Development. *Circ Res*, 2002, 91, 457-469.

[60] Gaussin, V., Van de Putte, T., Mishina, Y., Hanks, M. C., Zwijsen, A., Huylebroeck, D., Behringer, R. R. and Schneider, M. D. Endocardial Cushion and Myocardial Defects after Cardiac Myocyte-Specific Conditional Deletion of the Bone Morphogenetic Protein Receptor Alk3. *Proc Natl Acad Sci U S A*, 2002, 99, 2878-2883.

[61] Schneider, M. D., Gaussin, V. and Lyons, K. M. Tempting Fate: Bmp Signals for Cardiac Morphogenesis. *Cytokine Growth Factor Rev,* 2003, 14, 1-4.

[62] Olson, E. N. and Schneider, M. D. Sizing up the Heart: Development Redux in Disease. *Genes Dev.,* 2003, 17, 1937-1956.

[63] Schneider, V. A. and Mercola, M. Wnt Antagonism Initiates Cardiogenesis in Xenopus Laevis. *Genes Dev.*, 2001, 15, 304-315.

[64] Lickert, H., Kutsch, S., Kanzler, B., Tamai, Y., Taketo, M. M. and Kemler, R. Formation of Multiple Hearts in Mice Following Deletion of Beta-Catenin in the Embryonic Endoderm. *Dev.Cell,* 2002, 3, 171-181.

[65] Reya, T., Duncan, A. W., Ailles, L., Domen, J., Scherer, D. C., Willert, K., Hintz, L., Nusse, R. and Weissman, I. L. A Role for Wnt Signalling in Self-Renewal of Haematopoietic Stem Cells. *Nature*, 2003, 423, 409-414.

[66] Willert, K., Brown, J. D., Danenberg, E., Duncan, A. W., Weissman, I. L., Reya, T., Yates, J. R., III and Nusse, R. Wnt Proteins Are Lipid-Modified and Can Act as Stem Cell Growth Factors. *Nature*, 2003, 423, 448-452.

[67] Nakamura, T., Sano, M., Songyang, Z. and Schneider, M. D. A Wnt- and Beta - Catenin-Dependent Pathway for Mammalian Cardiac Myogenesis. *Proc Natl Acad Sci U S A*, 2003, 100, 5834-5839.

[68] Ventura, C., Zinellu, E., Maninchedda, E. and Maioli, M. Dynorphin B Is an Agonist of Nuclear Opioid Receptors Coupling Nuclear Protein Kinase C Activation to the Transcription of Cardiogenic Genes in Gtr1 Embryonic Stem Cells. *Circ Res*, 2003, 92, 623-629.

[69] Ventura, C., Zinellu, E., Maninchedda, E., Fadda, M. and Maioli, M. Protein Kinase C Signaling Transduces Endorphin-Primed Cardiogenesis in Gtr1 Embryonic Stem Cells. *Circ Res*, 2003, 92, 617-622.

[70] Papadimou, E., Menard, C., Grey, C. and Puceat, M. Interplay between the Retinoblastoma Protein and Lek1 Specifies Stem Cells toward the Cardiac Lineage. *Embo J*, 2005, 24, 1750-1761.

[71] Hidaka, K., Lee, J. K., Kim, H. S., Ihm, C. H., Iio, A., Ogawa, M., Nishikawa, S., Kodama, I. and Morisaki, T. Chamber-Specific Differentiation of Nkx2.5-Positive Cardiac Precursor Cells from Murine Embryonic Stem Cells. *Faseb J*, 2003, 17, 740-742.

[72] Takahashi, T., Lord, B., Schulze, P. C., Fryer, R. M., Sarang, S. S., Gullans, S. R. and Lee, R. T. Ascorbic Acid Enhances Differentiation of Embryonic Stem Cells into Cardiac Myocytes. *Circulation*, 2003, 107, 1912-1916.

[73] Wu, X., Ding, S., Ding, Q., Gray, N. S. and Schultz, P. G. Small Molecules That Induce Cardiomyogenesis in Embryonic Stem Cells. *J.Am.Chem.Soc.*, 2004, 126, 1590-1591.

[74] Klug, M. G., Soonpaa, M. H., Koh, G. Y. and Field, L. J. Genetically Selected Cardiomyocytes from Differentiating Embronic Stem Cells Form Stable Intracardiac Grafts. *J.Clin.Invest*, 1996, 98, 216-224.

[75] Moore, J. C., van Laake, L. W., Braam, S. R., Xue, T., Tsang, S. Y., Ward, D., Passier, R., Tertoolen, L. L., Li, R. A. and Mummery, C. L. Human Embryonic Stem Cells: Genetic Manipulation on the Way to Cardiac Cell Therapies. *Reprod Toxicol,* 2005, 20, 377-391.

[76] Odorico, J. S., Kaufman, D. S. and Thomson, J. A. Multilineage Differentiation from Human Embryonic Stem Cell Lines. *Stem Cells,* 2001, 19, 193-204.

[77] Reppel, M., Boettinger, C. and Hescheler, J. Beta-Adrenergic and Muscarinic Modulation of Human Embryonic Stem Cell-Derived Cardiomyocytes. *Cell Physiol Biochem*, 2004, 14, 187-196.

[78] Snir, M., Kehat, I., Gepstein, A., Coleman, R., Itskovitz-Eldor, J., Livne, E. and Gepstein, L. Assessment of the Ultrastructural and Proliferative Properties of Human Embryonic Stem Cell-Derived Cardiomyocytes. *Am.J.Physiol Heart Circ.Physiol,* 2003, 285, H2355-H2363.

[79] Braude, P., Bolton, V. and Moore, S. Human Gene Expression First Occurs between the Four- and Eight-Cell Stages of Preimplantation Development. *Nature,* 1988, 332, 459-461.

[80] Luckett, W. P. Origin and Differentiation of the Yolk Sac and Extraembryonic Mesoderm in Presomite Human and Rhesus Monkey Embryos. *Am J Anat,* 1978, 152, 59-97.

[81] Thomson, J. A. and Odorico, J. S. Human Embryonic Stem Cell and Embryonic Germ Cell Lines. *Trends Biotechnol,* 2000, 18, 53-57.

[82] Eriksson, H. Heart Failure: A Growing Public Health Problem. *J Intern Med,* 1995, 237, 135-141.

[83] Lanza, R. P., Cibelli, J. B. and West, M. D. Human Therapeutic Cloning. *Nat Med,* 1999, 5, 975-977.

[84] Lanza, R. P., Cibelli, J. B. and West, M. D. Prospects for the Use of Nuclear Transfer in Human Transplantation. *Nat Biotechnol,* 1999, 17, 1171-1174.

[85] Hwang, W. S., Ryu, Y. J., Park, J. H., Park, E. S., Lee, E. G., Koo, J. M., Jeon, H. Y., Lee, B. C., Kang, S. K., Kim, S. J., Ahn, C., Hwang, J. H., Park, K. Y., Cibelli, J. B. and Moon, S. Y. Evidence of a Pluripotent Human Embryonic Stem Cell Line Derived from a Cloned Blastocyst. *Science,* 2004, 303, 1669-1674.

[86] Hwang, W. S., Roh, S. I., Lee, B. C., Kang, S. K., Kwon, D. K., Kim, S., Kim, S. J., Park, S. W., Kwon, H. S., Lee, C. K., Lee, J. B., Kim, J. M., Ahn, C., Paek, S. H., Chang, S. S., Koo, J. J., Yoon, H. S., Hwang, J. H., Hwang, Y. Y., Park, Y. S., Oh, S. K., Kim, H. S., Park, J. H., Moon, S. Y. and Schatten, G. Patient-Specific Embryonic Stem Cells Derived from Human Scnt Blastocysts. *Science,* 2005, 308, 1777-1783.

[87] Miake, J., Marban, E. and Nuss, H. B. Gene Therapy: Biological Pacemaker Created by Gene Transfer. *Nature,* 2002, 419, 132-133.

[88] Xue, T., Chan, C., Henrikson, C., Sang, D., Marban, E. and Li, R. Lentivirus-Mediated Genetic Manipulations of Human Embryonic Stem Cells and Their Cardiac Derivatives. *Circulation,* 2003, 108:IV33,

[89] Robinson, R. B. and Siegelbaum, S. A. Hyperpolarization-Activated Cation Currents: From Molecules to Physiological Function. *Annu Rev Physiol,* 2003, 65, 453-480.

[90] Rubart, M., Pasumarthi, K. B., Nakajima, H., Soonpaa, M. H., Nakajima, H. O. and Field, L. J. Physiological Coupling of Donor and Host Cardiomyocytes after Cellular Transplantation. *Circ Res,* 2003, 92, 1217-1224.

[91] Rosen, M. R., Robinson, R. B., Brink, P. and Cohen, I. S. Recreating the Biological Pacemaker. *Anat Rec A Discov Mol Cell Evol Biol,* 2004, 280, 1046-1052.

[92] Xue, T. and Li, R. A. *Circulation,* 2005, 112, e82-83.

[93] Robinson, R. B., Rosen, M. R., Brink, P. R. and Cohen, I. S. *Circulation,* 2005, 112, e82.

[94] Boyett, M. R., Honjo, H. and Kodama, I. The Sinoatrial Node, a Heterogeneous Pacemaker Structure. *Cardiovascular Research,* 2000, 47, 658-687.

[95] Maitra, A., Arking, D. E., Shivapurkar, N., Ikeda, M., Stastny, V., Kassauei, K., Sui, G., Cutler, D. J., Liu, Y., Brimble, S. N., Noaksson, K., Hyllner, J., Schulz, T. C., Zeng,

X., Freed, W. J., Crook, J., Abraham, S., Colman, A., Sartipy, P., Matsui, S., Carpenter, M., Gazdar, A. F., Rao, M. and Chakravarti, A. Genomic Alterations in Cultured Human Embryonic Stem Cells. *Nat Genet*, 2005, 37, 1099-1103.

[96] Xue, T., Cho, H.C., Akar, F.G., Tsang, S.-Y., Jones, S.P., Marban,E., Tomaselli, G.F., Li, R.A. Functional integration of electrically active cardiac derivatives from genetically engineered human embryonic stem cells with quiescent recipient ventricular cardiomyocytes. *Circulation*, 2005, 111,11-20.

[97] Boheler, K.R., Wobus, A.M. Myocardial Aging and Embryonic Stem Cell Biology. Advances in Cell Aging and Gerontology. In *Stem Cells: A Cellular Fountain of Youth?* (Mattson MP, van Zant G, Eds) Elsevier Press. 2002, 141-177.

In: Progress in Stem Cell Research
Editor: Prasad S. Koka, pp. 171-200

ISBN: 978-1-60456-065-7
© 2008 Nova Science Publishers, Inc.

Chapter 10

STEM CELLS IN AGING: INFLUENCE OF ONTOGENIC, GENETIC AND ENVIRONMENTAL FACTORS

Edmond J. Yunis[* 1,2]*, Joaquin Zúñiga*[*1,2,3]*, Prasad S. Koka*[*4]*,
Zaheed Husain*[*1,2]*, Viviana Romero*[1]*,
Joel N.H. Stern*[1] *and Masha Fridkis-Hareli*[1,2]

[1] Department of Cancer Immunology and AIDS,
Dana Farber Cancer Institute, Boston MA
[2] Department of Pathology, Harvard Medical School, Boston, MA
[3] Instituto Nacional de Enfermedades Respiratorias, Mexico City, Mexico
[4] Laboratory of Stem Cell Biology, Torrey Pines Institute for Molecular Studies,
San Diego, CA.

ABSTRACT

Aging is a genetically programmed decline in the functional effectiveness of the organism. It is manifested by a collective group of changes in cells or organs that occur over the course of a lifespan, limiting the duration of life. Longevity usually refers to long-lived members of a population within species. Organs develop and can involute according to specific timetables. Such timetables correlate with a preordained proliferative capacity of cells mediated by cell and organ clocks. In this review, we discuss different aspects related to genetic and environmental factors that are involved in determining life span. We discuss the influence of ontogenic, genetic and environmental factors in aging. The genetic factors can be studied in embryonic stem cells (ESC) and in niches (microenvironments) of stem cells (SC) using cellular or experimental animal models. We discuss molecular mechanisms involving genes and proteins associated with death pathways, niches, or hubs, on longevity. Moreover, we also discuss genes and proteins, associated with death pathways, on longevity. Unraveling these mechanisms

* These authors contributed equally to the work. Corresponding author: Edmond J. Yunis, M.D., Department of Cancer Immunology and AIDS, Dana Farber Cancer Institute, 44 Binney St, Boston, MA, 02115. Phone (617) 632-3347, Fax (617)632-4468, email: edmond_yunis@dfci.harvard. edu

may further our understanding of human aging leading to development of therapeutic interventions with the potential of prolonging life.

ABBREVIATIONS

BM, bone marrow;
ESC, embryonic stem cells;
HSC, hematopoietic stem cells;
RA, rheumatoid arthritis;
ROS, reactive oxygen species;
RI, recombinant inbreed,
Niches, microenvironment of stem cells.

INTRODUCTION

Studies in animal models and in human populations have documented a decline in the functional effectiveness with age. Aging is likely to be mediated by several overlapping mechanisms that work simultaneously. The mechanisms commonly cited include progressive accumulation of damage to DNA leading to genomic instability [reviewed in ref. 1], telomere shortening due to telomerase suppression during embryogenesis [reviewed in ref. 2], damage to macromolecules by reactive oxygen species (ROS) [reviewed in ref. 3] and changes in gene expression patterns brought about by epigenetic alterations that include changes influenced by the environment [reviewed in ref. 4]. While the aging process may have these common mechanisms, pathways leading to death may follow different paths. Embryonic stem cells (ESC) and experimental animal models have been used to study the role of genetic factors in aging. Among the genetic changes occurring in the ESC, the p53, Rb, Akt and telomerase genes have been found to be important [5]. The genetic and environmental factors known to affect aging are related to the role of the immune system, and specifically the thymus, as well as dietary manipulations. In this regard, one of the most important "clocks" studied during aging has been the thymus, which is associated with immune dysfunction including infections, autoimmune phenomena [6-11] and cancer [reviewed in ref.12]. Recombinant inbred (RI) strains of mice enabled identification of potential genetic regions associated with short or long life span as well as genes that control variability at death [13].

This review describes how genetics of animal models has aided in understanding the aging phenomena, with the potential prediction of those factors affecting lifespan in humans. These mouse strains, which have been generated several decades ago, as well as the more recent ones, continue to provide a source for addressing unresolved questions of aging paradigms.

We will discuss the difficulties of finding genes and proteins involved in aging because of the many interactions that can be produced in many microenvironments or niches, which can also be affected by environmental factors. However, these experimental models are useful to map genetic regions or markers to guide the discovery of encoded proteins involved in long life of cells, niches, organs and the organism using methods such as microarrays. The use of experimental animals such as the RI strains are a first step to map certain genetic regions and can be used to test their relevance of such functions in relation to lifespan. Such studies combined with searches of other proteins encoded by genes (for example using microarrays along with proteomics) would help to elucidate the complexities of molecules involved in aging.

EMBRYONIC STEM CELLS DURING AGING: REGULATION OF SENESCENCE

Mammalian cells experience limited number of cell divisions when placed in culture before entering into a stage of proliferation arrest, also known as replicative senescence [14]. The number of cell divisions in culture shows variability based on the cell type or the species, and the phenomenon called the Hayflick limit [15], suggests the existence of a mitotic clock. Senescence is invariable in most cells, including transformed cells [14]. In contrast, ESC [16] and some somatic cells [17] do not have demonstrable senescence. Several pathways that are activated independently or together with others can allow the cells to bypass senescence: the telomerase pathway required to maintain telomere ends [2], the p53 and Rb pathways needed to direct senescence in response to DNA damage [5], telomere shortening and mitotic signals [2], and the insulin-like growth factor–Akt pathway that may regulate lifespan, cell proliferation and the mitochondrial/oxidative stress pathway [18, 19]. One experimental design that has been successful in defining these pathways is based on the fact that senescence is dominant over immortality [20, 21]. These pathways are summarized in Table 1. The senescence pathway in ESCs can be characterized by the presence of activity of p53 and Rb pathways, inactivity of Akt pathway, absence of telomerase and short telomere length. By contrast, ESCs express inactive p53 and Rb, active Akt, and maintain telomerase and telomere length. These pathways include a large number of proteins encoded by different genes. Several of them can be mapped using genetic mouse models or by the use of microarrays.

The protein p53 is a tumor suppressor that normally responds to DNA damage by inducing apoptosis and preventing cell transformation [22, 23]. It is also a regulator of senescence in response to several signals including telomere shortenings, DNA damage, oncogene activation and over-expression of tumor suppressor genes [24-29]. Significantly, suppression of telomerase activity in differentiated ESC requires histone deacetylation in early hTERT gene downregulation and DNA methylation for maintenance of silencing of hTERT gene [30]. In addition, over-expression of the catalytic subunit of telomerase (TERT) allows cells to maintain a normal karyotype and proliferative capacity for prolonged periods of time beyond the Hayflick limits [30]. By contrast, loss of proliferative potential or cell death is associated with loss of telomeres. [31]. Similar to p53, Rb is an important regulator of senescence that interacts with p53 [32, 33]. Another important regulator of senescence, demonstrated in flies and worms, is the IGF/Akt pathway [34, 35]. Recently, signaling pathways of insulin/IGF-1/phosphatidylinositol-3-kinase (P13K/Akt), also known as protein kinase B, has been shown to extend the lifespan of the nematode *C. elegans* [36-38]. In mammalian cells, where Akt is activated, proliferation and cell survival is induced as well.

This pathway is important in regulating cell size, as suggested by the phenotypes of PTEN (a phosphatase that inhibits the Akt pathway [reviewed in 39]).

Table 1. Pathways of senescence of embryonic stem cells and genes involved (ESCs)

Senescence pathways	Senescent cells	ESC	ESC over-expressed genes*
Telomerase	absent	Present	HSPCA, TEBP, DKC1,
Telomere length	short	Maintenance	TERF1, RAD50, Rif1, MRE11A, TNKS,
P53 and Rb pathway	active	Inactive or unknown	MDM2, CDC25A, CDK2, CDK4, CCND1, CCND2
Akt pathway	inactive	Active or unknown	PTEN, FKHR

GENETICS OF AGING MODELS

The difficulties of finding genes and proteins involved in aging are due to the multiple interactions occurring in numerous microenvironments or niches, which can also be affected by environmental factors. Experimental mouse models are useful for mapping genetic regions or markers to guide the discovery of encoded proteins involved in long life of cells, niches, organs and the organism, using methods such as microarrays. The use of experimental animals such as the RI strains is a first step in mapping certain genetic regions and testing their relevance in relation to lifespan. Such studies combined with searches for other proteins encoded by candidate genes using microarrays would help to elucidate the complexities of molecules involved in aging. Thymic involution that occurs earlier in some individuals than others may result from complex interactions between genetic factors and the environment. Such interactions may produce defects of thymus-dependent immune regulation associated with aging.

Using different experimental protocols to study the influence of the MHC in life span resulted in inconsistent findings, particularly following viral infections [40]. In the case of Sendai virus infection, T cells and the MHC were involved in susceptibility to acute infection and early death [41], with highest incidence in H-2^d/H-2^d mice. However, the H-2^d conferred longer life in mice not infected or not exposed to the virus, suggesting that mice exposed to virus can change the profile of life span [42]. Genes important for lifespan need to be studied against many genetic backgrounds and under different environmental conditions because of its complexity. Several genetic models have been used, in backcross and intercross mice. In (C57BL/6xDBA/2) F1xDBA/2 backcross the F1 lived longer than H-2^d homozygous in animals heterozygous for the brown locus b or homozygous b. The Bb mice lived longer than bb females; however, the dilute locus d on chromosome 9 did not influence life span. The dilute locus and the brown locus have shorter lifespan in females. The longest-lived mice were females heterozygous at the H-2 and Brown (b) loci. The shortest were males homozygous at the H-2 and Brown loci. The (C57BL/6XDBA/2) F1xF1 intercross revealed that females lived longer than males. The longest- lived females were homozygous H-2^d of dominant black phenotype at the Brown locus of chromosome 4 and homozygous at the dilute locus of chromosome 9. The longest and shortest- lived male genotypes were dilute brown H-2^d/H-2^d and dilute brown H-2^b/H-2^d, respectively [42].

In B10 congenic mice, males lived longer than females, H-2^d mice were not disadvantaged when compared to H-2^b that had not been exposed to Sendai virus infection, but the reverse was true when they were exposed [43]. In experiments using RI strains, known genes or genetic regions from the BxD (C57BL/6 and DBA/2) lifespan data were originally published by Gelman et al. [44]. These data can be retrieved from Web QTL Published Phenotypes database.

In 22 different strains BxD recombinant mice, lifespan was studied and we identified 3 (strains 2, 14, 32) that have a short survival and 4 (19, 24, 9 and 15) with long lifespan. COX models for multiple gene analyses of 1692 gene markers available demonstrated potential genes: HDC in chromosome 2, Rho in chromosome 6, CYP2A in chromosome 7, and IL-5 of chromosome 11. Of interest, the gene variants associated with longer lifespan came from DBA/2 in chromosomes 2, 14 and 6 and from C57Bl/6 in chromosome 7 and 11. Figure 1, Tables 2 and 3 (unpublished data).

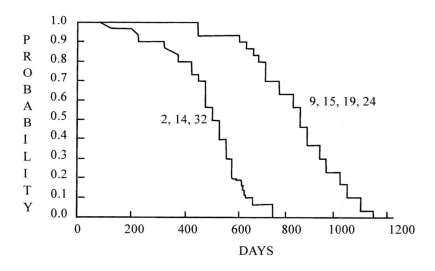

Figure 1. Survival of 7 recombinant inbred strains of the F1 hybrids of C57BL/6 and DBA/2 mice. This figure shows separate survival curves using the shortest possible survival times for strains 2, 14 and 32 and the long lived span trains 9, 15, 19 and 24. The linear regression of survival on strain used ordinary least squares and analysis of variance. The linear regression of average survival in each strain on genes was based on the R-squared and Cp selection criteria and used the algorithm explained with details in Gelman et al. 1988 [44].

The use of recombinant strains of mice with short or long life spans and the variability of age at death need to be studied by comparing adaptor proteins controlling stress response during life span. Another possible mechanism may involve the telomere lengths between these strains because telomere length was highly variable among genotypically identical siblings [45]. In this regard it is interesting that RI that are genotipically identical differ in one genetic region of chromosome 11, Gls-ps1 as was reported before [46], but in re-analyses of the data another region of genes associated with variability of age at death was discovered, including Hba, Hba-x, Lamrl-rs5 and Tel-rs1 (Figure 2, Table 4).

Table 2. Recombinant strains of mice
(short and long lived), proportional hazards model

	Strains	Median	Mean	SD	Range	Significance level Proportional hazards model
Short lived	2	479	490	128	531	<0.0001
	14	493	529	138	548	0.0002
	32	440	419	238	842	0.04
	9	816	884	176	610	0.05
	15	798	783	179	678	0.02
Long lived	19	904	939	151	647	0.003
	24	835	854	157	620	0.03
	11*	750	847	266	950	0.04

Summary statistics ** [44]

Table 3. Recombinant strains of mice (short and long lived) proportional hazards model

Chromosome	Mapped genes	BXD content
2	Hdc (histidine decarboxilase)	D
	Gabpb1 (GA repeat binding protein, beta 1)	D
	Il1a (Interleukin 1 alpha)	D
4	Iapls1-10 (intracisternal A particle lymphocyte specific 10)	D
	Adft (adipose differentiation related protein)	D
	Ifna (interferon alpha gene family, leukocyte	D
6	Rho (rhodopsin)	D
	Tpi1 (triosephosphate isomerase 1)	D
7	Cyp2b10 (cytochrome p450, family 2, subfamily b, polypeptide 10)	B
	Tam1 (tosyl arginine methylesterase 1)	B
	Iapls1-11 (intracisternal A particle, lymphocyte specific 1-11)	B
	Iapls3-4 (intracisternal A particle, lymphocyte specific)	B
	Zfp30 (zinc finger protein 30)	B
	Pmv18 (polytropic murine leukemia virus 18)	B
	Xmv30 (xenotropic murine leukemia virus 30)	B
	Ngfg (nerve growth factor, gamma)	B
11	IL5 (Interleukin 5)	B
Chromosome	**Mapped sequences**	
2	D2Bir1 (DNA segment)	D
	D2Mit493 (DNA segment)	D
	D2Mit304 (DNA segment)	D
4	D4Rik108 (DNA segment)	D
	D4Rik109 (DNA segment)	D
	D4Rik110 (DNA segment)	D
	D4Bir5 (DNA segment)	D
	Ms6hm (minisatellite 6 hypermutable)	D
	D4Mc2 (DNA segment)	D
	D4Mit327 (DNA segment)	D
6	D6Nds2 (DNA segment)	D

Table 3. (Continued)

Chromosome	Mapped sequences	
7	D7Mit178 (DNA segment)	B
	Mr66-2 (middle repeat MR66-2)	B
	Tel7p (telomerase sequence)	B
	D7Mc2 (DNA segment)	B
	D7Mit114 (DNA segment)	B
	D7Rik79 (DNA segment)	B
	D7Rik80 (DNA segment)	B
	D7Mit145 (DNA segment)	B
11	D11Mit140 (DNA segment)	B
	D11Mit86 (DNA segment)	B
	D11Mit23 (DNA segment)	B
13	D13Mit18 (DNA segment)	B

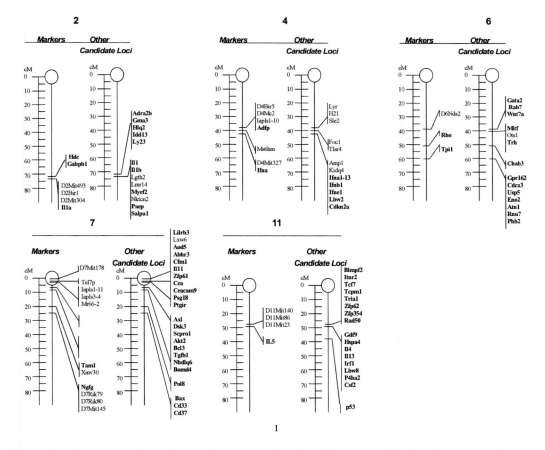

Figure 2. The genes and genetic markers summarized in Table 2 are placed at the position in mouse chromosome (left). The genes known at the same region are listed (right). These genes are classified accordingly: a) angiogenesis b) immune functions c) nucleic and transcription d) signal transduction e) metabolism f) cell metabolism g) protein mutation h) disease markers i) for non coded markers. Description of genes displayed in the figure: Mapping of genes involved in a) Angiogenesis: Adra2b: adrenergic receptor, α 2b.b) Immune function: Gma3: granulocyte macrophage antigen 3; Ly23: lymphocyte antigen 23; Il1:

interleukin 1 complex; Il1b: interleukin 1 β; Ifna1-13: interferon α family, genes 1-13; Ifnb1: interferon 1β, fibroblast; Ifne1: interferon epsilon 1; Lilrb3: leukocyte immunoglobulin-like receptor, subfamily B, with TM and ITIM domains; Il11: interleukin 11; Ptgir: prostaglandin I receptor (IP); Tgfb1: transforming grow factor, beta 1; Cd33: CD33 antigen; Cd37: CD37 antigen; Il4: interleukin 4; Il13: interleukin 13; Irf1: interferon regulatory factor 1; Csf2: colony stimulating factor 2 (granulocyte-macrophage).c) Nucleic acid transcription: Myef2: myelin basic protein expression factor 2, repressor; Gata2: GATA binding protein 2; Mitf: microphtalmia-associated transcription factor; Rnu 7: U7 small nuclear RNA; Phb2: prohibitin 2; Tcf7: transcription factor 7 T-cell specific; Zfp62: zinc finger protein 62; Zfp354a: zinc finger protein 354A. d) Signal transduction: Rab 7: RAB7, member RAS oncogene family; Wnt7a: wingless-related MMTV integration site 7A; Gpr162: G protein-coupled receptor 162; e) Metabolism: Paep: progestagen-associated endometrial protein; Trh: thyrotroponin releasing hormone; Atn1: atrophin 1; Ceacam 9: CEA-related cell adhesion molecule 9; Psg18: pregnancy specific glycoprotein 18. f) Cell metabolism: Cdca3: cell division cycle associated 3; Bax: Bcl2-associated X protein; Gdf9: growth differentiation factor 9. g) Protein metabolism: Usp5: ubiquitin specific peptidase 5 (isopeptidase T); Eno2: enolase 2, gamma neuronal; Zfp61: zink finger protein 61; Axl: AXL receptor tyrosine kinase; Hspa4: heat shock protein 4; P4ha2: procollagen-proline, 2-oxoglutarate 4-dioxigenase (proline 4-hydroxylase), alpha II polypeptide; h) Disease Markers: Cea: carcinoembryonic antigen gene family. i) Non coding susceptibility loci: Lyr: lymphoma resistance; H21: histocompatibility 21; Sle2: systemic lupus erythematosus susceptibility 2; Hlq2: heat loss QTL 2; Idd13: insulin dependent diabetes susceptibility 13; Lgth2: body length 2; Lmr14: leishmaniasis resistance 14; Nktcn 2: natural killer T cell numbers 2; Foc1: follicular center cell lymphoma 1; Tlsr4: thymic lymphoma suppressor region 4; Amp1: Amplitude circadian rhythm 1; Kidq4: kidney weight QTL4; Lbw2: lupus NZB x NZW 2; Ots1: ovarian teratoma susceptibility 1; Chab3: cholesterol absorption 3; Lxw6: lupus BXSB x NZW 6; Aod5: autoimmune ovarian dysgenesis 5; Abhr3: allergen-induced bronchial hyperresponsiveness 3; Cfm1: cystic fibrosis modifier 1; Dsk3: dark skin 3; Scpro1: stem cell proliferation 1; Akt2: thymoma viral proto-oncogene 2; Bcl3: B-cell leukemia/lymphoma 3; Nhdlq6: non-HDL QTL 6; Bomd4: bone mineral density 4; Pol8: viral polymerase 8; Blmpf2: bleomycin-induced pulmonary fibrosis 2; Itnr2: lentinan responsive 2; Tcpm1: T-cell phenotype modifier 1; Tria 1: T-cell receptor induced activation 1; Lbw8: lupus NZB x NZW 8.

Table 4. Variability of age at death in recombinant strains of mice, B allele for broad variability, and D allele for narrow variability

	Strains	Median	Mean	SD	Range
Broad	1	519	394	261	803
	5	452	528	317	920
	11	847	750	266	950
	12	774	738	209	907
	16	617	642	191	862
Narrow	6	641	680	115	366
	18	750	742	140	483
	28	775	765	104	331
	29	704	703	114	349

Summary statistics * [44].

This genetic control of phenotype variability could result from environmental effects such as infections or from nutrition and this together with other unknown genes may produce short or long life span. We believe that caloric restriction and or addition of antioxidants to the diets will correct the defective adaptor proteins controlling oxidative stress, the p53 stress response and the telomere length in mice with premature immunosenescence. For this, it will be necessary to study by microarrays the possible differences in expression of these genes in recombinant strains of mice.

Table 5. Reported associations with MHC and cytokine genes in different ethnic groups

Gene	Finding	Population	Ref
A1, B8, DR3	Increased in elderly men, decreased T cell function and decreased survival in women.	Caucasian, NAm	[154]
A1, B8, Cw7, DR3	Increased in Nonagenarian men	Caucasian, Ireland	[155]
DRB1*1401, DQB1*0503, DQA1*0101	Increased in Centenarians	Oriental, Japan	[146]
B16	Increased in elderly	Greek	[147]
DR7	Increased in elderly	Greek	[147]
B15	Decreased in elderly	Greek	[147]
DR4	Decreased in elderly	Greek	[147]
DR11	Increased in elderly women	Caucasian, French	[156]
DR7	Increased in elderly men	Caucasian, French	[156]
DR13	Increased in elderly men and women	Caucasian, French	[156]
A31, B7, Cw7, DQ1	Increased in elderly	Caucasian, Italy	[157]
A1, B8, DR3, TNF	No association	Caucasian, Ireland	[143]
DRB1*15	Increased in Centenarians	Sardinian	[148]
HSP70-1 -110A>C	Association of heterozygosity in aged twins	Caucasian, Danish	[158]
TNF −308 A	Increased in elderly with bronchoalveolar infections	Caucasian, Italy	[142]
IL-6 −174 C	Increased in Centenarian men	Sardinian	[159]
IFN-γ +874A	Increased in centenarian women	Sardinian	[159]
IL-6 −174 G/G	Homozygous genotype G/G increased in elderly	Caucasian, Denmark	[160]
IL-10 −1082G/A, -819C/C, -592C/C	Increased in elderly	Caucasian, Bulgaria	[161]
IL-10 −1082G	Increased in centenarian men	Caucasian, Italy	[162]
TGF-β1 +915G/C	Decreased in centenarians	Caucasian, Italy	[163]

ROLE OF THE MICROENVIRONMENT AND NICHES FOR STEM CELLS DURING AGING

The distribution of lymphoid cells in autoimmune susceptible and resistant mice was studied by the capacity to trace ^{51}Cr-labeled lymphoid cells (Yunis et al., unpublished observations). Splenocytes of old NZB mice were distributed in abnormally large numbers in the liver, and in abnormally small numbers in the spleen and lymph nodes, as compared to the distribution of labeled cells from young donors given to young recipients. The cells from old donors did not home to the bone marrow (BM) of old mice, but homed better to the BM of young mice. Cells from young animals given to old animals with significant autoimmunity also were deployed excessively to the liver and poorly to the spleen and marrow, as compared to tagged cells of young animals injected intravenously into old animals. These findings indicate that in NZB mice there is a significant age-related pathology of the normal ecotaxis, which has both cellular and organ-determined components.

One of the most interesting findings was that spleen cells from young NZB donors homed well to lymph nodes of both young and old recipients, whereas spleen cells from old donors homed very poorly to lymph nodes of either young or old recipients [7]. By contrast, cells from young and old CBA/H mice, which are long lived, were able to home to lymph nodes very well. Also, in unpublished experiments we showed that BM cells from young and aging CBA/H and NZB mice were comparable in their capacity to repopulate spleen of irradiated syngeneic mice. More research is needed to test the microenvironment of spleen, lymph nodes and BM during aging. It appears that the microenvironment of the BM during aging is not as affected as that of the spleen or lymph nodes.

Thus, it appears that there are intrinsic and extrinsic defects in the generation of hematopoietic cells in autoimmune susceptible strains and in aging animals. Recently, it has been shown that long-term hematopoietic stem cells from old mice expressed elevated levels of many genes involved in leukemic transformation. The data supports the concept that there is an age-dependent alteration in gene expression at the stem-cell level presage that contributes to age-dependent immune decline in the elderly [47].

New evidence indicates that cells of the connective tissue and blood vessels are part of the microenvironments or niches, for hematopoietic stem cells (HSCs) in adult BM as well as stromal fibroblasts are associated with cancer cells with respect to the self-renewal activity [48]. The most protected niche is the BM. The skin is composed of units in which every hair follicle has a tiny niche of stem cells, responsible for generating a new hair and to generate sebaceous glands and epidermis [49, 50, 51]. Also, the intestine is composed of many units each containing a villous and a crypt, their stem cells are located above the vase of the crypt [52]. In the adult central nervous system, stem cells are in the sub-ventricular zone where they generate glia and neurons [53]. Stem cells depend on their surrounding environment to maintain their functions and proliferation potentials [50]. It is important to mention that whenever SCs exit the niche it must be replenished, perhaps by self-renewal. Leaving the niche is due to changes in the microenvironment or loss of certain important components of the niche. These changes could be different in individual niches. This is important because the administration of stem cells to correct a disease or to prolong lifespan is not sufficient. An example is related to the role of signaling of Wnt and Notch in BM morphogenesis; Notch has pleotropic effects on stem cells and their lineages, which are different in distinct SC [54].

It is noteworthy mentioning that infections, such as HIV, nutrition and other non-genetic factors can influence the microenvironment of the niches. For example, measurable amounts of cytokine responses could vary depending on the genetic background. It is possible that these measurements will be variable in some animals and less variable but decreased in others, which may be genetically controlled. Such studies can be done in RI strains of mice where a gene in chromosome 11 distinguishes strains with short variability at death as compared with other that have wide variability of age at death. It is generally known that aging is characterized by upregulation of genes involved in oxidative stress responses [55-57], suggestive of an increased need to cope with the accumulation of macromolecular abnormalities. The studies of one cell type cannot address the question of the effect of tissues, which can also be altered during aging.

The quiescence of HSCs is controlled in the individual by signaling of receptors-ligands and cell-adhesion molecules [58]. Stem cells are cells with self-renewal capacity and also have the capacity to differentiate into single or multiple lineages [59]. A small subset of HSCs can be isolated using cell phenotype markers (Kit receptor, Sca-1 and Thy-1 but negative for lineage-specific antigens) [60, 61]. They differentiate into different lineages with specific cytokines [62]. During postnatal life, the BM supports both self-renewal and differentiation of HSCs in specialized microenvironmental niches (ecotaxis). Of interest, in fish blood cells are not produced by BM but rather by the kidney. But, in other animals including mammals, BM is found in bone cavities where cells of the niche are composed of fat, stromal cells and other components including blood sinusoids. There is a balance between self-renewal and commitment of stem cells controlled by both cell-intrinsic and external regulatory mechanisms. There is a significant information about the intrinsic molecular properties of stem cells as well as the specific microenvironment in which they reside. Not only the niches have been studied for hematopoiesis, but also for epidermis, intestinal epithelium, nervous system and gonads [49, 50].

The quiescence of stem cells is maintained in part by cyclin-dependent kinase inhibitor such as (Cdkn1a) [58]. Also, shortening of telomere length of chromosomes occurs during every cell division. HSCs have high proliferative potential and telomerase activity to protect the ends of the chromosomes [63]. However, they show telomeric shortening during replicative aging. The gene encoding p21 is repressed directly by c-Myc and HSCs lacking c-Myc overexpresses p21, indicating that the c-Myc-p21 pathway could be important in regulating the switch from resting to active HSCs [59].

Experiments with the ataxia telangiectasia mutated protein (ATM), show that it regulates reconstitutive capacity and a key cell cycle checkpoint in response to DNA damage of HSCs but not the proliferation or differentiation into progenitors [64]. The ATM protein maintains genomic stability by activation of a key cell cycle checkpoint in response to DNA damage, telomeric instability or oxidative stress. Elevated radical oxygen species (ROS) is maintained without telomere dysfunction. Elevated ROS induces upregulation of the cyclin-dependent kinase (C d k) inhibitor p16NK4A, also named Cdkn2a, (maps together with Ifna and Interferon cluster 1-13) (Fig 2) and the retinoblastoma (Rb) gene in ATM negative HSCs. Treatment of cells with antioxidative reagents restores them to normal state. Also, polycomb group ring finger 4 (bmi-1) is essential for self-renewal via the p16NK4a/Rb pathway; antioxidants produce inactivation of p16 and inactivation of Rb that result in restoration of stem cell function. In addition, studies of interactions of stem cells and niche cells with each other will help the understanding of growth of cancer cells; stromal fibroblasts associated with cancer cells are capable of self-renewal. Also, quantitative genetic variation in hematopoietic stem cell and progenitor cell compartment and lifespan were found closely linked at multiple loci in BxD recombinant strain of mice. Genes on chromosome 4 and 7 are involved in the number of LSK cells [65].

The Thymus: A Temporary Niche

Thymic involution and involution of the thymus-dependent system of cells responsible for cell-mediated immunity occur in man as they do in all animals that possess a thymus. Specific thymic alterations related to aging have been described and extensively discussed. It has been known for many years that beginning at the time of sexual maturation, an apparent programmed involution begins in the central lymphoid organs [7]. The interaction between different hormones and the involution has been reviewed in 1976 by Fabris et al. [66, 67]. More recently, this subject has been reviewed and it will not be discussed in this review. Instead, we will summarize recent studies of molecular events occurring in the thymus during aging. In order to understand the basis for age-associated thymic involution, microarray analyses on the thymi from young, middle-aged, and old mice have been recently performed to identify differences in gene expression patterns, that may be attributed to aging (reviewed in ref. 68). For this analysis, a total of 67 mice were used, divided into multiple categories. There were four age groups: 1, 6, 12, and 24 months. Of the 17 000 genes on the murine cDNA array, 788 genes demonstrated significant changes in gene expression with progressive thymic aging. Dramatic changes in gene expression were observed between mice aged 1 month and 6 months (107 genes changed; 26 up and 81 down) and those aged 12 months (203 genes changed; 95 up and 108 down) or 24 months (788 genes changed; 418 up and 370 down). The early changes in expression may possibly reflect the known peak of thymic decline between the age of onset of puberty to the midlife period in mice. Genes involved in various biological processes (e.g. cell-cycle progression, transcriptional regulators, maintenance and remodeling of extracellular matrix, protein binding and transport, proteasomal proteins, apoptosis, stress response, inflammation and immune function, growth factors, energy metabolism, and mitochondrial function) and molecular functions (e.g. ATP, DNA and chromatin-binding proteins, RNA and protein binding, and transcriptional regulators) were observed to change with thymus age. On the basis of the fact that the thymus is undergoing involution, one would expect to see changes in genes that are known to be involved with thymus and involution, and indeed such changes were observed. Examples include genes such as LIF, several thymosin family members, trkA, and BDNF [69, 70]. Some of the gene expression changes associated with certain biological and molecular functions observed in our thymic analysis were quite similar to other microarray studies profiling age-associated alterations in liver, kidney, brain, muscle, and fibroblasts [4]. However, the majority of the specific genes found to change with thymic aging were quite distinct from these other organ systems suggesting that there is only a limited degree of overlap in the major categories of genes associated with aging and that age-induced modifications are for the most part species, organ, and tissue-specific. In addition, effects of caloric restriction (CR) on the age-associated changes in thymic gene expression have been examined. CR is currently considered one of the major life extension interventions in primates and rodents, and it has been utilized in numerous microarray studies to examine its effects on organ and cellular aging [71, 72]. Interestingly, aged CR thymi demonstrated a significant reversal in their gene expression profile compared with their AL-fed aged counterparts and revealed a significant profile match with AL-fed young animals. The microarray analysis to uncover specific biological processes at play during thymic aging has provided some excellent gene targets for further examination.

CHANGES PRODUCED IN NEURAL AND HEMATOPOIETIC NICHES BY HIV INFECTION: NICHE PATHOLOGY OR DEFECTIVE ECOTAXIS

Ontogenic control of the HSC microenvironment during human development [66] seems to be an accepted feature of the aging process. Comparison between fetal liver and adult BM derived stromal cells led to the information that these two microenvironments that support human HSC contain age dependent differences [73]. However, intra-species and ontogenic conservation of stem cell niches is also not an uncommon occurrence [74, 75]. The microenvironments or niches control the self-renewal and regeneration through cell division of neural and hematopoietic progenitor stem cells among others through cell cycle regulation and signaling processes involving transcription factors [76, 81]. Maintenance and differentiation of stem cells following their migration from the niches of "origin" to those niches, which are the sites of "development" suggests the existence of function specific microenvironments [82, 83]. Cytotoxic T lymphocytes also execute their protective action through available or designated niches and have to deal with invading organisms that are thriving in separate niches [84-87]. Thus, niches can be present in both extracellular and intracellular compartments within a living being [78, 79, 82].

The proliferative or maintenance stage in the niches of progenitor stem cells is followed by the migratory stage that brings about cell cycle changes [88]. C-Myc has been reported to regulate the interaction between the self-renewal and differentiation niches of the HSC [59]. C-Myc deficiency causes severe cytopenias arising from impaired differentiation and enforced c-Myc expression leads to loss of self-renewal activity and concomitantly supports differentiation [59].

Reproduction of in vivo niches ex vivo, that is, niche-independent simulation using putative molecular entities of normal physiology or pathology has been reported [89, 90] but is unclear and is fraught with deficiencies that support the multitude of functions that occur in vivo. Osteopontin is a stem cell niche component that maintains the size of the stem cell pool [91, 92] and therefore may reduce the risk of uncontrolled proliferation. Angiopoietin-1 is a regulator of cell cycle in the stem cell niche [93, 94]. Notch and Wingless (Wnt) are some of the signaling pathways that occur in the hematopoietic microenvironment to regulate self-renewal of the stem cells [95, 96]. Ontogenic differences in the human development include the Wnt signaling regulation in the human fetal liver stem cell niche compared to the control of Notch signaling in the adult bone marrow microenvironment [73]. The niches, in addition to molecular entities, also include cellular components such as the endothelial cells present in a neural stem cell niche secrete soluble factors that promote self-renewal and inhibit their differentiation [97]. Similarly, the AFT024 stromal cell line confers or delivers the properties of an *in vivo* stem cell niche [98, 99].

HIV infection of stem cell microenvironments or niches causes hematopoietic inhibition and hence cytopenias [100-105]. Hematopoietic CD34+ progenitor stem cells are reported to be resistant to HIV-1 infection, *in vitro*, or *in vivo* [106, 107]. Those cells that experienced the indirect effects of HIV-1 infection exhibit inhibition of their multilineage hematopoiesis as determined by colony forming activity ex vivo [106, 108-110]. It is reported that the hematopoietic stem cell microenvironment is damaged due to the indirect effects of HIV-1 infection of the thymocytes on the CD34+ progenitor stem cells but in a reversible manner, in the human fetal Thymus/Liver conjoint hematopoietic organ of the transplanted chimeric severe combined immunodeficiency mouse (SCID-hu) model system [108, 110]. It is therefore highly plausible that this implanted human organ in the SCID-hu mouse, which serves as a niche, not only for thymocyte expansion but also supports hematopoiesis, suffers niche dysfunction due to HIV-1 infection. Continued presence of the CD34+ progenitor stem cells in the infected niche seem to suffer due to exacerbation resulting from persistent virus mediated niche disruption via infection of thymocytes and consequent interactions and signaling network of the hubs. Thus cellular and molecular niches and involvement of their hubs might be at play in the pathology of this infected microenvironment within the human hematopoietic organ of SCID-hu mouse. Thus, this model is useful in understanding the cellular and molecular events that occur in human stem cell niches.

MAPPING OF GENES OF LIFESPAN, USING RI, STEM CELLS AND STUDIES OF NICHES

In Fig 2 we placed candidate genes and genetic markers (life span genes) that have been mapped to the regions summarized in Table 2. The cytokine genes cluster in a region of chromosome 11 includes: growth differentiation factor 9, colony stimulating factor 2, IL-3 IL-5, IL-13, IL-4 [111-113]. It is of interest that recombinant strains of mice showed the IL-5 gene to be associated with lifespan. But the cytokines IL-3, IL-4, IL-13 and Irf1 (Interferon regulatory factor 1) have also been mapped in the same region. This is of interest because cytokines made by TH2 cells are spaced widely, but are kept primed for action by one master control region on the same chromosome [114]. It is suggested that there is an interaction between chromosome 11 and the initiation of activation of interferon-gamma on a different chromosome. But that this relationship falls apart when the T cells have differentiated into helper cells.

The regulation of the molecules involved in niches is more complex, since some of them could be upregulated while others are downregulated. Of interest, two genes identified thus far in the RI or in the studies of stems cells that are also involved in niches, are the Akt2 on chromosome 7, which is near Bcl3, and the other one is p16NK-4 which is on chromosome 4, near the IFN-gamma and -beta [115].

We have reanalyzed the data of genes of variability of age at death and discovered a new group of genes in chromosome 11 - Hba, Hba-x, Lamrl-rs5 and Tel-rs1. The chromosomal location of these genes is depicted in Figure 3. Other candidate genes involved were mapped to different chromosomes or regions involved in niches and include: bcl-2 and Akt3 on chromosome 1 [116, 117], bmi-1 [118] on chromosome 2, ATM on chromosome 9 [119], ROS-1 and LSK (also named Matk, (megakaryocyte-associated tyrosine kinase) on chromosome 10 [120, 121], p53 on chromosome 11 [122, 123], Akt-1 on chromosome 12 [124], Rb1 on chromosome 14 [125], c-Myc on chromosome 15 [126] and p21 on chromosome 17 [127]. Other genes mentioned were p66 (Shc1), a transforming factor on chromosome 3 [128], IL-2 and PLC-gamma on chromosomes 3 and 2 respectively [129, 130].

Recently it was reported that a significant number of proteins are interactive with one another (interactomes) [131]. The interactome is composed of hubs that are interconnected via specific proteins [132]. Hubs are composed of highly interactive proteins. This concept of interactive proteins is reminiscent of the existence of niches. Is it possible that the anatomical concept of niches would be related to hubs and that protein components of them are needed for the integrity of hubs. Since there are many genetic interactions, particularly in niches, it would be important to know the relationship among such protein interactions with the proteins involved in the microenvironment of niches. It needs to be determined what are the proteins involved in the maintenance of the health of niches and ultimately which interactomes are involved in the process of aging resulting in the determination of life span.

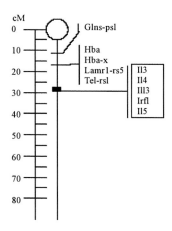

Figure 3. Genes on chromosome 11 associated and life span variability in mice. Variability genes and the cytokine cluster. Glns-ps1: Glutamine sythetase pseudogene 1; Hba: hemoglobin alpha chain complex; Hba-x: hemoglobin X, alpha-like embryonic chain in Hba complex; Lamr1-rs5: laminin receptor 1 (ribosomal protein SA), related sequence 5; Tel-rs1: telomere, related sequence 1; Rcvrn: Recoverin.

INFLUENCE OF NUTRITION ON THE DECLINE OF IMMUNITY WITH AGING IN MICE

Although the regulation of the immune response is predominantly under genetic control, environmental factors such as nutrition are also influential. Earlier studies have demonstrated that in the autoimmune-prone NZB mouse strain diets low in fat and high in protein and fiber content produced a delayed development of autoimmunity and was associated with prolonged life span in both males and females [133]. However, restriction of protein intake alone, while conferring beneficial influences on T-cell functions, did not significantly suppress the occurrence of autoimmune disease or prolong the life span or NZB mice. In contrast, B/W mice fed a normal diet in restricted amount (12 cal/day) lived at least twice as long as mice fed a normal diet (24 cal/day) [134]. This dramatic influence of nutrition was accompanied by prolonged maintenance of T cell-mediated functions, inhibition of the development of spontaneously active suppressor cells, and maintenance of inducible suppressor cells. Dietary restriction also inhibited immuno-complex-dependent renal injury and anti-DNA antibody production in B/W mice as well as preventing the development of circulating immune complexes. Furthermore, the high caloric diet was accompanied with cardiovascular diseases. In C3H mice, which develop spontaneous breast tumors, two methods, alternate-day feeding and daily caloric restriction, have been successful in the prevention or delay of tumor development [134]. In an unpublished study using the same alternate-day feeding schedule versus the ad libitum feeding in CBA/H (a long lived strain of mice), we have seen 70% survival of the experimental mice and only 42% survival of the control mice at 960 days of age. The difference in survival at 1,080 days of age was 40% and 5%, respectively, for the experimental and control mice. The final number of days was 1,260 for the mice with the diet restriction and 1,099 for those fed ad libitum.

MHC Genes in Aging

Studies of genetics of aging using mouse models that differ only in the MHC region demonstrated MHC association, but in recombinant strains of mice, non-MHC genes were found to be involved. Furthermore, it was of interest that MHC congenic strains of mice showed interaction between MHC alleles and production of IL-4 and low production of IFN-γ by NK and NKT cells [135]. It has been known for a long time that mice susceptible to autoimmunity showed deficient T cell functions [136]. Furthermore, studies of human aging using MHC markers have described associations with MHC alleles or haplotypes that are known to be markers for autoimmune disease, such as the HLA-DRB1*0301 and the haplotypes A1, B8, DR3, which were described in some ethnic groups [137]. Also, the TNFα –308 polymorphism is known to be a marker of such haplotypes [138, 139]. Our observations are relevant for ethnically matched aged and young individuals; for example, Caucasian markers such as TNF2 are associated with genetics of aging in Mexicans. In this regard, only 3 out of 12 elderly individuals carrying this mutation were of the B8, DR3 extended haplotype, suggesting that in Mexicans the association is not due to linkage disequilibrium (unpublished data). The TNF-α promoter polymorphisms have been associated with the pathogenesis of autoimmune disorders [138, 139]. In Mexicans, TNF2 has been associated with severity of RA [140]. The risk of developing autoimmune diseases such as systemic lupus or RA varies between populations [141]. Other studies suggest that TNF2 polymorphism may be a susceptible factor to bronchoalveolar infections in old hospitalized patients from Caucasian origin [142]. TNF2 is a marker for autoimmunity but we suggest that it could be a marker that promotes efficient immune inflammatory response against pathogens in older people with specific genetic background. However, this hypothesis does not support previous findings in Caucasians [143]. Since case control studies should take into account the possibility of genetic stratification, such studies should include information about the contribution of genes in both the elderly and young groups, as we showed in our studies. Mexican mestizos, who constitute about 90% of the country's population (National Population Census 1992), can be defined as the descendants of the mixture of the autochthonous inhabitants with other genetic groups, mainly Spaniards. Genetic admixture between populations with high prevalence of RA, such as Amerindians, and populations with lower prevalence (Caucasians) has occurred, demonstrating the role of genetic admixed background and environmental factors that contributed to disease risk. Current approaches to mapping disease susceptibility genes within MHC, such as the analysis of DNA conserved blocks [144] or SNPs, and the methods to eliminate confounding have been important in defining the population stratification and genetic distance between admixed and ancestral populations [145].

The MHC class I and class II gene frequencies did not reveal significant associations with aging. However, the frequency of distribution of the DRB1*DQB1 blocks were used as a marker of genetic admixture and also as a measure of population diversity. There was higher diversity in the young group than in the elderly group, a proportion of 48.3% of Caucasian and Amerindian component of 27.5% compared with 40.4% and 30.8%, respectively, in the young group (unpublished observations). Although, these results showed comparable Amerindian admixture, there is a non-significant higher Caucasian component in the elderly group. In addition, it was remarkable that only 4 of the 120 DRB1*DQB1* block of the elderly group showed individual blocks with a frequency of less than 1% each, as compared to 45 of the young groups (p=0.0001). This finding suggests that multiple class II genes may be associated, reflecting a decreased diversity in aged individuals, as reported before [146, 147].

As described above (Table 1), the HLA associations with elderly individuals showed significant ethnic and nationality effects. In some cases a combination of HLA class II alleles was involved. Also, other genetic polymorphisms have been found to be important. For example, the potential relevance of IL-10 promoter region polymorphisms in longevity has been suggested [148]. In some of the studies, inflammatory cytokines were increased as well as genetic polymorphisms of cytokines, and it has been suggested that the infections in elderly individuals could explain such findings.

Our findings suggested that genetic admixture with Caucasian ethnic groups might promote the incorporation of genes associated with autoimmune disorders and that these genes could be associated with immunity against pathogens that frequently affect aged people, and are important for protection from infection. The mechanism by which the MHC genes participate in the longevity can be partially explained by the function of the product of these genes in the regulation of the specific immune response, although, the role of MHC genes in the susceptibility to infections and the potential connection with the innate immunity is not well understood. This study suggests that genes located within the MHC cluster, specifically those, which are close to TNF region, could influence longevity in Mexican individuals. Also, genetic diversity studies are important for the future attempts to understand the genetics of longevity in admixed populations. Our findings support the hypothesis that specific genes can have different roles in different stages of life and that they could be involved both in autoimmunity and longevity.

In summary, studies of genetics of longevity has yielded complex results, this is due in part to the need to assess the degree of genetic admixture and to determine the degree of genetic diversity of the elderly and control individuals. Good candidates for the studies of genetics of cytokines, related to serum secretion for determination of the role of pro-inflammatory cytokines, are TNF-α, IFN-γ and IL-6, as compared to cytokines involved in regulatory immune function such as IL-10. Our data, showing increased incidence of TNF-α mutation associated with increased levels of production of this cytokine in elderly Mexicans that have comparable Amerindian and Caucasian genes, support the above prediction. Our results are consistent with the concept that phenotypic interactions of genes within the MHC are operative in the elderly and that genes associated with autoimmunity may also be markers of longevity in populations with admixture, suggesting the possibility that one group of non-MHC genes can interact with the same MHC gene (i.e. TNF2) to produce autoimmunity, while other non-MHC genes could be associated with the same MHC gene (i.e. TNF2) with longevity. Associations with MHC and cytokine genes in different ethnic groups are shown in Table 4.

DISCUSSION

In mammals, the mechanisms that regulate stress responses and increased life span involving reactive oxygen species (ROS) are poorly understood. Mice that are genetically deficient for the p66shc gene are less sensitive to the toxic effects of ROS and live 30% longer than their wild-type littermates. Ablation of p66shc enhances cellular resistance to apoptosis induced by H_2O_2. A serine-phosphorylation defective mutant of p66shc cannot restore the normal stress response in p66shc-/- cells. The p53 and p21 stress response is also impaired in p66-/- cells and p66-/- mice have a 30% increase of life span [149]. We have described the early immune abnormalities in the B10.AKM mice [40] similar to those reported by others in p53 knock-out mice with the accumulation of memory T cells and increased production of IL-4 by NKT cells [135]. Our results suggested that young B10.AKM mice have a primary immune abnormality that ultimately results in an early senescence phenotype.

Our studies in another murine experimental model (BxD recombinant mice) identified several potential candidate genes in short- and long-lived strains. Among them were in chromosome 2, histone deacetylase (HD), in chromosome 6 the Rho, and in chromosome 7, p450 gene (CYP2A) and apoptosis related BAX genes. In this regard, the human HD showed its involvement in cell cycle progression and activation in one report [150]. In addition, the inhibition of HDC was associated with early abrogation of IFN-γ production by Th1 lymphocytes and with p53 mRNA downregulation. Thus, HDC participates in IFN-γ gene regulation and cell survival. Interestingly, p53 deficient (p53-/-) mice have accelerated aging of the immune system (increased accumulation of memory cells, stronger Th2 cytokine profile). This has been suggested to be due to dysregulation of cell cycle, DNA repair and apoptosis in the lymphocyte population. In normally dividing cells, p53 is highly unstable with a short half-life. DNA damage leads to accumulation of p53 and transcription of target genes such as Bax and p21. It can also be hypothesized that a relationship between increased oxidative stress and transcriptional activation of Bax could lead to increased loss of naïve cells and accumulation of apoptosis-resistant memory cells in these animals.

CYP2A subfamily includes enzymes that catalyze oxidation of several compounds of chemical or toxicological interest. Little is known about associations between variant CYP2A alleles and diseases. Thus, we have the opportunity to study the role of ROS in cell death and life span using an experimental model with one genetic factor in chromosome 7. Also, we hypothesize that HDC may be defective in the DBA/2 background, since the contribution of recombinant short-lived BxD strains carry the D marker. Therefore, it is of importance to investigate the role of oxygen in mice and to investigate the possible role of genes involved in the downregulation of p53.

We believe that these defects could be corrected with low caloric diets or diets rich in antioxidants. We will test this hypothesis in congenic strains and recombinant strains of mice with short and long survival. In addition, we have identified candidate genes on chromosome 2, chromosome 6 and chromosome 7 which could provide additional information on molecules involved in oxidation such as a gene in chromosome 7 (CYP2A), and a gene on chromosome 2 involved in apoptosis. In this regard, two candidate genes mapped to different regions of chromosome 11 were Hsp-a4, important in longer life span in the cM 28, and tel-rs1m in cM 16 associated with variability at the age of death. A possible mechanism may involve the telomere lengths between these strains since telomere length was highly variable among genotypically identical siblings [151]. We believe that modifying caloric restriction and or addition of antioxidants to the diets will correct the defective adaptor proteins controlling the oxidative stress and the p53 stress response, as well as the telomere length in mice with premature immunosenescence. For this purpose, it will be necessary to study the possible differences between these proteins in recombinant strains of mice by microarrays. However, in the case of viral infection such as HIV, the defects of niches cannot be corrected by replacing stem cells without treating the viremia and defects produced in the niche of hematopoietic cells because the continued presence of the CD34+ stem cells in the infected niche seems to maintain the disruption by the infection of thymocytes [100].

CONCLUDING REMARKS: PERSPECTIVES FOR FUTURE RESEARCH IN AGING

Pathways leading to death are affected by multiple genetic and environmental factors. We have been able to partially define two such pathways. The first involves increased sensitivity to infections due to early onset of immune senescence in a congenic mouse strain, and the second defines decreased life span in recombinant strains of mice that develop lymphomas due to possible deregulation of apoptotic pathways and non-limitation of proliferative capacity of cells (that is a component of cellular senescence). In the future, the use of microarrays will be beneficial in analysis of differentially expressed genes between three recombinant mouse inbred (RI) strains (2, 14 and 32) that are short-lived and four (9, 15, 19 and 24) that are long-lived. Several thousand genes can be surveyed in the spleen, and we have observed that a small proportion displayed greater than three-fold increase or decrease in expression levels between them. Such analyses combined with the results of studies in the mapping of the genes of long lifespan could give important results of proteins that are unique or part of niches associated with survival.

We have recently completed DNA oligonucleotide microarray studies of differentially expressed genes between two recombinant inbred strains, strain 2 (short-lived) and 15 (long-lived). Of the 11,406 genes surveyed in the spleen, only 109 (0.9%) displayed greater than three-fold increase or decrease in expression levels between the two strains. This frequency is in agreement with a differential display analysis of gene expression and a study involving caloric restriction gene profiling in mice. While a variety of genes were differentially expressed between the two strains, the most significant difference observed was in the expression of a gene that has high homology to the Bcl2-like gene Boo/Diva/Bcl-2111. This sequence might represent a new member of the BH-domain family of proteins involved with mediating apoptosis and involved in proliferative disorders. Interestingly, in a separate system where we have been studying human immune deficiency disorders, we have observed upregulation of survival genes associated with abnormal B cell proliferation. It is proposed that mice that are short-lived may develop lymphomas following upregulation of a similar BH-family survival gene that inhibits apoptosis by inhibiting caspase activity. The lack of regulated expression of this gene, may be involved in lymphomagenesis in mice.

Disruption of the normal molecular processes within the niches such as those due to infection can result in abnormal functioning of the systems that are affected and lead to pathological consequences within the niche, or ecotaxic defects or failure, which is a disruption from the normal cell migration to physiological distribution. Abnormal transition or failure of ecotaxis including a premature, disruptive, delay, or failure can result in disease pathology. HIV infection of stem cell microenvironments or niches causes hematopoietic abnormalities and associated cytopenias [100-105]. Therefore, alterations of niches produced by environmental factors including infections should be taken into account when considering how important it is to correct defects produced in the niches together with those of the stem cells. Such alterations explain why the autoimmune susceptible strains of mice have abnormalities of homing of transplanted cells as reported before [152].

Our observations presented in this report suggested that the age at death is variable in the majority of the BxD recombinant strains of mice; this variability being controlled by a gene in chromosome 11. This gene confirmed by experiments in C57/B/L/6 was significant and produced age at death with higher variability than that of DBA/2 [46]. Genes affecting variability in phenotype expression of genetically identical populations have been suggested previously [46]. It is possible that these genes invoke sensitivity to environmental factors. In spite of the difficulties of cloning of this gene, it is reasonable to use experimental mice to correct the variability of age at death by calorie restriction or antioxidant administration to strains with extreme variability at age at death (strains 1, 5,11,12 and 16) compared to strains with short variability at death (strains 6, 18, 28 and 29). In such studies comparisons of not only the role of caloric restriction or treatment with antioxidants in the duration of life, but also correlation with functions of stem cells and other cell types are essential.

The use of RI strains is limited by the number of genomes used in the generation of the strains as well as the number of individual strains generated for given genomes. The probability of mapping accurately such genetic regions or individual genes is proportional to those variables. Also, such discoveries cannot be generalized for the animal or human population at large. Nevertheless, the identification of genes, proteins or niches of mortality or immortality in these experimental models should be necessary in designing strategies to determine important genes or proteins associated with long or short life in outbreed populations. But, ultimately it would require the use of multiple genetic and environmental manipulations to correct the defects that occur during aging. In this regard, the interacting proteins within hubs and their interconnections should be compared with those described in relation to the genes and proteins associated with embryonic stem cells, and stem cells and their niches associated with life span as summarized in this report. Therefore, since the genetics of life span and aging are complex, we suggest that it will be necessary in the future to categorize the genes and proteins of hubs and niches into groups that need to be investigated in relation to aging.

Although we did not discuss it in this review, aging is even more complex than the mechanisms controlled by genetics or the environment, because it is possible that embryogenesis, development which includes organs, niche development and germ cells result from genetic programs of patterns of DNA methylation in multiple cell types. This is the science of epigenetics, the study of epigenotypes, which provide the basis for switching of gene activities and the maintenance of stable phenotypes. A challenge is to determine the extent of epigenetic defects during aging, a most difficult task because such defects will be heterogeneous or random in any one tissue [153].

ACKNOWLEDGEMENTS

This work was supported by NIH grants HL29583 and HL59838 (to E.J.Y). J.Z. was supported in part by grants from the Instituto Nacional de Enfermedades Respiratorias, Mexico and by Fundación México en Harvard A.C. ZH was supported by grant HL-29583 from the National Heart, Lung and Blood Institute of the NIH. P.S.K. is a recipient of a grant from the National Institutes of Health (RO1HL079846).

REFERENCES

[1]   Lombard, DB; Chua, KF; Mostoslavsky, R; Franco, S; Gostissa, M; Alt, FW. DNA repair, genome stability, and aging. *Cell,* 2005, 120(4), 497-512.

[2]   Hathcock, KS; Chiang, YJ; Hodes, RJ. In vivo regulation of telomerase activity and telomere length. *Immunol. Rev.,* 2005, 205, 104-113.

[3]   Colavitti, R; Finkel, T. Reactive oxygen species as mediators of cellular senescence. *IUBMB Life,* 2005, 57(4-5), 277-81.

[4]   Jaenisch, R; Bird, A. Epigenetic regulation of gene expression: how the genome integrates intrinsic and environmental signals. *Nat Genet.,* 2003, 33 Suppl, 245-254.

[5]   Miura, T; Mattson, MP; Rao, MS. Cellular lifespan and senescence signaling in embryonic stem cells. *Aging Cell,* 2004, 3, 333-343.

[6]   Yunis, EJ; Fernandez, G; Stutman, O. Susceptibility to involution of the thymus-dependent lymphoid system and autoimmunity. *Am. J. Clin. Pathol.,* 1971, 56, 280-292.

[7]   Yunis, EJ; Ferndades, G; Good, RA. Aging and Involution of the Immunological apparatus. In *The immunopathology of Lymphoreticular Neoplasms.* Ed. JJ Twomey and Robert A. Good. Plenum Publishing Corporation, 1978, 53-80.

[8]   Teague, PO; Yunis, EJ; Rodey, G; Martinez, C; Good, RA. Autoimmune phenomena and renal disease in mice. Role of thymectomy, aging and evolution of immunologic capacity. *Lab. Invest.,* 1970, 22, 121-138.

[9]   Stutman, O; Yunis, EJ; Good, RA. Studies on thymus function. III duration of the thymic function. *J. Exp. Med.,* 1972, 135, 339-356.

[10]   Hallgren, H; Buckley, CE; Gilbertsen, VA; Yunis, EJ. Lymphocyte PHA responsiveness, immunoglobulins and autoantibodies in aging humans. *J. Immunol.,* 1973, 111, 1101-1107.

[11]   Good, RA; Yunis, EJ. Association of autoimmunity, immunodeficiency and aging in man, rabbits and mice. *Fed. Proc.,* 1975, 33, 2040-2050.

[12]   Bodey, B; Bodey, B; Siegel, SE; Kaiser HE. Involution of the mammalian thymus, one of the leading regulators of aging. *In Vivo.* 1997, 11, 421-40.

[13]   Van Zant, G; de Haan, G. Genetic control of lifespan: studies from animal models. *Expert. Rev. Mol. Med.,* 1999, 28, 1-12.

[14]   Smith, JR; Pereira-Smith, OM. Replicative senescence: implications for in vivo aging and tumor suppression. *Science,* 1996, 273, 63-67.

[15]   Hayflick, L; Moorhead, PS. The serial cultivation of human diploid cell strains. *Exp. Cell Res.,* 1961, 25, 585-621.

[16] Thomson, JA; Itskovitz-Eldor, J; Shapiro, SS; Waknitz, MA; Swiergel, JJ; Marshall, VS; Jones, JM. Embrynic stem cell lines derived from human blastocysts. *Science,* 1998, 282, 1145-1147.

[17] Kyono, T; Foster, SA; Koop, JI; McDougall, JK; Galloway, DA; Klingelhutz, AJ. Both Rb/p16INK4a inactivation and telomerase activity are required to inmortalize human epithelial cells. *Nature,* 1998, 396, 84-88.

[18] Szibor, M; Holtz, J. Mitochondrial ageing. *Basic Res. Cardiol.,* 2003, 98, 210-218.

[19] Bertram, MJ; Berube, NG; Hang-Swanson, X; Ran, Q; Leung, JK; Bryce, S; Spurgers, K; Bick, RJ; Baldini, A; Ning, Y; Clark, LJ; Parkinson, EK; Barret, JC; Smith, JR; Pereira-Smith, OM. Identification of a gene that reverses the immortal phenotype of a subset of cells and is a member of a novel family of transcription factor-like genes. *Mol. Cell Biol.,* 1999, 19, 1479-1485.

[20] Tominaga, K; Olguin A; Smith JR; Pereira-Smith OM. Genetics of cellular senescence. *Mech. Ageing Dev.* 200, 123, 927-36.

[21] Sandhu AK; Kaur GP; Reddy DG; Rane NS; Athwal RS. A gene on 6q 14-21 restores senescence to immortal ovarian tumor cells. *Oncogene.,* 1996, 12, 247-52.

[22] Oren, M; Rotter, V. Introduction p53-the first twenty years. *Cell Mol. Life Sci.,* 1999, 55, 9-11.

[23] Bargonetti, J; Manfredi, JJ. Multiple roles of the tumor suppressor p53. *Curr. Opin. Oncol.,* 2002, 14, 86-91.

[24] Di Leonardo, A; Linke, SP; Clarkin, K; Wahl, GM. DNA damage triggers a prolonged p53-dependent G1 arrest and long-term induction of Cip1 in normal human fibroblasts. *Genes Dev.,* 1994, 8, 2540-2551.

[25] Serrano, M; Lin, AW; McCurrach, ME; Beach, D; Lowe, SW. Oncogenic ras provokes premature cell senescence associated with accumulation of p53 and p16INK4a. *Cell,* 1997, 88, 593-602.

[26] Lin, AW; Barradas, M; Stone, JC; van Aelst, L; Serrano, M; Lowe, SW. Premature senescence involving p53 and p16 is activated in response to constitutive MEK/MAPK mitogenic signaling. *Genes Dev.,* 1998, 12, 3008-3019.

[27] Sherr, CJ. Tumor surveillance via the ARF-p53 pathway. *Genes Dev.,* 1998, 12, 2984-2991.

[28] Dimri, GP; Itahana, K; Acosta, M; Campisi, J. Regulation of a secescence ckeckpoint response by the E2F1 transcription factor and p14 (ARF) tumor suppressor. *Mol. Cell Biol.,* 2000, 20, 273-285.

[29] Pearson, M; Carbone, R; Sebastiani, C; Cioce, M; Fagioli, M; Saito, S; Higashimoto, Y; Appella, E; Minucci, S; Pandolfi, PP; Pelicci, PG. PML regulates p53 acetylation and premature senescence induced by oncogenic Ras. *Nature,* 2000, 406, 207-210.

[30] Lopatina, NG; Poole, JC; Saldanha, SN; Hansen, NJ; Key, JS; Pita, MA; Andrews, LG; Tollefsbol, TO. Control mechanisms in the regulation of telomerase reverse transcriptase expression in differentiating human terocarcinoma cells. *Biochem. Biophys. Res. Commmun.,* 2003, 306, 650-659.

[31] Forsyth, NR; Wright, WE; Shay, JW. Telomerase and differentiation in multicellular organisms: turn it off, turn it on, and turn it off again. *Differentiation,* 2002, 69, 188-197.

[32] Lee, SW; Fang, L; Igarashi, M; Ouchi, T; Lu, KP; Aaronson, SA. Sustained activation of Ras/Raf/mitogen-activated protein kinase cascade by the tumor suppressor p53. *Proc. Natl. Acad. Sci.* USA, 2000, 97, 8302-8305.

[33] Ferbeyre, G; de Stanchina, E; Lin, AW; Querido, E; McCurrach, ME; Hannon, GJ; Lowe, SW. Oncogenic ras and p53 cooperate to induce cellular senescence. *Mol. Cell Biol.,* 2002, 22, 3497-3508.

[34] Staveley, BE; Ruel, L; Jin, J; Stambolic, V; Mastronardi, FG; Heiltzer, P; Woodgett, JR; Manoukian, AS. Genetic analysis of protein kinase B (AKT) in Drosophila. *Curr. Biol.,* 1998, 8, 599-602.

[35] Vanfleteren, JR; Braeckman, BP. Mechanisms of life span determination in Caenorhabditis elegans. *Neurobiol. Aging,* 1999, 20, 487-502.

[36] Kenyon, C. A conserved regulatory system for aging. *Cell,* 2001, 105, 165-168.

[37] Lin, K; Libina, N; Kenyon, C. Regulation of Caenorhabiditis elegans longevity protein DAF-16 by insulin/IGF-1 and germline signaling. *Nat. Genet.,* 2001, 28, 139-145.

[38] Longo, VD; Finch, CE. Evolutionary medicine: from dwarf model systems to healthy centenarians? *Science, 2003,* 299, 1342-1346.

[39] Backman, S; Stambolic, V; Mak, T. PTEN function in mammalian cell size regulation. *Curr. Opin. Neurobiol.,* 2002, 12, 516-522.

[40] Yunis, EJ; Salazar, M. Genetics of lifespan in mice. *Genetica,* 1993, 91, 211-223.

[41] Parker, JC; Whiteman MD; Richter CB. Susceptibility of inbred and outbred mouse strains to Sendai virus and prevalence of infection in laboratory rodents. *Infect Immun.* 1978, 19, 123-30.

[42] Dear, KB; Salazar, M; Watson, AL; Gelman, RS; Bronson, R; Yunis, EJ. Traits that influence longevity in mice: a second look. *Genetics,* 1992,132, 229-39.

[43] Gelman, R; Watson E; Yunis EJ; Williams RM. Genetics of survival in mice: subregions of the major histocompatibility complex. *Genetics.,* 1990, 25, 167-174.

[44] Gelman, R; Watson, A; Bronson, R; Yunis, EJ. Murine chromosomal regions correlated with longevity. *Genetics,* 1988, 118, 693-704.

[45] Zijlmans, JM; Martens, UM; Poon, SS; Raap, AK; Tanke, HJ; Ward, RK; Lansdorp, PM. Telomeres in the mouse have large inter-chromosomal variations in the number of T2AG3 repeats. *Porc. Natl. Acad. Sci.* USA, 1997, 94, 7423-7428.

[46] de Haan, G; Gellman, R; Yunis, EJ; Van Zant, G. A putative gene causes variability in lifespan among genotypically identical mice. *Nature Genet.,* 1998, 19, 114-116.

[47] Rossi, DJ; Bryder, D; Zahn, JM; Ahlenius, H; Sonu, R; Wagers, AJ; Weissman, IL. Cell intrinsic alterations underlie hematopoietic stem cell aging. *Porc. Natl. Acad. Sci.* USA, 2005, 102, 9194-9199.

[48] Bhowmick, NA; et al. Stromal fibroblasts in cancer initiation and progression. *Nature,* 2004, 432, 332-337.

[49] Suda, T; Arai F; Hirao A. hematopoietic stem cells and their niche. *Trends in Immunology,* 2005, 26, 426-433.

[50] Fuchs, E; et al. Socializing with the neighborgs: stem cells and their niche. *Cell,* 2004, 116, 769-778.

[51] Reya, T; Morrison SJ; Clarke MF; Weissman IL. Stem cells, cancer, and cancer stem cells. *Nature, 2001,* 414, 105-111.

[52] Loeffler, M; Birke A; Winton D; Potten C. Somatic mutation, monoclonality and stochastic models of stem cell organization in the intestinal crypt. *J. Theor. Biol.,* 1993, 160, 471-491.

[53] Doetsch, F; Caille I; Lim DA; Garcia-Verdugo JM; Alvarez-Buylla A. Subventricular zone astrocytes are neural stem cells in the adult mammalian brain. *Cell.* 1999, 97, 703-716.

[54] Duncan, AW; Rattis FM; DiMascio LN; Congdon KL; Pazianos G; Zhao C; Yoon K; Cook JM; Willert K; Gaiano N; Reya T. Integration of Notch and Wnt signaling in hematopoietic stem cell maintenance. *Nat. Immunol.,* 2005, 6, 314-22.

[55] Welle, S; Brooks AI; Delehanty JM; Needler N; Thornton CA. Gene expression profile of aging in human muscle. *Physiol Genomics.,* 2003, 14, 149-59.

[56] Hamatani, T; Falco G; Carter MG; Akutsu H; Stagg CA; Sharov AA; Dudekula DB; VanBuren V; Ko MS. Age-associated alteration of gene expression patterns in mouse oocytes. *Hum. Mol. Genet.,* 2004, 13, 2263-78.

[57] Pansarasa, O; Bertorelli L; Vecchiet J; Felzani G; Marzatico F. Age-dependent changes of antioxidant activities and markers of free radical damage in human skeletal muscle. *Free Radic Biol Med.,* 1999, 27, 617-622.

[58] Cheng, T; et al. Hematopoietic stem cell quiescence maintained by p21$^{cip1/waf1}$. *Science,* 2000, 287, 1804-1808.

[59] Wilson, A; Murphy MJ; Oskarsson T; Kaloulis K; Bettess MD; Oser GM; Pasche AC; Knabenhans C; Macdonald HR; Trumpp A. c-Myc controls the balance between hematopoietic stem cell self-renewal and differentiation. *Genes Dev* 2004, 8, 2747-63.

[60] Spangrude, GJ; Heimfeld S; Weissman IL. Purification and characterization of mouse hematopoietic stem cells. *Science,* 1988, 241, 58-62.

[61] Okada, S; Nakauchi H; Nagayoshi K; Nishikawa S; Nishikawa S; Miura Y; Suda T. Enrichment and characterization of murine hematopoietic stem cells that express c-kit molecule. *Blood,* 1991, 78, 1706-1712.

[62] Akashi, K; Traver D; Miyamoto T; Weissman IL. A cologenic common myeloid progenitor that give rise to all myeloid lineages. *Nature,* 2000, 404, 193-197.

[63] Greenwood, MJ; Lansdoep, PM. Telomeres, telomerase, and hematopoietic stem cell biology. *Arch. Med. Res.,* 2003, 34, 489-495.

[64] Ito, K; Hirao A; Arai F; Matsuoka S; Takubo K; Hamaguchi I; Nomiyama K; Hosokawa K; Sakurada K; Nakagata N; Ikeda Y; Mak TW; Suda T. Regulation of oxidative stress by ATM is required for self-renewal of hematopoietic stem cells. *Nature,* 2004, 431, 997-1002.

[65] Henckaerts, E; Langer JC; Snoeck HW. Quantitative genetic variation in the hematopoietic stem cell and progenitor cell compartment and in lifespan are closely linked at multiple loci in BXD recombinant inbred mice. *Blood,.* 2004, 104, 374-379.

[66] Fabris N. Hormones and Aging. In , Comprehensive Immunology. Ed Rober A. Good and Stacey B. Day. Plenum Publishing Corporation, NY, 1977, p 72-89.

[67] Montecino-Rodriquez, E; Min, H; Dorshkind, K. Reevaluating current models of thymic involution. *Semin Immunol.,* 2005,17(5), 356-61.

[68] Taub, DD; Longo, DL. Insights into thymic aging and regeneration. *Immunol Rev.,* 2005, 205, 72-93.

[69] Shen, MM; Skoda, RC; Cardiff, RD; Campos-Torres, J; Leder, P; Ornitz, DM. Expression of LIF in transgenic mice results in altered thymic epithelium and apparent

interconversion of thymic and lymph node morphologies. *EMBO J.*, 1994, 13, 1375–1385.

[70] Hannestad, J; Monjil, DF; Diaz-Esnal, B; Cobo, J;, Vega, JA. Age-dependent changes in the nervous and endocrine control of the thymus. *Microsc. Res. Tech.*, 2003, 63, 94–101.

[71] Han, E; Hilsenbeck, SG; Richardson, A; Nelson, JF. cDNA expression arrays reveal incomplete reversal of age-related changes in gene expression by calorie restriction. *Mech. Ageing. Dev.*, 2000, 115, 157–174.

[72] Butler, RN; et al. Biomarkers of aging: from primitive organisms to humans. *J. Gerontol. Biol. Sci. Med. Sci.*, 2004, 59, B560–B567.

[73] Martin, MA; Bhatia, M. Analysis of the human fetal liver hematopoietic microenvironment. *Stem Cells Dev.*, 2005, 14, 493-504.

[74] LaFever, L; Drummond-Barbosa, D. Direct control of germline stem cell division and cyst growth by neural insulin in Drosophila. *Science,* 2005, 309, 1071-3.

[75] Shi, S; Gronthos S. Perivascular niche of postnatal mesenchymal stem cells in human bone marrow and dental pulp. *J. Bone Miner. Res.*, 2003, 18, 696-704.

[76] Yamashita, YM; Fuller MT; Jones DL. Signaling in stem cell niches: lessons from the Drosophila germline. *J. Cell Sci.*, 2005, 118, 665-672.

[77] Ma, DK; Ming, GL; Song, H. Glial influences on neural stem cell development: cellular niches for adult neurogenesis. *Curr. Opin. Neurobiol.*, 2005, 15, 514-520.

[78] Haylock, DN; Nilsson, DK. Stem cell regulation by the hematopoietic stem cell niche. *Cell Cycle,* 2005 (In press).

[79] Heissig, B; Ohki, Y; Sato, Y; Rafii, S; Werb, Z; Hattori, K. A role for niches in hematopoietic cell development. *Hematology,* 2005, 10, 247-253.

[80] Suzuki, T; Chiba, S. Notch signaling in hematopoietic stem cells. *Int. J. Hematol.*, 2005, 82, 285-294.

[81] Doetsch, F. A niche for adult neural stem cells. *Curr. Opin. Genet. Dev.*, 2003, 13, 543-550.

[82] Nilsson, SK; Simmons, PJ. Transplantable stem cells: home to specific niches. *Curr. Opin. Hematol.*, 2004, 11, 102-106.

[83] Schaerli, P; Willimann, K; Ebert, LM; Walz, A; Moser, B. Cutaneous CXCL14 targets blood precursors to epidermal niches for Langerhans Cell differentiation. *Immunity,* 2005, 23, 331-342.

[84] Starnbach, MN; Bevan, MJ. Cells infected with Yersinia present an epitope to class I MHC-restricted CTL. *J. Immunol.*, 1994, 153, 1603-1612.

[85] Buckner, FS; Wipke, BT; Van Voorhis, WC. Trypanosoma cruzi infection does not impair major histocompatibility complex class I presentation of antigen to cytotoxic T lymphocytes. *Eur. J. Immunol.*, 1997, 27, 2541-2548.

[86] Liu, Z; Savoldo, B; Huls, H; Lopez, T; Gee, A; Wilson, J; Brenner, MK; Heslop, HE; Rooney, CM. Epstein-Barr virus (EBV)-specific cytotoxic T lymphocytes for the prevention and treatment of EBV-associated post-transplant lymphomas. *Recent Results Cancer Res.*, 2002, 159, 123-133.

[87] San Mateo, LR; Chua, MM; Weiss, SR; Shen, H. Perforin-mediated CTL cytolysis counteracts direct cell-cell spread of Listeria monocytogenes. *J. Immunol.*, 2002, 169, 5202-5208.

[88] Choi, Y; Borghesani, PR; Chan, JA; Segal, RA. Migration from a mitogenic niche promotes cell-cycle exit. *J. Neurosci.*, 2005, 25, 10437-10445.

[89] Conti, L; Pollard, SM; Gorba, T; Reitano, E; Toselli, M; Biella, G; Sun, Y; Sanzone, S; Ying, QL; Cattaneo, E; Smith, A. Niche-independent symmetrical self-renewal of a mammalian tissue stem cell. *PLoS Biol.*, 2005, 3, e283.

[90] Garcion, E; Halilagic, A; Faissner, A; French-Constant, C. Generation of an environmental niche for neural stem cell development by the extracellular matrix molecule tenascin C. *Development*, 2004, 131, 3423-3432.

[91] Stier, S; Ko, Y; Forkert, R; Lutz, C; Neuhaus, T; Grunewald, E; Cheng, T; Dombkowski, D; Calvi, LM; Rittling, SR; Scadden, DT. Osteopontin is a hematopoietic stem cell niche component that negatively regulates stem cell pool size. *J. Exp. Med.*, 2005, 201, 1781-1791.

[92] Nilsson, SK; Johnston, HM; Whitty, GA; Williams, B; Webb, RJ; Denhardt, DT; Bertoncello, I; Bendall, LJ; Simmons, PJ; Haylock, DN. Osteopontin, a key component of the hematopoietic stem cell niche and regulator of primitive hematopoietic progenitor cells. *Blood*, 2005, 106, 1232-1239.

[93] Hirao, A; Arai, F; Suda, T. Regulation of cell cycle in hemetopoietic stem cells by the niche. *Cell Cycle*, 2004, 3, 1481-1483.

[94] Moore, KA; Limischka IR. "Tie-ing" down the hematopoietic niche. *Cell*, 2004, 118, 149-161.

[95] Moore, KA. Recent advances in defining the hematopoietic stem cell niche. *Curr. Opin. Hematol.*, 2004, 11, 107-111.

[96] Rattis, FM; Voermans, C; Reya, T. Wnt signaling in the stem cell niche. *Curr. Opin. Hematol.*, 2004, 11, 88-94.

[97] Shen, Q; Goderie, SK; Jin, L; Karanth, N; Sun, Y; Abramova, N; Vincent, P; Pumiglia, K; Temple, S. Endothelial cells stimulate self-renewal and expand neurogenesis of neural stem cells. *Science*, 2004, 304, 1253-1255.

[98] Hackney, JA; Charbord, P; Brunk, BP; Stoeckert, CJ; Lemischka, IR; Moore, KA. A molecular profile of a hematopoietic stem cell niche. *Proc. Natl. Acad. Sci. USA.*, 2002, 99, 13061-13066.

[99] Nolta, JA; Thiemann, FT; Arakawa-Hoyt, J; Dao, MA; Barsky, LW; Moore, KA; Lemischka, IR; Crooks, GM. The AFT024 stromal cell line supports long-term ex vivo maintenance of engrafting multipotent human hematopoietic progenitors. *Leukemia* 2002, 16, 352-361.

[100] Koka, PS; Reddy, ST. Cytopenias in HIV infection: Mechanisms and alleviation of hematopoietic inhibition. *Curr. HIV Res.*, 2004, 2, 275-282.

[101] Miles, SA; Mitsuyasu, RT; Moreno, J; Baldwin, G; Alton, NK; Souza, L; Glaspy, JA. Combined therapy with recombinant granulocyte colony-stimulating factor and erythropoietin decreases hematologic toxicity from zidovudine. *Blood*, 1991, 77, 2109-2117.

[102] Miles, SA; Lee, S; Hutlin, L; Zsebo, KM; Mitsuyasu, RT. Potential use of Human stem cell factor as adjunctive therapy for Human immunodeficiency virus-related cytopenias. *Blood*, 1991, 78, 3200-3208.

[103] Ratner, L. Human immunodeficiency virus-associated autoimmune thrombocytopenic purpura: A review. *Am. J. Med.*, 1989, 86, 194-198.

[104] Fauci, AS. Host factors and the pathogenesis of HIV-induced disease. *Nature,* 1996, 384, 529-534.

[105] Harbol, AW; Liesveld, JL; Simpson-Haidaris, PJ; Abboud, CN. Mechanisms of cytopenia in human immunodeficiency virus infection. *Blood Rev.,* 1994, 8, 241-251.

[106] Shen, H; Cheng, T; Preffer, FI; Dombkowski, D; Tomasson, MH; Golan, DE; Yang, O; Hofmann, W; Sodroski, JG; Luster, AD; Scadden, DT. Intrinsic Human immunodeficiency virus type 1 resistance of hematopoietic stem cells despite coreceptor expression. *J. Virol.,* 1999, 73, 728-737.

[107] Koka, PS; Jamieson, BD; Brooks, DG; Zack, JA. Human immunodeficiency virus type-1 induced hematopoietic inhibition is independent of productive infection of progenitor cells in vivo. *J. Virol.* 1999, 73, 9089-9097.

[108] Koka, PS; Fraser, JK; Bryson, Y; Bristol, GC; Aldrovandi, GM; Daar, ES; Zack, JA. Human immunodeficiency virus type 1 inhibits multilineage hematopoiesis in vivo. *J. Virol.,* 1998, 72, 5121-5127.

[109] Jenkins, M; Hanley, MB; Moreno, MB; Wieder, E; McCune, JM. Human immunodeficiency virus-1 infection interrupts thymopoiesis and multilineage hematopoiesis in vivo. *Blood,* 1998, 91, 2672-2678.

[110] Koka, PS; Kitchen, CM; Reddy, ST. Targeting c-Mpl for revival of human immunodeficiency virus type 1-induced hematopoietic inhibition when CD34+ progenitor cells are re-engrafted into a fresh stromal microenvironment in vivo. *J. Virol.,* 2004, 78, 11385-11392.

[111] Lee, JS; Campbell, HD; Kozak, CA; Young, IG. The IL-4 and IL-5 genes are closely linked and are part of a cytokine gene cluster on mouse chromosome 11. Somat. *Cell Mol. Genet.,* 1989, 15, 143-152.

[112] D'Eustachio, P; Brown, M; Watson, C; Paul, WE. The IL-4 gene maps to chromosome 11, near the gene encoding IL-3. *J. Immunol.,* 1988, 141, 3067-3071.

[113] Barlow, DP; Bucan, M; Lehrach, H; Hogan, BL; Gough, NM. Close genetic and physical linkage between the murine haemopoietic growth factor genes GM-CSF and Multi-CSF (IL3). *EMBO J.,* 1987, 6, 617-623.

[114] Spilianakis, CG; Lalioti, MD; Town, T; Lee, GR; Flavell, RA. Interchromosomal associations between alternatively expressed loci. *Nature,* 2005, 435, 637-645.

[115] Altomare, DA; Guo, K; Cheng, JQ; Sonoda, G; Walsh, K; Testa JR. Cloning, chromosomal localization and expression analysis of the mouse Akt2 oncogene. *Oncogene,* 1995, 11, 1055-1060.

[116] Mock, BA; Givol, D; D'Hoostelaere, LA; Huppi, K; Seldin, MF; Gurfinkel, N; Unger, T; Potter, M; Mushinski, JF. Mapping of the bcl-2 oncogene on mouse chromosome 1. *Cytogenet Cell Genet.,* 1988, 47, 11-15.

[117] Murthy, SS; Tosolini, A; Taguchi, T; Testa, JR. Mapping of AKT3, encoding a member of the Akt/protein kinase B family, to human and rodent chromosomes by fluorescence in situ hybridization. *Cytogenet. Cell. Genet.,* 2000, 88, 38-40.

[118] Haupt, Y; Barri, G; Adams JM. Nucleotide sequence of bup, an upstream gene in the bmi-1 proviral insertion locus. *Mol. Biol. Rep.,* 1992, 17, 17-20.

[119] Pecker, I; Avraham, KB; Gilbert, DJ; Savitsky, K; Rotman, G; Harnik, R; Fukao, T; Schrock, E; Hirotsune, S; Tagle, DA; Collins, FS; Wynshaw-Boris, A; Ried, T; Copeland, NG; Jenkins, NA; Shiloh, Y; Ziv, Y. Identification and chromosomal

localization of Atm, the mouse homolog of the ataxia-telangiectasia gene. *Genomics,* 1996, 35, 39-45.

[120] Justice, MJ; Siracusa, LD; Gilbert, DJ; Heisterkamp, N; Groffen, J; Chada, K; Silan, CM; Copeland, NG; Jenkins, NA. A genetic linkage map of mouse chromosome 10: localization of eighteen molecular markers using a single interspecific backcross. *Genetics,* 1990, 125, 855-866.

[121] Avraham, S; Jiang, S; Ota, S; Fu, Y; Deng, B; Dowler, LL; White, RA; Avraham, H. Structural and functional studies of the intracellular tyrosine kinase MATK gene and its translated product. *J. Biol. Chem.,* 1995, 270, 1833-1842.

[122] Czosnek, HH; Bienz, B; Givol, D; Zakut-Houri, R; Pravtcheva, DD; Ruddle, FH; Oren, M. The gene and the pseudogene for mouse p53 cellular tumor antigen are located on different chromosomes. *Mol. Cell. Biol,* 1984, 4, 1638-1640.

[123] Rotter, V; Wolf, D; Pravtcheva, D; Ruddle, FH. Chromosomal assignment of the murine gene encoding the transformation-related protein p53. *Mol. Cell. Biol.,*1984, 4, 383-385.

[124] Cho, M; Villani, V; D'Eustachio, P. A linkage map of distal mouse chromosome 12. *Mamm Genome,* 1991, 1, 30-36.

[125] Stone, JC; Crosby, JL; Kozak, CA; Schievella, AR; Bernards, R; Nadeau, JH. The murine retinoblastoma homolog maps to chromosome 14 near Es-10. *Genomics,* 1989, 5, 70-75.

[126] Banerjee, M; Wiener, F; Spira, J; Babonits, M; Nilsson, MG; Sumegi, J; Klein, G. Mapping of the c-myc, pvt-1 and immunoglobulin kappa genes in relation to the mouse plasmacytoma-associated variant (6;15) translocation breakpoint., *EMBO J.,* 1985, 4, 3183-3188.

[127] Huppi, K; Siwarski, D; Dosik, J; Michieli, P; Chedid, M; Reed, S; Mock, B; Givol, D; Mushinski, JF. Molecular cloning, sequencing, chromosomal localization and expression of mouse p21 (Wafl). *Oncogene,* 1994, 9, 3017-3020.

[128] Kojima, T; Yoshikawa, Y; Takada, S; Sato, M; Nakamura, T; Takahashi, N; Copeland, NG; Gilbert, DJ; Jenkins, NA; Mori N. Genomic organization of the Shc-related phosphotyrosine adapters and characterization of the full-length Sck/ShcB: specific association of p68-Sck/ShcB with pp135. *Biochem. Biophys. Res. Commun.,* 2001, 284, 1039-1047.

[129] Webb, GC; Campbell, HD; Lee, JS; Young, IG. Mapping the gene for murine T-cell growth factor, Il-2, to bands B-C on chromosome 3 and for the alpha chain of the IL-2-receptor, Il-2ra, to bands A2-A3 on chromosome 2. Cytogenet. *Cell. Genet.,* 1990, 54, 164-168.

[130] Nelson, KK; Knopf, JL; Siracusa, LD. Localization of phospholipase C-gamma 1 to mouse chromosome 2. *Mamm Genome.,* 1992, 3, 597-600.

[131] Vidal, M. Interactome modeling. *FEBS Lett.,* 2005, 579, 1834-1838.

[132] Rual, JF; et al. Towards a proteome-scale map of the human protein-protein interaction network. *Nature,* 2005, 437,1173-1178.

[133] Fernandes, G; Good, RA; Yunis, EJ. Responses of autoimmune diseases and diseases of aging to dietary restriction, in: *Immunological Aspects of Aging.* D. Segre and L. Smith, eds., Marcel Dekker, Inc., New York 1981; p. 207.

[134] Anderson, DJ; Watson, ALM; Yunis, EJ. Environmental and genetic factors that influence immunity and longevity in mice. *Mol. Biol. Aging,* 1985, 1, 231-240.

[135] Dubey, DP; Husain, Z; Levitan, E; Zurakowski, D; Mirza, N; Younes, S; Cononell, C; Yunis, D; Yunis, EJ. The MHC influences NK and NKT cell functions associated with immune abnormalities and lifespan. *Mech. Ageing Dev.,* 2000, 113, 117-134.

[136] Strelkauskas, AJ; Andrews, JA; Yunis, EJ. Autoantibodies to a regulatory T cell subset in human ageing. *Clin. Exp. Immunol.,* 1981, 45, 308-315.

[137] Caruso, C; Candore, G; Colonna-Romano, G; Lio, D; Bonafe, M; Valensin, S; Franceschi, C. HLA, aging and longevity a critical reappraisal. *Human Immunol.,* 2000, 61, 942-949.

[138] Wilson, AG; Gordon, C; di Giovine, FS; de Vries, N; van de Putte, LB; Emery, P; Duff, GW. A genetic association between systemic lupus erythematosus and tumor necrosis factor alpha. *Eur. J. Immunol.,* 1994, 24, 191-195.

[139] Waldron-Lynch, F; Adams, C; Amos, C; Zhu, DK; McDermott, MF; Shanahan, F; Molloy, MG; O'Gara, F. Tumour necrosis factor 5' promoter single nucleotide polymorphisms influence susceptibility to rheumatoid arthritis (RA) in immunogenetically defined multiplex RA families. *Genes Immun.,* 2001, 2, 82-87.

[140] Rodriguez-Carreon, AA; Zuniga, J; Hernandez-Pacheco, G; Rodriguez-Perez, JM; Perez-Hernandez, N; Montes de Oca, JV; Cardiel, MH; Granados, J; Vargas-Alarcon, G. Tumor necrosis factor-alpha -308 promoter polymorphism contributes independently to HLA alleles in the severity of rheumatoid arthritis in Mexicans. *J. Autoimmun.,* 2005, 24, 63-68.

[141] Molokhia, M; McKeigue, P. Risk for rheumatic disease in relation to ethnicity and admixture. *Arthritis Res.,* 2000, 2, 115-125.

[142] Cipriano, C; Caruso, C; Lio, D; Giacconi, R; Malavolta, M; Muti, E; Gasparini, N; Franceschi, C; Mocchegiani, E. The -308G/A polymorphism of TNF-alpha influences immunological parameters in old subjects affected by infectious diseases. *Int. J. Immunogenet.,* 2005, 32, 13-18.

[143] Ross, OA; Curran, MD; Rea, IM; Hyland, P; Duggan, O; Barnett, CR; Annett, K; Patterson, C; Barnett, YA; Middleton, D. HLA haplotypes and TNF polymorphism do not associate with longevity in the Irish. *Mech Ageing Dev.,* 2003, 124, 563-567.

[144] Yunis, EJ; Larsen, CE; Fernandez-Vina, M; Awdeh, ZL; Romero, T; Hansen, JA; Alper, CA. Inheritable variable sizes of DNA stretches in the human MHC: conserved extended haplotypes and their fragments or blocks. *Tissue Antigens,* 2003, 62, 1-20.

[145] Rosenberg, NA; Pritchard, JK; Weber, JL; Cann, HM; Kidd, KK; Zhivotovsky, LA; Feldman, MW. Genetic structure of human populations. *Science,* 2002, 298, 2381-2385.

[146] Akisaka, M; Suzuki, M; Inoko, H. Molecular genetic studies on DNA polymorphism of the HLA class II genes associated with human longevity. *Tissue Antigens,* 1997, 50, 489-493.

[147] Papasteriades, C; Boki, K; Pappa, H; Aedonopoulos, S; Papasteriadis, E; Economidou, J. HLA phenotypes in healthy aged subjects. *Gerontology,* 1997, 43, 176-181.

[148] Lio, D; Pes, GM; Carru, C; Listi, F; Ferlazzo, V; Candore, G; Colonna-Romano, G; Ferrucci, L; Deiana, L; Baggio, G; Franceschi, C; Caruso, C. Association between the HLA-DR alleles and longevity: a study in Sardinian population. *Exp. Gerontol.,* 2003, 38, 313-317.

[149] Purdom, S; Chen, QM. p66(Shc): at the crossroad of oxidative stress and the genetics of aging. *Trends Mol. Med.,* 2003, 9, 206-210.

[150] Dangond, F; Gullans, SR. Differential expression of human histone deacetylase mRNA in response to immune cell apoptosis induction by trichostatin A and butyrate. *Biochem. Biophys. Res. Commun.,* 1998, 242, 648-652.

[151] McClearn, GE. Prospects for quantitative trait locus methodology in gerontology. *Exp. Gerontol.,*1997, 32, 49-54.

[152] Fernandez, G; Good, RA; Yunis EJ. Attempts to correct age-related immuodeficiency and autoimmunity by cellular and dietary manipulation in inbred mice. *Immunology and Aging,* edited by T. Makinodan and EJ Yunis, New York Plenum. 1977, 111-133.

[153] Holliday, R. DNA methylation and epigenotypes. *Biochemistry,* 2005, 70, 500-504.

[154] Greenberg, LJ; Yunis, EJ. Histocompatibility determinants, immune responsiveness and aging in man. *Fed. Proc.,* 1978, 37, 1258-1262.

[155] Rea, IM; Middleton, D. Is the phenotypic combination A1B8Cw7DR3 a marker for male longevity? *J. Am. Geriatr. Soc.,* 1994, 42, 978-983.

[156] Ivanova, R; Hénon, N; Lepage, V; Charron, D; Vicaut, E; Schächter, F. HLA-DR alleles display sex-dependent effects on survival discriminate between individual and familial longevity. *Human Mol. Genet.,* 1998, 7, 187-194.

[157] Ricci, G; Colombo, C; Ghiazza, B; Illeni, MT. Association between longevity and allelic forms of human leukocyte antigens (HLA): population study of aged Italian human subjects. *Arch. Immunol. Ther. Exp.* (Warsz), 1998, 46, 31-34.

[158] Singh, R; Kolvraa, S; Bross, P; Gregersen, N; Andersen Nexo, B; Frederiksen, H; Christensen, K; Rattan, SI. Association between low self-rated health and heterozygosity for -110A > C polymorphism in the promoter region of HSP70-1 in aged Danish twins. *Biogerontology,* 2004, 5, 169-176.

[159] Pes, GM; Lio, D; Carru, C; Deiana, L; Baggio, G; Franceschi, C; Ferrucci, L; Oliveri, F; Scola, L; Crivello, A; Candore, G; Colonna-Romano, G; Caruso, C. Association between longevity and cytokine gene polymorphisms. A study in Sardinian centenarians. *Aging Clin. Exp. Res.,* 2004, 16, 244-248.

[160] Christiansen, L; Bathum, L; Andersen-Ranberg, K; Jeune, B; Christensen, K. Modest implication of interleukin-6 promoter polymorphisms in longevity. *Mech. Ageing Dev.,* 2004, 125, 391-395.

[161] Naumova, E; Mihaylova, E; Ivanova, M; Michailova, S; Penkova, K; Baltadjieva, D. Immunological markers contributing to successful aging in Bulgarians. *Exp. Gerontol.,* 2004, 39, 637-644.

[162] Lio, D; Scola, L; Crivello, A; Colonna-Romano, G; Candore, G; Bonafe, M; Cavallone, L; Marchegiani, F; Olivieri, F; Franceschi, C; Caruso, C. Inflammation, genetics, and longevity: further studies on the protective effects in men of IL-10 -1082 promoter SNP and its interaction with TNF-alpha -308 promoter SNP. *J. Med. Genet.,* 2003, 40, 296-299.

[163] Carrieri, G; Marzi, E; Olivieri, F; Marchegiani, F; Cavallone, L; Cardelli, M; Giovagnetti, S; Stecconi, R; Molendini, C; Trapassi, C; De Benedictis, G; Kletsas, D; Franceschi, C. The G/C915 polymorphism of transforming growth factor beta1 is associated with human longevity: a study in Italian centenarians. *Aging Cell.,* 2004, 3, 443-448.

In: Progress in Stem Cell Research
Editor: Prasad S. Koka, pp. 201-231

ISBN: 978-1-60456-065-7
© 2008 Nova Science Publishers, Inc.

Chapter 11

STEM CELLS IN AGING: CONTRIBUTION OF THE IMMUNE SYSTEM

Masha Fridkis-Hareli[*,1,2], *Joaquin Zúñiga*[1,2,3] *and Edmond J. Yunis*[*,1,2]

[1] Department of Cancer Immunology and AIDS, Dana Farber Cancer Institute, Boston MA.
[2] Department of Pathology, Harvard Medical School, Boston, MA.
[3] Instituto Nacional de Enfermedades Respiratorias, Mexico City, Mexico

ABSTRACT

Aging is associated with progressive decline in immune responses, resulting in increased frequency of infections, autoimmunity and cancer. The deterioration of the immune system with progressive aging is believed to contribute to morbidity and mortality in elderly humans. Among immune functions, lymphocyte production in the bone marrow (BM) and in the thymus is reduced during aging. Decrease in thymopoiesis is believed to occur as a result of thymic involution, during which the thymus undergoes a progressive reduction in size due to profound changes in its anatomy associated with loss of thymic epithelial cells. The decline in the output of newly developed cells results in diminished numbers of circulating naïve cells that reconstitute the peripheral lymphocyte pool, leading to impaired cell-mediated immunity. Together with the restricted function of mature lymphocytes, these age-related defects contribute to the diminished immune responses in the elderly. In this review, we discuss the role of the immune system in the process of development and aging as relates to the contribution of pathways of lymphocyte differentiation from hematopoietic stem cells (HSC) and the microenvironment to the weakened immune responses, resulting in increased susceptibility to autoimmunity, infections and cancer. With the rapidly evolving technology enabling isolation and manipulation of stem cells it becomes feasible to

[*] Corresponding authors: Masha Fridkis-Hareli, Ph.D., Department of Cancer Immunology and AIDS, Dana Farber Cancer Institute, 44 Binney St, Boston, MA, 02115. Phone (617)632-3344, Fax (617)632-4468, email: masha_fridkis-hareli@dfci.harvard.edu; Edmond J. Yunis, M.D., Department of Cancer Immunology and AIDS, Dana Farber Cancer Institute, 44 Binney St, Boston, MA, 02115. Phone (617)632-3347, Fax (617)632-4468, email: edmond_yunis@dfci.harvard .edu

targeting pathological conditions or expressing therapeutic genes. Unraveling these mechanisms may further our understanding of human processes during aging leading to development of therapeutic interventions with the potential of prolonging life.

ABBREVIATIONS

APC, antigen-presenting cells;
BM, bone marrow;
DC, dendritic cells;
DN, double negative;
DP, double positive;
FT, fetal thymus;
FTOC, fetal thymus organ culture;
HSC, hemopoietic stem cells;
NK, natural killer cells;
RTE, recent thymic emigrants;
SP, single positive;
TREC, T cell receptor excision circle

INTRODUCTION

The potential lifespan of a species, defined as the duration of life of the longest survivors, is determined by interaction of genetic factors which control the rate of cellular and organ development and involution. However, the incidence of disease increases with age [1], and longevity of individuals within species is also determined by an absence of genetic susceptibility to disease and the maintenance of a normal and balanced immune system, which copes with environmental and internal degenerative changes. The thymus, a principal lymphoid organ, is governed by a 'time clock', programming its involution with age; environmental influences such as infections can accelerate or delay this process.

Specific thymic alterations related to aging were described and discussed by Hammar [2] and were reviewed by others [3]. It has been known for many years that beginning at the time of sexual maturation, an apparent programmed involution begins in the central lymphoid organs. This is succeeded by a period of gradual involution of the peripheral lymphoid organs and declining vigor of immune functions [4-8]. Decline of thymic size, however, followed by decline in cell-mediated immune function and aging, occurs rapidly in some persons and in some inbred mouse strains [6], whereas others may show appreciable loss of immune vigor until later in life. The nature of the immunodeficiency that occurs in some in strains of mice relatively early in life, as, for example, during the second half of the first year in NZB mice and (NZBxNZB) F1 hybrid is similar to that produced or accelerated by neonatal thymectomy [4-9]. Cell-mediated immunioty deteriorates spontaneously at an earlier age in autoimmune prone strains than in autoimmune-resistant strains [6]. Progressive morphologic changes include a decrease in the cortical mass and number of cortical thymocytes [10] and infiltration of plasma cells [11]. The levels of thymic hormones and as well as thymic dependent functions decline with age [6].

Of interest, the MHC class II expression by epithelial cells diminish with age [11], which could affect the microenvironment during aging. These aspects need to be further investigated, as we have recently reviewed the role of the thymus in autoimmunity and discussed the acceleration of autoimmune diseases in neonatally thymenctomized mice that are susceptible to autoimmune disease [12]. Also, the thymus of auitoimmune susceptible strains involutes faster than long lived strains [13, 14].

The incidence of autoimmune, neoplastic and infectious diseases increases as immune and immunoregulatory functions decline, and they are hallmarks of the aging process. Such findings are based on the thymic clock theory of aging, which postulates that the thymus, which, in turn, affects immune competence resulting from environmental factors and intrinsic changes, is involved in the production of abnormal immunoregulatory mechanisms [4]. We propose that the optimal functional longevity is genetically based and controlled by a hypothetical homeostasis gene complex that includes immune response genes and genes that control endocrine balance. (We have described in a recent review that the balance between such a complex includes genetics, environment and interactions between cells of niches [15]). Such imbalance between external and internal environment could be produced by virus-host interactions and endocrine-immune dysfunctions [6]. The rates of aging including the immunology have time constraints. CBA mice tend to be very long-lived and to maintain immunological function much longer than do certain other strains, such as autoimmune susceptible [6]. Furthermore, numerous studies have shown that mice of different inbred strains differ in survival rate [14, 16]. Also, the MHC is involved in several autoimmune diseases [17]. It remains to be determined whether genes of the MHC could be markers for both autoimmune diseases and long life. In such case, other genes will be different in these two situations [18].

It has been showed that the diminished ability to mount a humoral or cell-mediated immune responses associated with aging relates, in part, to an age-associated defect in T cell function. This change is linked to decreased levels of both T-cell proliferation and IL-2 production following activation [19]. Studies of intracellular signaling after T-cell antigen receptor ligation have demonstrated that cells from aged mice display multiple signaling defects including reduced generation of inositol triphosphate, decreased mobilization of intracellular Ca^2 and impaired activation of protein kinase C [20].

Many studies have shown that mice of different inbred strains differ in survival rate. Molecular biology of aging, based on studies by Walford and Smith using congeneic mice, demonstrated that the median survival rate does correlate with certain H-2 haplotypes and immune responsiveness [21]. In another study, H-2 congenic mouse strain B10.RIII (H-2r) which is the longest -lived strain, displayed the highest response to PHA, whereas the B10.AKM (H-2m), the shortest-lived strain, was least responsive [22].

We have also reported early immune abnormalities in the B10.AKM mice and described the correction of immunosenescence in these mice by using N-Acetyl-cysteine or glutathione [20]. In addition, we described an increase in the frequency of memory T-cells in young mice of this strain. More importantly, young mice of this strain produced a significantly higher level of IL-4 by activated NKT cells [23]. Our results suggested that young B10.AKM mice have a primary immune abnormality that ultimately results in an early senescence phenotype.

One characteristic of the aging immune system is that lymphocyte production in the BM and the thymus is reduced [24]. As a result, fewer naïve cells are available to replenish the peripheral lymphocyte pool. Concomitant with changes in primary lymphopoiesis is the development of restricted function [24-26] and clonal hyperproliferation [27, 28] of mature lymphocytes already resident in secondary lymphoid organs. Together, these age-related defects in primary and secondary lymphopoiesis contribute to the constriction of the B- and T-cell repertoire and the diminished immune response in the elderly.

Observations in animal models pointed at the age-related differences on the genetic and biochemical levels correlating with the late-life diseases. Gene mapping studies have documented multiple quantitative trait loci (QTL) that influence the levels of age-sensitive T-cell subsets (reviewed in ref. 29). Moreover, biomarker studies showed that T-cell subset levels measured at 8 or 18 months are significant predictors of lifespan for mice dying of lymphoma, fibrosarcoma, mammary adenocarcinoma, or all causes combined. Biochemical analyses showed that T cells from aged mice are defective in the activation process within a few minutes of encountering a stimulus and that the defects precede the recognition by the T-cell receptor of agonist peptides on the antigen-presenting cell [29]. Another pathway, which is affected during the process of aging is the apoptosis of lymphocytes. Alterations in apoptotic pathways, in T and B lymphocytes during aging and the role of lymphocyte apoptosis in immune senescence have been recently investigated [30]. An important factor contributing to the decline in the immune functions with age is thymic involution, resulting in diminished T cell output (reviewed in ref. 31). Understanding of the potential mechanisms involved in thymic involution and optimizing interventional strategies aimed at restoring thymic function may provide a valuable avenue for immune reconstitution in the aged host.

Aging reduces the efficiency of physical barriers, decreasing protection against invasive pathogens, and exposing previously hidden antigens in the body's own tissues. Self-antigens acquire alterations that increase their immunogenicity. In addition, the ability of innate immunity to eliminate infectious agents deteriorates, resulting in inappropriate persistence of immune stimulation and antigen levels exceeding the threshold for the activation of B or T cells. B cell turnover is reduced and numbers of naïve T cells decline to the advantage of increasing numbers of memory T cells. In parallel, the loss of co-stimulatory T cell molecules may increase reactivity of T cells, and render them less susceptible to downregulation. Since optimal immune reactivity requires a tight balance of transduction pathways in both T and B lymphocytes, and because these pathways are altered in systemic autoimmune diseases, with age, alterations of the immune receptor signaling machinery might underlie the higher incidence of autoimmune phenomena in the elderly. Consistently, aging is associated with alterations in several components of the signaling complex in B cells, memory and naïve T cells, and a reduced activation of several lipid rafts-associated proteins (reviewed in ref. 32). Because the coincidence of autoimmune disease with other ailments increases the burden of disease and limits therapeutic options in the aged, further investigation of these pathways in the elderly represents a challenge that will need to be addressed in order to devise effective preventive and therapeutic interventions. The interest in postnatal thymic function and investigation of ways to restore it has been increased also due to exposure of the population to AIDS and cancer chemotherapy, causing damage to the immune system (reviewed in ref. 33). This chapter describes how aging affects lymphopoiesis in the thymus and the BM, the thymic structure and function, resulting in susceptibility to infections, cancer and autoimmunity, and discusses potential therapeutic options to restore thymic functions, with the goal of developing strategies to circumvent immune system declines that develop in the elderly.

EARLY MODELS OF T LYMPHOCYTE DEVELOPMENT

The ability of the thymus to restore the immune deficiency produced by neonatal thymectomy in mice decreases with the delay of treatment after thymectomy (reviewed in ref. 18). Lymphopoietic cells of adult and newborn origin act in cooperation with the thymic function in restoring the host; spleen, lymph nodes, thoracic duct, thymus, BM, or newborn hemopoietic liver [34]. Such studies were effective whether thymus and functional thymomas or thymus grafts or thymomas within diffusion chambers were used [35]. More importantly for this discussion is the fact that syngeneic newborn or embryonic hematopoietic liver cells together with thymus function. Thymus function alone or cells alone were ineffective. Newborn liver cells are effective in association with thymus or thymomas in diffusion chambers. Embryonic liver cells were ineffective, even in large numbers, when associated with humoral thymus function. Embryonic liver cells were effective in the cooperative effect only in association with viable thymus grafts. Thymic cells were ineffective in association with embryonic liver cells. Cells capable of cooperating with humoral thymic function start to appear to embryonic liver by day 19-21 of gestation and are detectable until day 5-6 postbirth. Embryonic hematopoietic liver cells from 12 to 18 days of gestation contain cels capable of cooperation only with viable free thymus grafts and not with humoral thymic function. A prethymic cell population of partially differentiated cells of hemopoietic origin, insensitive to humoral activity of the thymus but requiring thymic stroma and traffic through the thymus explain such results. This population of prethymic cells can become posthymic through this process and eventually develop into competent cells. Posthymic cells are characterized by their sensitivity to humoral activity of the thymus and by their wide distribution in the lymphopoietic tissues of newborn and young adult mice.

Thus, the processes underlying the developmental pathways of hemopoietic stem cells in the thymus have attracted considerable attention during the past 3 decades. The mechanisms that control differentiation of stem cells into functionally and phenotypically matrure T lymphocytes involve complex cell-cell interactions in the thymic microenvironment. It was shown that hemopoietic stem cells migrate from the BM through a set of blood vessels to the subcapsular region of the thymus, where they start differentiation, and subsequently move to the medulla [36-39]. The medullary compartment of the thymus is connected to the lymphoid circulation, and mature T lymphocytes migrate to the periphery. The precursor cells of thymocytes are included in a minor cortical thymus subpopulation characterized as double negative (DN) CD4-CD8- cells [37, 40, 41]. Since double positive (DP) CD4+CD8+ cortical cells appear before single positive (SP) CD4+CD8- or CD4-CD8+ mature T cells (38, 42-45], it was suggested that thymocytes first express both of these antigens and then some of them shut off one or the other determinant, depending on the specificity of their T cell receptors (TCRs), while most DP cells do not proceed to differentiate and die in the thymus by apoptosis [46-48]. An intermediate subpopulation between DN and DP was identified which expresses only CD8 [49] or CD4 [50], with various proportions in different mouse strains.

The mechanisms controlling the pattern of thymocyte development in aging have been extensively investigated. Altered proportions of CD4+CD8- and CD4-CD8+ T cells in the peripheral lymphoid tissues [51, 52] as well as the increase in memory vs. naïve CD4+CD8- subsets [53-55], have been documented. Cellular interactions in the course of thymic development have been studied extensively by transplanting BM cells into irradiated recipients and analyzing T lymphocytes in the radiation chimeras [56, 57]. It has been shown that a single thymic stem cell progenitor can give rise to all T cell lineages within the thymus *in vivo* [58] and *in vitro* [59, 60]. At the later stage, an *in vitro* model of thymocyte differentiation was developed in which lymphohemopoietic cells were seeded onto the lymphoid-depleted fetal thymuses (FT) [61]. Being the first *in vitro* system used in a number of studies of thymic repopulation and T cell development, it, however, bared some disadvantages as compared to the *in vivo* irradiation chimeras in which newly emigrating lymphoid progenitors interacted with the radio-resistant lymphocytes in the process of their maturation in the thymus. Subsequently, the *in vitro* system in which T cell progenitors from different sources were co-cultured with the irradiated fetal thymuses has been developed [62], enabling analysis of cellular and molecular interactions in the course of thymocyte reconstitution and maturation [63-68]. When BM cells from young and old donors were mixed and seeded onto the same FT explant, the proportion of cells, which arose from the old cell inoculum was smaller than that from the young [69, 70]. Here, BM cells from aged mice maintained their capacity to reconstitute FT explants and to differentiate into various T-cell subsets as assessed by distinct T-cell-specific surface markers (Thy-1, Lyt-1, Lyt-2, and L3T4) and functions (concanavalin A-induced proliferative and cytotoxic responses). However, when mixtures of old and young BM cells reconstituted FT explants, the cells of old mice were less efficient than those of young in their capacity to give rise to T cells. These results indicated that BM cells from aged mice can reconstitute the thymus and differentiate into T cells; however, their reconstituting capacity is inferior to that of BM cells from young mice. In a different study, when immature thymocytes from young and old mice were seeded onto the lymphoid-depleted FT, reduced DP and increased DN levels were found in cocultures containing cells of the old donors as compared to the young [67]. When cortical and medullary thymocytes from young and old mice were separated by peanut agglutinin PNA and seeded onto the FT, the emerging cells of the old mouse origin exhibited higher CD4- CD8+ and lower DN CD4-CD8- as compared to the young [67]. Seeding of BM cells from young and old mice onto the depleted FT revealed an age-related decline in the developmental potential [63]. When the FT was severely depleted [treated with either 2-deoxyguanosine (dGua) or exposed to an irradiation dose of 20 Gy], BM-type T lymphocytes were dominant, regardless of BM donor age. When the FT was only partially depleted of its proper lymphoid cells (by exposure to 10 Gy), the lymphocytes, which developed were from both BM and FT origins, yet the level of donor-type thymocytes from the young mice was higher than that of the old. The proportions of old BM-derived DP cells were lower than in the young. Co-cultures of thymocytes from young and old mice with partially depleted FT explants resulted in similar proportions of CD4/CD8 subsets from both donor and FT origins, with the exception that in the presence of old thymus-derived cells there was an increase in the level of FT-type CD4- CD8+ cells.

The strategy of using young and old mice as BM donors was based on the idea that T cell deficiency in aging [71, 72] is related to the developmental failure of the BM-derived thymocyte progenitors [73]. The effect of mature cells on thymocyte development was examined by coculturing mixtures of progenitor cells and the mature thymocytes from young and old donors within the FT [73-76]. The strategy was to seed sorted DN CD4-CD8- thymocytes on their own, or in the presence of mature T cells, onto lymphoid depleted FT explants, and to examine the resulting T cell subsets. The DN cells of the old mice gave rise to lower levels of DP CD4+CD8+ cells than those of the young. Cocultures containing a mixture of DN thymocytes and CD4+CD8- splenocytes showed higher CD4+CD8- and DN, and lower DP and CD4-CD8+ levels in the old-donor derived cells, as compared with the young ones. Similar results were obtained with CD4+CD8- thymocytes. In contrast, the presence of CD4-CD8+ splenocytes had no effect on the pattern of DN cell development, indicating that differentiation of CD4/CD8 thymocytes is affected by CD4+ cells in an age-associated differential manner [74]. Altogether, these observations suggested that stem cell differentiation in the thymus occurs through cellular interactions within the thymic microenvironment, and that the thymocyte progenitors from the old donors are inferior to the young, especially at the stage of DN to DP cell development.

CURRENT STUDIES OF THE EFFECTS OF AGING ON LYMPHOCYTE DEVELOPMENT FROM HEMOPOIETIC STEM CELL PROGENITORS

In the recent years there have been advances in the characterization and functional analysis of hemopoietic stem cells (HSC) developing into all blood cell lineages (reviewed in ref. 77), in spite of the difficulties posed by limited availability of experimental models for aging and the low frequency of early lymphoid precursors. HSC differentiate into all blood cell lineages, including T and B lymphocytes, as well as myeloid and erythroid cells, and have the capacity for self-renewal [78]. Murine HSC have been characterized as cells lacking the expression of antigens specific for mature differentiated cells (lineage negative (Lin) c-kit^{hi} Sca-1^{hi} phenotype). More detailed phenotyping of the early progenitors have been reported [79, 80], showing that the earliest HSC precursor expresses Flt receptor [80]. It has been suggested that B and T lymphocytes originate from the common lymphoid progenitor (CLP) which upon migration to the thymus develop into T cells, and those residing in the BM give rise to B cells [81, 82]. However, these data have been challenged by reports that thymocytes develop from the early T-lineage progenitor not derived from CLP [83-85].

The thymus is repopulated by HSC precursors derived from the BM, which possess the potential to develop into T lineages [85]. The most immature intrathymic progenitors do not express CD3, CD4 or CD8 co-receptors and therefore are denoted as triple negative (TN) cells, comprising approximately 3–5% of total thymocytes [86, 87]. TN cells have been further subdivided based on the differential expression of CD44 and CD25 into CD44+CD25- (TN1), CD44+CD25+ (TN2), CD44-CD25+ (TN3), and CD44-CD25- (TN4) subpopulations [86, 87]. The differentiation of TN1 into TN2, TN3 and TN4 stages accompanies by TCR rearrangements, leading to generation of DP and SP thymocytes [88-91]. The early thymocyte precursors (ETP) comprise a very small fraction of TN1 cells [83, 84]; they are significantly reduced in the thymus of old mice due to decreased proliferative potential and increased apoptosis [84]. In contrast, other studies showed increase in the number of ETP with aging [92, 93], probably due to methodological limitations and impurities by non-T-lineage cells in the examined TN1 fraction. Pathways of HSC differentiation are depicted in Fig. 1.

The age-related effects of the thymic microenvironment containing a heterogeneous population of stromal cells that supports T-cell development have been extensively studied [94] and are described below. The decline of the immune system during aging is related to changes that include the cells themselves, characteristics of populations of such cells, and the environment in which these cells must function. Approximatlely 10% of the decline of these functions has been attributed to factors of the environment extrinsic to the cells [95]. The environmental changes maybe due to systemic and noncellular effects,, consequences of viral or bacterial infections, products of other cells and nutriments. The distribution of lymphoid cells in autoimmune susceptible and resistant mice was studied by the capacity to trace ^{51}Cr-labeled lymphoid cells (Yunis et al., unpublished observations). Splenocytes of old NZB mice were distributed in abnormally large numbers in the liver, and in abnormally small numbers in the spleen and lymph nodes, as compared to the distribution of labeled cells from young donors given to young recipients. The cells from old donors did not home to the BM of old mice, but homed better to the BM of young mice. Cells from young animals given to old animals with significant autoimmunity also were deployed excessively to the liver and poorly to the spleen and marrow, as compared to tagged cells of young animals injected intravenously into old animals. These findings indicate that in NZB mice there is a significant age-related pathology of the normal ecotaxis, which has both cellular and organ-determined components.

Loss of stromal cells or decline in their function with age may also account for decreased lymphopoiesis. Among T-lymphopoietic cytokines, IL-7 has shown lower levels in old mice [96, 97]. In addition, presence of mature T cells in the thymus have been suggested to play an important role in the maintenance of the thymic structure [98], in line with our findings on feedback regulation of thymocyte development by mature T cells [74-76]. Thus, lower T cell numbers due to age-related effects on ETP would affect thymic microenvironment resulting in lower production of new thymocytes.

B cells develop in the BM through distinct stages defined by expression of phenotypic markers and rearrangement of immunoglobulin (Ig) genes [99, 100]. Similar to T cells, B cell production is decreased in aging [101-105], due to reduction of pre-B cells, CLP and pro-B cells [106]. These B cell precursors from aged mice have been shown to respond poorly to IL-7 [106], suggesting that they lost their proliferative potential for self-renewal. Another factor contributing to declines in their number with age might be the impaired mechanisms of stem cell entry into the CLP and pro-B compartments [77]. Also, BM microenvironment accumulates defects with age, as demonstrated by impaired generation of B cells in old mice injected with BM cells from young donors [107]. Collectively, these studies demonstrate that both intrinsic and microenvironmental defects contribute to the decline in B and T cell lymphopoiesis. Interestingly, aging does not affect myelopoiesis, as shown by a number of studies (reviewed in ref. 77), suggesting that defects in the development of B and T cells might be attributable to the impaired DNA repair mechanisms in the process of Ig and TCR gene rearrangement [108].

In addition to the changes occurring in the BM and in the thymus, other factors, e.g. endocrine hormones, whose receptors are expressed on both thymocytes and thymic stroma, affect lymphopoiesis in aging as negative regulators of proliferation or stromal interactions [109-114]. Decreased levels of growth hormone (GH) and insulin-like growth factor-I (IGF-I) with age might also contribute to thymic involution. Increased thymic cellularity in old mice upon exposure to these hormones supports the above notion [115-117]. In contrast to observations on the effect of hormones on T cell development in aging, little is known about these effects on B cells. Age-related effects on gene expression in HSC giving rise to lymphoid cell precursors have been reviewed [15]. Accumulated knowledge of the age-associated effects on lymphopoiesis might be applicable to BM transplantation or HIV infection, are conditions which depend on depletion of recipient hemopoietic cells and repopulation by healthy donor cells.

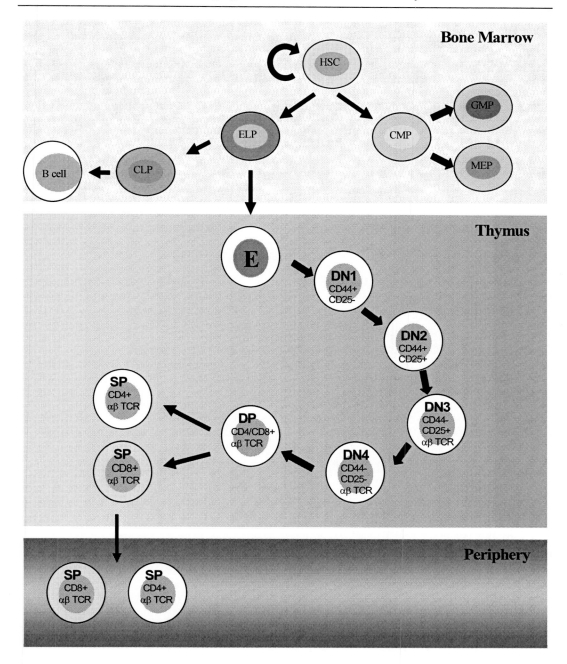

Figure 1. Pathway of thymocyte development and egress to the periphery. Hemopoietic stem cells (HSC) originating in the BM with self-renewal capacity differentiate into common myeloid progenitor (CMP) and progeny that includes granulocyte-macrophage (GMP) and megakaryocyte-erythroid (MEP) progenitors. Early lymphoid progenitors (ELP) differentiate into early T lineage cell progenitor (ETP) which undergos differentiation form double negative (DN) cells $CD4^-CD8^-$ to $\alpha\beta TCR^+CD4^+CD8^+$ double positive (DP) cells and single positive (SP) $CD4^+$ or $CD8^+$. These mature SP thymocytes then emigrate to the peripheral lymphoid organs.

BIOCHEMICAL BASIS FOR AGE-RELATED DEVELOPMENTAL CHANGES IN T CELLS

Molecular mechanisms of age-related changes in lymphocytes have been thoroughly investigated in the recent years (reviewed in ref. 29). Using genetically labeled mice, B and T cell subpopulations at different stages of maturation were examined for age-sensitive traits, and showed associations of certain loci with the cell levels in young adult and aged mice [29]. Interestingly, mice with the highest levels of CD4 memory phenotype, resembling the immune system of older animals, died at relatively early age [118-120]. In contrast, those with high levels of naïve CD4 cells and low levels of CD4 and CD8 memory cells lived longer [119]. Statistical analysis showed that mice with 'aged T cell phenotype' died at younger age of cancers, while those with delayed T cell subset pattern of aging survived longer [119]. Genetic analysis detected loci on chromosomes 4 and 13 associated with age-sensitive T-cell subset patterns [120].

T cell activation is also impaired in aging, as demonstrated by decline in calcium signals and T cell signal transduction pathways [121, 122]. Specifically, T cells from old mice were unable to form functional immunological synapses required for downstream stages of TCR activation [123], partially due to defects in relocation of cytoskeletal protein talin to the synapse [124]. These defects in cytoskeletal reorganization result in decreased T cell functions, e.g. cytokine production and blast formation. In addition to assembly of elements of the immunological synapse, cytoskeletal proteins are essential for movement of surface molecules to the area of the T-cell membrane opposite from the point of contact with the APC following activation [125]. Removal of a large glycosylated protein CD43, which is relocated to the cell surface upon T cell activation and interferes with functional interaction between T cell and APC, was decreased with age [126]. Moreover, CD4 T cells from old mice expressed higher levels of glycosylated forms of CD43, which might contribute to anergy. Noteworthy, enzymatic cleavage of CD43 glycoproteins restored synapse formation and improved activation of T cells from aged mice [126], consistent with the hypothesis that activation defects of T lymphocytes stem from hyperglycosylation of CD43 and other surface glycoproteins, together with alterations in the cytoskeletal processes required for removal of these molecules from the area of contact with APC [127].

THE ROLE OF APOPTOSIS IN AGING

A decline in T cell functions during aging is attributable partially to alterations in apoptotic pathways in T and B lymphocytes (reviewed in ref. 128). Apoptosis plays a central role in the immune system by deletion of non-desirable B and T cells following selection or immune response [129]. Two major signaling pathways of apoptosis, the death receptor pathway and the mitochondrial pathway, activated by a series of caspases, have been described [130, 131]. Apoptosis in human T and B cells in aging has been examined via death receptor signaling. Several studies have demonstrated lymphopenia of CD4 and CD8 T cells in older individuals [132, 133], possibly due to decreased BM precursors, decreased thymic output due to thymic involution, reduced proliferative capacity and increased apoptosis (reviewed in ref. 134), which was associated with higher levels of expression and activity of caspases [135]. In addition, CD4 and CD8 T cells are more susceptible to TNF-α-induced apoptosis as compared to young subjects [136], due to decreased activity of NF-κB [137].

There is a marked age-related reduction in naïve and central memory CD8+ and CD8+ CD28+ T cells [138] as a result of increased activation-induced cell death (AICD) [139]. In contrast, there is an accumulation of CD8+CD28- T cells, comprised of two subpopulations of effector memory CD8+ T cells, with age [134]. Memory T cell subsets are more susceptible to anti-CD95-induced apoptosis as compared to naïve T cells [140]; this observation is consistent with the demonstration of decreased Bcl-2 expression in memory subsets of CD4+ and CD8+ T cells in healthy adults [141]. Since Bcl-2 blocks anti-CD95-induced apoptosis in activated T cells, decreased Bcl-2 expression in aging may play a role in increased sensitivity of human T cell subsets.

The numbers of naïve B cells are significantly decreased, whereas memory B cells are increased with age [142]. This is associated with both quantitative and qualitative changes in humoral immunity, including decreased levels of IgM and increased levels of IgG and IgA, decreased B cell repertoire, decreased primary and secondary specific antibody response to vaccine antigens and changes in antibody affinity. A subpopulation of B cells expressing CD5 antigen, which is considered as auto-reactive due to secretion of IgM antibodies that often react with self antigens, has been analysed in aged individuals and was found in increased proportions concomitant with CD95 expression [128]. Altogether, these studies demonstrate that increased apoptosis in T cells in aging appears to contribute to lymphopenia, which might be responsible for decline in T cell functions, leading to increased susceptibility to viral infections and higher frequency of cancer.

CONTRIBUTION OF THE THYMIC MICROENVIRONMENT (TEMPORARY NICHE) TO AGING

Increased prevalence of infections, autoimmunity and cancers with age is attributable to the deteriorating immune system (reviewed in ref. 31). Numerous studies have focused on the role of the thymus in aging, since, being the source of T lymphocytes which develop through thymic selection and emerge to the peripheral pool, it undergoes atrophy with age, resulting in low capability to produce new T cells [31]. To compensate for this loss, peripheral T cells undergo thymus-independent proliferation, leading to accumulation of replicative-senescent T cells with limited TCR repertoire and weakened immune responses.

The structure of the thymus has been studied for several decades [31, 143]. It is a primary lymphoid organ cituated above the heart, consistsing of two lobes enclosed in a capsule [143, 144]. Lobes contain thymocytes at different stages of development, which are spread over a network of epithelial cells forming the thymic stroma. These structures form a cortex, an area where immature thymocyte precursors repopulate the thymus and initiate differentiation, following by their migration and advanced development in the medulla. During embryonic development, the epithelial cells of the thymic cortex arise from ectodermal cells, while the epithelial cells of the medulla derive from endodermal cells [31, 145]. While at birth the thymus is mainly composed of thymic epithelial cells that support thymocyte development and selection, with aging, the thymus begins to involute due to the loss of epithelial cells and increase in the perivascular space [146, 147].

Pathways of thymocyte development from the hemopoietic stem cells, the stages of selection and acquisition of the phenotypic markers have been described at the beginning of the present chapter. In addition to thymocyte progenitors, which are capable of developing into T cells, dendritic cells or natural killer (NK) cells, the thymus is colonized by BM-derived macrophages. Hemopoietic stem cells enter the thymic subcapsular zone and undergo antigen-independent expansion, followed by TCR rearrangement and selection, which occurs in the cortex and the medulla [148, 149]. As a result of thymic selection, more than 95% of thymocytes are lost based on their αβTCR specificities recognizing self-antigens, while mature SP CD4+ or CD8+ thymocytes expressing competent αβ TCR chains migrate from the medulla into the peripheral T-cell pool as mature and functional T lymphocytes.

While thymic function is critical during embryogenesis, as shown by lethal effects of its removal, it can be taken after birth with no harmful effects [31]. Involution of the thymus with aging correlates with the loss of thymic stroma, expansion of the perivascular space progressively filled with adipose tissue, reduction in the number of naïve T cells in the periphery, decline in immune functions, and, consequently, increased susceptibility to infections, cancers and autoimmunity. In spite of the atrophy, aged thymus is still capable of supporting differentiation and producing naïve T cells [150, 151]. The causative linkage of thymic involution to puberty suggests that hormones may influence or possibly induce age-associated thymic loss.

Development of methods enabling to measure thymic output (TCR excision circle, TREC) significantly advanced identification of recent thymic emigrants [152]. It has been shown that TREC content in the peripheral blood CD4+ and CD8+ T cells has declined with age [153]. In spite of the continuing production of thymocytes, aged thymus is unable to increase its T cell output upon decline in peripheral T cells due to infection or cancer therapy, resulting in slower recovery. It has been shown that in aged mice the number of thymocyte precursors at the DN1 stage was increased, suggesting that progression to the DN2 stage is blocked [154]. Interestingly, exposure to IL-7 restored DN1-DN2 pathway and subsequent maturation steps in the aged thymus [155]. Age-associated thymic involution has been studied in several animal models and in humans [156]. Genetic analysis in mice revealed a product of the Klotho gene, similar to the β-glucosidase enzyme, which delays thymic atrophy [157]. Several other studies identified loci associated with thymic involution on chromosomes 3 and 9 [158]. With the advances in microarray analysis, it is now possible to focus on gene expression changes within the aging thymus [31]. It should be noted that under certain physiological and pathological conditions, unrelated to aging, which include puberty, pregnancy, inflammation, bacterial and viral infections, physical and emotional stress, environmental conditions, exposure to glucocorticoid (GC) therapy or chemotherapy, thymus may undergo transient reduction in size and function [31]. Interestingly, deficiency in Zn, a catalytic component of numerous enzymes and an inhibitor of apoptosis, has been shown to lead to thymic involution regardless of age and to increase the frequency of microbial infections [159].

It has been proposed that age-related thymic involution in humans and in rodents might occur due to decline in migration of BM-derived stem cell progenitors into the thymus; alterations in the TCR rearrangements; loss of cells within the thymic microenvironment; or extrinsic changes in the levels of hormones, cytokines, and growth factors. Support of the hypothesis on decreased numbers of T cell progenitors was brought by studies on reconstitution of young mice with BM from old donors, showing low repopulation efficiency

[160-162]. However, other reports indicated that the thymic tissue is more important for the process of age-associated involution [31]. The involvement of TCR rearrangement alterations in thymic atrophy remains controversial. Studies in TCR transgenic mice and other genetic models suggest that alterations in the generation or selection of mature T cells might trigger thymus involution [31]. Loss of thymic epithelial cells is another possible cause of thymic involution, based on several reports in rodents [163]. Alterations in the levels of circulating and intrathymic hormones, cytokines, and/or growth factors with age also play an important role in thymic function. A number of studies suggest that the cytokine IL-7, through the induction of the antiapoptotic gene bcl-2, permits maturation of DN1 thymocytes [164, 165]. Although measuring IL-7 levels in aged mice resulted in controversial findings, the evidence accumulated so far points at the potential of IL-7 to augment thymic function [31]. The expression of several other cytokines show decline (IL-2, IL-9, IL-10, IL-13, and IL-14) with age, while levels of LIF, OSM, IL-6, SCF, and M-CSF are increased in the old murine and human thymi [31, 166]. It is possible that higher levels of certain cytokines produced in the thymus during aging contribute to suppression of thymopoiesis and facilitate thymic involution. Among neuroendocrine hormones, reduced levels of growth hormone (GH) with age were shown to coincide with thymic involution [167], while administration of exogenous GH restored thymic function [168] also in HIV-infected patients [169]. Diminished production of GH with age may contribute to the decline of thymopoiesis and loss of thymic tissue with progressive aging. Similarly to GH, IGF-1 hormone levels are reduced with age, while exposure to this hormone results in higher thymic cellularity [170]. The expression of some neurotrophins (NTs), (nerve growth factor (NGF) and brain-derived neurotrophic factor (BDNF)), have also been shown to change with age within the thymus [171]. In addition, many of the thymus-derived hormones (thymosin, thymopoietin, thymulin, and thymopentin) have been observed to decline with age and are associated with thymic atrophy and immune senescence [172].

Accumulation of fat tissue in the perivascular space within the aging thymus deserves special attention, since this process leads to structural changes in the thymic microenvironment resulting in loss of thymocytes [31]. It has been recently reported that adipocytes and adipose-stromal cell-derived proteins regulate fat cell differentiation, as well as metabolism and growth of adjacent tissues [173]. Moreover, age-related increase in production of several factors by adipocytes, e.g IL-6, LIF, leptin and glucocorticoids contributes to thymic atrophy or thymocyte apoptosis [173-175]. Apparently, adipogenic progenitors have been detected within the thymus, suggesting that adipocyte differentiation is taking place in the thymus involving various transcription factors [176].

Secretion of inflammatory cytokines by adipocyte progenitors may lead to elimination of thymocytes or thymic epithelial cells [176]. Overall, accumulation of adipose tissue within the thymic compartments may affect entry of thymic precursors from the BM, positive and negative selection, thymocyte growth, and stromal cell network.

Potential therapeutic strategies to recover age-related thymic involution have been considered by administration of cytokines and growth factors, resulting so far, however, in inconclusive data. The role of calorical restriction in suppressing oxidative damage, tumor development, autoimmunity, and extending lifespan in rodents and primates has been described [177-179] and is discussed in our adjacent chapter [15].

APPROACHES TO RESTORE THYMIC FUNCTION IN HUMANS AS RELATED TO AGING, AUTOIMMUNITY AND AIDS

Studies of postnatal thymic function have been important for developing therapeutic approaches aimed at restoring a damaged T-cell repertoire following cancer chemotherapy or AIDS (reviewed in ref. 33). Moreover, changes resembling normal thymic aging have been shown to occur in several autoimmune diseases. These include myasthenia gravis, in which the thymus is often hyperplasic due to massive immune cell infiltration of the perivascular space. In these patients, thymectomy is beneficial as treatment, since in adult and even pediatric patients the thymus has already supplied the periphery with an initial repertoire of T cells. In AIDS, the damage caused by human immunodeficiency virus includes destruction not only of CD4 T cells but also of the microenvironments supporting lymphocyte proliferation peripherally and thymopoiesis centrally. Combination antiretroviral therapy has been reported to increase a patient's T-cell count [180]. Several treatments, including cord blood transplantation to repopulate the recipient's hematopoietic stem cells, have been employed in cancer chemotherapy, in which damage to the immune system often leads to prolonged T-cell deficiency. However, some patients show low repopulation capacity and poor functions leading to increased susceptibility to infections.

THYMIC FUNCTION DURING HUMAN DEVELOPMENT

The human thymus shows its most extensive immunologic function prenatally, when it produces mature T cells, which migrate to the periphery. The epithelial thymic rudiment is formed by the sixth week of fetal development, while by the seventh to eighth week the epithelium is colonized by hematopoietic stem cells from the liver and other mesenchymal tissues [181, 182]. During the third trimester, BM becomes the source of HSC thymocyte progenitors. Two thymic compartments, the outer cortex and the inner medulla, are evident by week 14, with the presence of Hassall's bodies in the medulla by week 15. During 16 to 20 weeks, the thymus is fully formed, with the T cell differentiation processes ongoing. Mature T cells emerging from the thymus first colonize lymph nodes, gut, and spleen at 12 weeks, and by week 20 the peripheral immune system is competent to mount both T- and B-cell responses to infections.

Stem cells derived from the BM enter the thymus, where they interact with thymic epithelial cells in the cortex and the medulla, followed by their exit as mature T lymphocytes. Within the cortex, the thymocytes undergo maturation stages from cells lacking cell-surface expression of CD3, CD4, and CD8 (TN) to a double positive (DP) stage, expressing both CD4 and CD8, along with CD3. By the time they reach the medulla, they have become single-positive (SP) thymocytes expressing either CD4 or CD8 for ultimate function as helper or cytotoxic T cells, respectively. The overall process of thymocyte differentiation is thought to take about three weeks. Thymocyte development is associated with the formation of the thymic network, indicating that intercellular signals coordinate both thymocyte cell populations and the thymic microenvironment. The involvement of cytokine communication is suggested by thymocyte expression of receptors for cytokines such as interleukin-1 and granulocyte-macrophage colony-stimulating factor (GM-CSF). On the other hand, the epithelial cells express receptors for IFN-γ and IL-1. Cellular contacts are mediated not only by interaction between TCRs on the thymocytes and HLA molecules on the epithelial cells but also by thymocyte expression of adhesion molecules such as CD11/18 (LFA-1) and CD2, which bind to epithelial cells CD54 (ICAM-1) and CD58 (LFA-3), respectively. The process of thymic positive and negative selection has been described in detail throughout this chapter. As a result of massive elimination of autoreactive T cells and selection of those interacting weakly with self antigens, only about 5% of mature T cells leave the thymus to enter the periphery. These newly emigrated T cells are called 'recent thymic emigrants' (RTE). The rest are phagocytosed by mononuclear cells, often seen adjacent to Hassall's bodies. Mature RTE express CD45RA, a surface marker characteristic of naive T cells, while those surviving as memory cells following immune response express CD45RO. It has been reported that after elimination of the antigen some memory cells can revert to the immunologically naive CD45RA phenotype.

ANALYSIS OF THE THYMIC OUTPUT

Evidence suggesting thymic function in adult life has emerged from a number of studies involving HIV-infected patients. In these studies, the radiographic demonstration of abundant thymic tissue among some HIV-infected patients was correlated with a higher CD4 count, as also supported by flow cytometric analysis showing higher levels of CD4 T cells [183, 184]. Establishment of the experimental protocols for measuring the TCR rearrangement excision circles (TRECs) enabled precise analysis of the thymic output in adult life [185]. Studies of TRECs as a means of assessing thymic output in aging, in thymectomized subjects, and in HIV infection showed presence of TRECs only in naive αβTCR T cells, but not in memory cells and not in B or γδTCR T cells [183]. Over a lifetime, TREC levels in both CD4 and CD8 T-cell populations declined exponentially. Interestingly, the decline continued even though the percentage of naive cells remained fairly constant, supporting a belief that TRECs are characteristic of RTE production more than the totality of naive T cells. In addition, TREC levels studied in patients who had been thymectomized during surgery for myasthenia gravis were an order of magnitude lower than in nonthymectomized subjects, suggesting that thymic function in normal individuals continues during adulthood. In untreated HIV-infected subjects, TREC levels were significantly lower than in age-matched healthy controls, most likely due to HIV-induced decline in thymic function. Following antiretroviral therapy, TREC levels increased within 4 to 16 weeks of initiating therapy. Noteworthy, peripheral expansion of T cells also contributes to the total cell numbers, as found in studies of thymectomized vs. normal HIV-infected twins, indicating that adult's T-cell pool can maintain itself by mitotic division of mature peripheral T cells [186]. It seems that in adults, lack of a thymus does not preclude an increase in naive T cells, as TREC levels were extremely low at the time of CD4 T-cell increase, proving the peripheral origin of the cells. Altogether, these findings suggest that both thymic output and peripheral T-cell proliferation contribute to maintaining the T-cell pool during adult life. While the thymus contributes to T cell diversity by TCR rearrangements and selection of new repertoire, peripheral proliferation leads to expansion of the existing T cell specificities.

Discovering how to maintain or restore thymic function is now a matter of great importance. For HIV-infected patients, antiretroviral therapy has been the only clinical approach currently available. Thymic transplantation has been tried in several cases of hypoplastic thymus at birth, resulting in survival and functional capability of the implant [33]. In autoimmune disorders, tracking of the self-reactive T cells, which escaped thymic negative selection, to the periphery and further to the affected organs, would be helpful for their targeted elimination.

INFLUENCE OF NUTRITION ON THE DECLINE OF IMMUNITY WITH AGING IN MICE

Although the regulation of the immune response is predominantly under genetic control, environmental factors such as nutrition are also influential. Earlier studies have demonstrated that in the autoimmune-prone NZB mouse strain diets low in fat and high in protein and fiber content produced a delayed development of autoimmunity and was associated with prolonged life span in both males and females (reviewed in ref. 15). However, restriction of protein intake alone, while conferring beneficial influences on T-cell functions, did not significantly suppress the occurrence of autoimmune disease or prolong the life span or NZB mice. In contrast, B/W mice fed a normal diet in restricted amount (12 cal/day) lived at least twice as long as mice fed a normal diet (24 cal/day) [15]. This dramatic influence of nutrition was accompanied by prolonged maintenance of T cell-mediated functions, inhibition of the development of spontaneously active suppressor cells, and maintenance of inducible suppressor cells. Dietary restriction also inhibited immuno-complex-dependent renal injury and anti-DNA antibody production in B/W mice as well as preventing the development of circulating immune complexes. Furthermore, the high caloric diet was accompanied with cardiovascular diseases. In C3H mice, which develop spontaneous breast tumors, two methods, alternate-day feeding and daily caloric restriction, have been successful in the prevention or delay of tumor development [15]. In an unpublished study using the same alternate-day feeding schedule versus the ad libitum feeding in CBA/H (a long lived strain of mice), we have seen 70% survival of the experimental mice and only 42% survival of the control mice at 960 days of age. The difference in survival at 1,080 days of age was 40% and 5%, respectively, for the experimental and control mice. The final number of days was 1,260 for the mice with the diet restriction and 1,099 for those fed ad libitum.

SIGNALING BY IMMUNE RECEPTORS IN AGING AND AUTOIMMUNITY

In the process of aging, the immune system becomes more susceptible to autoimmune diseases, due to exposure of self-antigens, which undergo structural changes leading to their increased immunogenicity. In addition, the ability of innate immunity to eliminate infectious agents deteriorates, resulting in inappropriate persistence of immune stimulation and antigen levels exceeding the threshold for the activation of B or T cells. The numbers of both B and T cells are reduced, while memory T cells are increased (reviewed in ref. 32). Also, due to the loss of co-stimulatory molecules, T cells may increase their reactivity and initiate anti-self responses. It is possible that alterations in signal transduction pathways of B and T cells with age result in higher incidence of autoimmune phenomena. Investigation of these processes is of importance for clinical diagnosis and therapy.

Epidemiologic data show a rising incidence of autoimmunity with increased age, although the onset of the disease may vary in males and females [187]. Mechanisms that account for increased autoimmunity in the elderly may include prolonged exposure of T cells with high threshold for activation to autoantigen in higher concentrations than normal. In addition, self-antigens might get exposed due to alterations caused by inflammation, or may undergo age-associated post-translational modifications, such as isoaspartyl formation [188] and oxidation [189]. Autoimmune disease may also be triggered by infections leading to cross-reactivity [190-192].

Alterations in the innate immune system with age may have an impact on the development of autoimmunity. For example, reduced Ca^{2+} influx, diminished surface receptors, and a lower response of activated neutrophils to cytokines that protect against apoptosis have been reported [32]. Circulating levels of the proinflammatory cytokines IL-6 and TNF-α are raised in the aged [193], while toll-like receptor expression is significantly reduced in macrophages of aged mice [194]. NKT cell dysfunction has been associated with defective clearance of infection and autoimmunity, in which NKT cell numbers are decreased [195]. In the adaptive immune system, a variety of T cell functions, especially proliferation and cytokine production, are perturbed with aging, due to decrease in the generation of T cells triggered by thymic involution, and, consequently, the impaired replenishment of naïve T cells [31]. Moreover, the expression of co-stimulatory (CD28), adhesion and growth factor receptors and antigen- or mitogen-induced proliferation are reduced, while the levels of Bcl-2 are increased with age [32].

B cell development, antibody repertoire, and B cell subsets are also perturbed with aging [196]. In mice, a decreased number of pre-B cells and an increased number of surface Ig^{low}-expressing cells as a result from a block in pre-B cell maturation and in development of mature IgM^{+} B cells has been reported [197]. In spite of the fact that B cell lymphopoiesis is significantly decreased with age, peripheral B cell numbers stay relatively constant throughout life, largely due to prolongation in the life span of B cells [197]. In addition, B-1 cell subpopulation expressing the CD5 differentiation antigen is expanded. These cells home to peritoneal cavity, spleen, mantle zone of lymph nodes; recognize antigens with repeating subunit structure, such as polysaccharides; respond in the absence of cognate T cell antigen recognition; produce low-affinity IgM antibodies, and generate autoreactive antibodies [198]. The data on B cell numbers and functions in aged humans is inconclusive. A large number of elderly people have low-affinity autoantibodies in their serum, and the prevalence of autoantibodies associated with systemic autoimmune diseases increases with age [199].

ROLE OF NICHES, CYTOKINES, T, B AND NK CELLS

New evidence indicates that cells of the connective tissue and blood vessels are part of the microenvironments or niches, for HSCs in adult BM, as well as stromal fibroblasts are associated with cancer cells with respect to the self-renewal activity [200]. The most protected niche is the BM. The skin is composed of units in which every hair follicle has a tiny niche of stem cells, responsible for generating a new hair and to generate sebaceous glands and epidermis [201-203]. Also, the intestine is composed of many units each containing a villous and a crypt, their stem cells are located above the vase of the crypt [204]. In the adult central nervous system, stem cells are in the sub-ventricular zone where they generate glia and neurons [205]. Stem cells depend on their surrounding environment to maintain their functions and proliferation potentials [202].

It is noteworthy mentioning that infections, such as HIV, nutrition and other non-genetic factors can influence the microenvironment of the niches. For example, measurable amounts of cytokine responses could vary depending on the genetic background. It is possible that these measurements will be variable in some animals and less variable but decreased in others, which may be genetically controlled. Such studies can be done in RI strains of mice where a gene in chromosome 11 distinguishes strains with short variability at death as compared with other that have wide variability of age at death. It is generally known that aging is characterized by upregulation of genes involved in oxidative stress responses [206-208], suggestive of an increased need to cope with the accumulation of macromolecular abnormalities. The studies of one cell type cannot address the question of the effect of tissues, which can also be altered during aging.

The changes of pro-inflammatory cytokines during aging may reflect immune system effectiveness, the disability and age related diseases, including cancer [209]. Stem cells in their niches (as well as cancer cells in their microenvironment) could be affected by production of cytokines or other molecules, determining the progression of cancer cells or preservation of the cells in the niches [15].

Selection of the B cell repertoire and B cell development, have been investigated as related to aging [210]. Importantly, mechanisms of impairment of pro-B to pre-B cells in BM have been observed in old mice. The rearrangement of IgH VDJ gene segments is required for the differentiation from pro-B to pre-B cells. Recent studies have reported a decreased germline transcription of VH genes in BM of old mice deficient for IL-7R. New reports have expanded the research of aging into different phenotypes that are related to the role of immune functions in aging, particularly the postnatal rearrangements of immunoglobulins and TCRs. For example, BM- derived cell clones of pre-B cells and mechanism of B cell development are also affected in aging [211]. Other changes associated with BM function had been described, such as an increased apoptosis of pre-B cells [212]. Whereas several studies have shown that B cell number decreases in old mice, others have suggested that these age-related changes are the result of the decline in the rate of pre-B cell production in the BM [213].

New investigations have produced data suggesting that there is a collapse of the CD4 T cell diversity during the seventh and eight decades of life, primarily of naïve T cells that are important to initiate T cell responses to new antigens. While this represented a lack of thymic activity, it was not determined whether some individuals that maintained T cell diversity exhibited longer life span [214]. Also, it has been observed that there is a reciprocal age-related change in the expression of the MHC class I ligands for killer immunoglobulin-like receptors and for lectin-like receptors. It appears that the expression patterns of these ligands change with age. This is a novel finding that demonstrates that the change with age is not in the NK receptors but in the class I ligand expression that is required for inhibition of killing [215]. This finding needs to be investigated in the context of diseases of aging such as autoimmunity or malignancies.

FUTURE PERSPECTIVES FOR STEM CELL RESEARCH RELATED TO IMMUNOLOGY OF AGING

At the moment it seems remote to anticipate prolongation of life far beyond the limits imposed by ultimate genetic determinants. Manipulations directed toward achieving expression of full genetic potential by forestalling appearance of diseases of aging seem promising. Reversal of autoimmune disease by cellular transplantation has been accomplished when the disease occurs spontaneously, was accelarated in autoimmune susceptible strains of mice, or when autoimmunity was induced in autoimmune susceptible strains by neonatal thymectomy [216]. The possibility of developing a clinically useful cellular engineering can be accomplished using syngeneic donor cells. Another possibility exists of producing compatible hematopoietic cells using cellular somatic cloning. On the other hand, allogeneic cells might be used, provided that the donor and recipient mismatched at the major histocompatibiliity loci, provided that these cells are obtained from fetal liver cells in mice and perhaps from umbilical cord in humans [217, 218]. Also, it needs to be investigated whether transplants of embryonic cells, when used to correct the immunodeficiencies of aged mice, were used together with thymus obtained from fetuses in order to achieve optimal benefits. Such experiments will need to be done using histocompatible as well as histoincompatible transplants, and such comparisons need to be studied in strains of mice with genetic susceptibility or resistance to develop autoimmunity.

We have reviewed the genetic aspects involved in life span and variability at age of death in mice [15]. Additional studies of cytokine profiles, NK and T cells have to be performed in experimental mouse models, such as recombinant strains of mice, in order to understand the possible role of cytokines during aging. We suggested that genes in chromosome 11 encode a cluster of cytokines that could be markers of long life or variability of age at death [15].

ACKNOWLEDGEMENTS

This work was supported by NIH grants HL29583 and HL59838 (to E.J.Y). J.Z. was supported in part by grants from the Instituto Nacional de Enfermedades Respiratorias, Mexico and by Fundación México en Harvard A.C. ZH was supported by grant HL-29583 from the National Heart, Lung and Blood Institute of the NIH.

REFERENCES

[1]   Sims, HS. Logarithmic increase in mortality as a manifestation of aging. *J. Gerontol.,* 1946, 1, 13-26.

[2]   Hammar, JA. Die Menschen-Thymus in Gesundheit und Krankheit. I. Das normale Organ. *Z. Microsk.-Anat. Forsch.,* 1926, 6, 1-18.

[3]   Good, RA; Gabrielson, AE. The thymus in immunobiology. Hoeber-Harper, New York. 1964.

[4]   Walford, RL. The immunologic Theory of Aging. Munksgaard, Copenhagen, 1969.

[5]   Roberts-Thompson, I; Whittingham, S; Youngchaiyud, U; MacKay, IR. Aging, immune response, and mortality. *Lancet,* 1974, 2, 368-370.

[6]   Yunis, EJ; Fernandes, G; Good, RA. Aging and involution of the immunological apparatus. Immunopathology of lymphoreticular neoplasms. Editors: Tworney, JJ; Good, RA. Plenum Publishing Corporation, 1978. 53-80.

[7]   Stutman, O; Yunis, EJ; Good, RA. Deficient immunologic functions of NZB/Bl mice. *Proc. Sic. Exp. Biol. Med.,* 1968, 127, 1204-1207.

[8]   Good, RA; Yunis, EJ. Association of autoimmunity, immunodeficiency, and aging in man, rabbits and mice. *Fed. Proc. Fed. Am. Soc. Exp. Biol.* 1974, 33, 2040-2050.

[9]   Teague, PO; Yunis, EJ; Rodey, G; Fish, AJ; Stutman, O; Good, RA. Autoimmune phenomena and renal disease in mice: Role of thymectomy, aging and involution of immunologic capacity. *Lab. Invest.* 1970, 22, 121-130.

[10] Tosi, P; Kraft, R; Luzi, P; Cintroino, M; Fankhauser, G; Hess, MW; Cottier, H. Involution patterns of the humanthymus. I. Size of the cortical area as a function of age. *Clin. Exp. Immunol.,* 1982, 47, 497-504.

[11] Farr, AG; Sidman, CL. Reduced expression of Ia antigens by thymic epithelial cells of aged mice. *J. Immunol.,* 1984, 133, 98-103.

[12] Fridkis-Hareli, M; Joaquin Zúñiga, J; Yunis, EJ. Hemopoietic stem cells and autoimmunity: impaired mechanisms of thymic selection or genetic predisposition? *J. Stem Cells,* 2006 (in press).

[13] Yunis, EJ; Fernandes, G; Greenberg, LJ. Immune deficiency, autoimmunity and aging. In: Immunodeficiency in man and animals. (Bergsma, D; Good, RA; Finstad, J. Eds.), 1975, Sinauer Associates, Sunderland, Massachusetts.

[14] Yunis, EJ; Salazar, M. Genetics of life span in mice. *Genetica,* 1993, 9, 211-223.

[15] Yunis, EJ; Zúñiga, J; Koka, P; Husain, Z; Romero, V; Stern, JNH; Fridkis-Hareli, M. Stem Cells in Aging: Influence of Ontogenic, Genetic and Environmental Factors. *J. Stem Cells,* 2006 (in press).

[16] Anderson, DJ; Watson, AL; Yunis, EJ. Environmental and genetic factors that influence immunity and longevity in mice. *Basic Life Sci.,* 1985, 35, 231-240.

[17] Yunis, EJ; at al. Single nucleotide polymorphism blocks and haplotypes: human MHC block diversity. In: *Encyclopedia of Molecular Cell Biology and Molecular Medicine. Meyers,* RA, ed. Wiley-VCH Verlag, Weinheim, 2005, Vol. 13, 194-215.

[18] Fridkis-Hareli, M; Zúñiga, J; Yunis, EJ. Hemopoietic stem cells in autoimmunity: impaired mechanisms of thymic selection or genetic predisposition? *J. Stem Cells,* 2006 (in press).

[19] Haynes, L; Eaton, SM. The effect of age on the cognate function of CD4+ T cells. *Immunol. Rev.,* 2005, 205, 220-228.

[20] Weber, GF; Mirza, NM; Yunis, EJ; Dubey, D; Cantor, H. Localization and treatment of an oxidation-sensitive defect within the TCR-coupled signaling pathway that is associated with normal and premature immunologic aging. *Growth, Devel. Aging,* 1997, 61, 191-207.

[21] Smith, GS; Walford, RL. Influence of the main histocompatibility complex on ageing in mice. *Nature,* 1977, 270, 727-729.

[22] Meredith, PJ; Walford, RL. Effect of age on response to T- and B-cell mitogens in mice congenic at the H-2 locus. *Immunogenetics,* 1977, 5, 109-128.

[23] Dubey, DP; Husain, Z; Levitan, E; Zurakowski, D; Mirza, N; Younes, S; Coronell, C; Yunis, D; Yunis, EJ. The MHC influences NK and NKT cell functions associated with immune abnormalities and lifespan. *Mech. Ageing Dev.,* 2000, 7, 113, 117-134.

[24] Makinodan, T; Kay, MM. Age influence on the immune system. *Adv. Immunol.,* 1980, 29, 287–330.

[25] Globerson, A; Effros, RB. Ageing of lymphocytes and lymphocytes in the aged. Immunol. *Today, 2000,* 10, 515–521.

[26] Nel, AE; Slaughter, N. T-cell activation through the antigen receptor. Part 2. A role of signaling cascades in T-cell differentiation, anergy, immune senescence, and development of immunotherapy. *J. Allergy Clin. Immunol.,* 2002, 109, 901–915.

[27] Effros, RB; Cai, Z; Linton, PJ. CD8 T cells and aging. *Crit. Rev. Immunol.,* 2002, 23, 45–64.

[28] Ku, CC; Kotzin, B; Kappler, J; Marrack P. CD8+ T cell clones in old mice. *Immunol. Rev.,* 2000,160, 139–144.

[29] Miller, RA; Berger, SB; Burke, DT; Galecki, A; Garcia, GG; Harper, JM; Sadighi Akha, AA. T cells in aging mice: genetic, developmental, and biochemical analyses. *Immunol. Rev.,* 2005, 205, 94-103.

[30] Sudhir, G; Su, H; Bi, R; Agrawa, S; Gollapudi, S. Life and death of lymphocytes: a role in immunesenescence. *Immunity and Ageing,* 2005, 2, 12.

[31] Taub, DD; Longo, DL. Insights into thymic aging and regeneration. *Immunol. Rev.,* 2005, 205, 72-93.

[32] Hasler, P; Zouali, M. Immune receptor signaling, aging, and autoimmunity. *Cell. Immunol.,* 2005, 233, 102-108.

[33] Haynes, BF; Hale, LP. Thymic Function, Aging, and AIDS. *Hospital Practice,* 1999.

[34] Stutman, O; Yunis, EJ; Good, RA. Thymus: An essential factor in lymphoid repopulation. *Transplant. Proc.,* 1969, 1, 614-618.

[35] Stutman, O; Yunis, EJ; Good, RA. Studies on thymus function. II. Cooperative effect of newborn and embryonic hemopoietic liver cells with thymus function. *J. Exp. Med.,* 1970, 132, 601-612.

[36] Scollay, R; Shortman, K. Thymocyte subpopulations: an experimental review, including flow cytometric cross-correlations between the major murine thymocyte markers. *Thymus,* 1983, 5, 245-295.

[37] Fowlkes, BJ; Edison, L, Mathieson, BJ; Chused, TM. Early T lymphocytes: differentiation in vivo of adult intrathymic precursor cells. *J. Exp. Med.,* 1985, 162, 802-822.

[38] Scollay, R; Shortman, K. Identification of early stages of T lymphocyte development in the thymus cortex and medulla. *J. Immunol.,* 1985, 134, 3632-3642.

[39] Weissman, IL. Thymus cell migration: studies on the origin of cortisone-resistant thymic lymphocytes. *J. Exp. Med.,* 1973, 137, 504-510.

[40] Crispe, IN; Moore, MW, Husmann, LA; Smith, L; Bevan, MJ; Shimonkevitz, RP. Differentiation potential of subsets of CD4-CD8- thymocytes. *Nature,* 1987, 329, 336-339.

[41] Scollay, R; Wilson, A; D'Amico, A; Kelly, K; Egerton, M; Pearse, M; Wu, L; Shortman, K. Developmental status and reconstitution potential of subpopulations of murine thymocytes. *Immunol. Rev.,* 1988, 104, 81-120.

[42] Ceredig, R; Dialynas, DP; Fitch, FW; MacDonald, HR. Precursor of T cell growth factor producing cells in the thymus: ontogeny, frequency, and quantitative recovery in a subpopulation of phenotypically mature thymocytes defined by monoclonal antibody GK-1.5. *J. Exp. Med.*, 1983, 158, 1654-1671.

[43] Mathieson, BJ; Fowlkes, BJ. Cell surface antigen expression on thymocytes: Development and phenotypic differentiation of intrathymic subsets. *Immunol. Rev.*, 1984, 82, 141-173.

[44] Scollay, R; Bartlett, P; Shortman, K. T cell development in the adult murine thymus: changes in the expression of the surface antigens Ly 2, L3T4 and B2A2 during development from early precursor cell to emigrants. *Immunol. Rev.*, 1984, 82, 79-103.

[45] Wilson, A; Petrie, HT; Scollay, R; Shortman, K. The acquisition of CD4 and CD8 during the differentiation of early thymocytes in short-term culture. *Int. Immunol.* 1989, 1, 605-612.

[46] McPhee, D; Pye, J; Shortman, K. The differentiation of T lymphocytes. V. Evidence for intrathymic death of most thymocytes. *Thymus,* 1979, 1, 151-162.

[47] Jenkinson, EJ; Kingston, R; Smith, CA; Williams, GT; Owen, JJT. Antigen-induced apoptosis in developing T cells: a mechanism for negative selection of the T cell receptor repertoire. *Eur. J. Immunol.* 1989, 19, 2175-2177.

[48] MacDonald, HR; Lees, RK. Programmed death of autoreactive thymocytes. *Nature* 1990, 343, 642-644.

[49] Paterson, DJ; Williams, AF. An intermediate cell in thymocyte differentiation that expresses CD8 but not CD4 antigen. *J. Exp. Med.*, 1987, 166, 1603-1608.

[50] Hugo, P; Waanders, GA; Scollay, R; Petrie, HT; Boyd, RL. Characterization of immature CD4+CD8-CD3- thymocytes. *Eur. J. Immunol.* 1991, 21, 835-838.

[51] Utsuyama, M; Hirokawa, K. Age-related changes of splenic T cells in mice- a flow cytometrical analysis. *Mech. Ageing Dev.,* 1987, 40, 89-102.

[52] Brill, S; Ben-Menahem, D; Kukulansky, T;, Tal, E; Globerson, A. Do peripheral blood T lymphocytes reflect splenic T lymphocyte functions in individual young and old mice? *Aging: Immunology and Infectious Disease,* 2, 221-230.

[53] Sanders, ME; Makgoba, MW; Shaw, S. Human naïve and memory T cells: reinterpretation of helper-inducer and suppressor-inducer subsets. *Immunol. Today,* 1988, 9, 195-199.

[54] Dianzani, U; Luqman, M; Rogo, J; Yagi, J; Baron, JL; Woods, A; Janeway, CA; Bottomly, K. Molecular associations of the T cell surface correlate with immunological memory. *Eur. J. Immunol.*, 1990, 20, 2249-2257.

[55] Utsuyama, M; Hirokawa, K; Kurashima, C; Fukayama, M; Inamatsu, T; Suzuki, K; Wataru, H; Sato, K. Differential age-change in the numbers of CD4+CD45RA+ and CD4+CD29+ T cell subsets in human peripheral blood. *Mech. Ageing Dev.,* 1992, 63, 57-68.

[56] Wallis, VJ; Leuchars, E; Chawlinski, S; Davis, AJS. On the sparse seeding of bone marrow and thymus in radiation chimaeras. *Transplantation,* 1975, 19, 2-11.

[57] Boersma, WJA; Kokenberg, E; van der Westen, G; Haaijman, JJ. Postirradiation thymocyte regeneration after bone marrow transplantation. III. Intrathymic differentiation and development of thymocyte subpopulations. *Eur. J. Immunol.,* 1982, 12, 615-619.

[58] Ezine, S; Weissman, IL; Rouse, RV. Bone marrow cells give rise to distinct cell clones within the thymus. *Nature, 1984,* 309, 629-631.

[59] Kingston, R; Jenkinson, EJ; Owen, JJ. A single stem cell can recolonize an embryonic thymus, producing phenotypically distinct T-cell populations. *Nature,* 1985, 317, 811-813.

[60] Williams, GT; Kingston, R; Owen, MJ; Jenkinson, EJ; Owen, JJ. A single micromanipulated cell gives rise to multiple T-cell receptor gene rearrangements in the thymus in vitro. *Nature, 1986,* 324, 63-64.

[61] Jenkinson, EJ; Franchi, LL; Kingston, R; Owen, JJ. Effect of deoxyguanosine on lymphopoiesis in the developing thymus rudiment in vitro: application in the production of chimeric thymus rudiments. *Eur. J. Immunol.,* 1982, 12, 583-587.

[62] Fridkis-Hareli, M; Sharp, A; Abel, L; Globerson, A. Thymocyte development in an in vitro constructed chimera of irradiated fetal thymus and lymphohemopoietic cels. *Thymus,* 1991, 18, 225-235.

[63] Fridkis-Hareli, M; Abel, L; Globerson, A. Patterns of dual lymphocyte development in co-cultures of foetal thymus and lymphohaemopoietic cells from young and old mice. *Immunology,* 1992, 77, 185-188.

[64] Fridkis-Hareli, M; Abel, L; Eisenbach, L; Globerson, A. Differentiation patterns of CD4/CD8 thymocyte subsets in cocultures of fetal thymus and lymphohemopoietic cells from c-fos transgenic and normal mice. *Cell. Immunol.,* 1992, 141, 279-292.

[65] Fridkis-Hareli, M; Eren, R; Sharp, A; Abel, L; Kukulansky, T; Globerson, A. MHC recognition in colonization of the thymus by bone marrow cells. *Cell. Immunol.,* 1993, 149, 91-98.

[66] Fridkis-Hareli, M; Abel, L; Globerson, A. In vitro analysis of thymic microenvironmental effects on bone marrow cells of severe combined immunodeficient (SCID) mice. *Cell. Immunol.,* 1993, 147, 237-246.

[67] Fridkis-Hareli, M; Abel, L; Globerson, A. Developmental pathways of cortical and medullary thymocytes in aging. *Aging: Immunol. Infect. Dis.,* 1993, 4, 245-250.

[68] Fridkis-Hareli, M; Mehr, R; Abel, L; Globerson, A. Developmental interactions of CD4 T cells and thymocytes: age-related differential effects. *Mech. Ageing Dev.,* 1994, 173, 169-178.

[69] Eren, R; Zharhary, D; Abel, L; Globerson, A. Age-related changes in the capacity of bone marrow cells to differentiate in thymic organ cultures. *Cell. Immunol.* 1988, 112, 449-455.

[70] Sharp, A; Kukulansky, T; Globerson, A. In vitro analysis of age-related changes in the developmental potential of bone marrow thymocyte progenitors. *Eur. J. Immunol.,* 1990, 20, 2541-2546.

[71] Makinodan, T. Biology of aging: retrospect and prospect. *Compr. Immunol.,* 1977, 1, 1-7.

[72] Thoman, ML; Weigle, WO. The cellular and subcellular bases of immunosenescence. *Adv. Immunol.,* 1989, 46, 221-261.

[73] Globerson, A; Sharp, A; Fridkis-Harel,i M; Kukulansky, T; Abel, L; Knyszynski, A; Eren, R. Aging in the T lymphocyte compartment. A developmental view. *Ann. N. Y. Acad. Sci.,* 1992, 673, 240-251.

[74] Fridkis-Hareli, M; Mehr, R; Abel, L; Globerson, A. Developmental interactions of CD4
      T cells and thymocytes: age-related differential effects. *Mech. Ageing Dev.,* 1994,
      73(3), 169-178.

[75] Mehr, R; Perelson, AS; Fridkis-Hareli, M; Globerson, A. Feedback regulation of T cell
      development: manifestations in aging. *Mech. Ageing Dev.,* 1996, 91(3), 195-210.

[76] Mehr, R; Perelson, AS; Fridkis-Hareli, M; Globerson, A.Regulatory feedback pathways
      in the thymus. *Immunol, Today,* 1997, 18(12), 581-585.

[77] Min, H; Montecino-Rodriguez, E; Dorshkind, K. Effects of aging on early B- and T-cell
      development *Immunol. Rev.,* 2005, 205, 7-17.

[78] Kondo, M; et al. Biology of hematopoietic stem cells. *Annu. Rev. Immunol.,* 2003, 21,
      759–806.

[79] Akashi, K; Traver, D; Miyamoto, T; Weissman, IL. A clonogenic common myeloid
      progenitor that gives rise to all myeloid lineages. *Nature,* 2000, 404, 193–197.

[80] Sitnicka, E; et al. Key role of flt3 ligand in regulation of the common lymphoid
      progenitors but not in maintenance of the hematopoietic stem cell pool. *Immunity,* 2002,
      17, 463–472.

[81] Kondo, M; Weissman, IL; Akashi, K. Identification of common lymphoid progenitors
      in mouse bone marrow. *Cell,* 1996, 91, 661–672.

[82] Bhandoola, A; Sambandam, A; Allman, D; Meraz, A; Schwarz, B. Early T lineage
      progenitors: new insights but old questions remain. *J. Immunol.,* 2003, 171, 5653–5658.

[83] Allman, D; et al. Thymopoiesis independent of common lymphoid progenitors. *Nat.
      Immunol.* 2003, 4, 168–174.

[84] Min, H; Montecino-Rodriguez, E; Dorshkind, K. Reduction in the developmental
      potential of intrathymic T cell progenitors with age. *J. Immunol.,* 2004, 173, 245–250.

[85] Schwarz, B; Bhandoola, A. Circulating hematopoietic progenitors with T lineage
      potential. *Nat. Immunol.,* 2004, 5, 953–960.

[86] Ceredig, R; Rolink, T. A positive look at double-negative thymocytes. *Nat. Rev.
      Immunol.,* 2002, 2, 888–897.

[87] Porritt, HE; et al. Heterogeneity among DN1 prothymocytes reveals multiple
      progenitors with different capacities to generate T cell and non-T cell lineages.
      Immunity, 2004, 20, 735–745.

[88] Godfrey DI, Kennedy J, Suda T, Zlotnik A. A developmental pathway involving four
      phenotypically and functionally distinct subsets of CD3-CD4-CD8- triple-negative
      adult mouse thymocytes defined by CD44 and CD25 expression. *J. Immunol.,* 1993,
      150, 4244–4252.

[89] Rothenberg EV. T-lineage specification and commitment: a gene regulation
      perspective. *Semin. Immunol.,* 2002, 14, 431–440.

[90] Anderson G, Moore NC, Owen JJ, Jenkinson EJ. Cellular interactions in thymocyte
      development. *Annu. Rev. Immunol.,* 1996, 14, 73–99.

[91] von Boehmer H. Selection of the T-cell repertoire: receptor controlled checkpoints in T
      cell development. *Adv. Immunol.,* 2004, 84, 201–238.

[92] Thoman, ML. Early steps in T cell development are affected by aging. *Cell. Immunol.,*
      1997, 178, 117–123.

[93] Aspinall, R; Andrew, D. Thymic atrophy in the mouse is a soluble problem of the
      thymic environment. *Vaccine,* 2000, 18, 1629–1637.

[94] Farr, AG; Dooley, JL; Erickson, M. Organization of thymic medullary epithelial heterogeneity: implications for mechanisms of epithelial differentiation. *Immunol. Rev.,* 2002, 189, 20–27.

[95] Makinodan, T; Adler, W. The effects of aging on the differentiation and proliferation potentials of cells of the immune system. *Fed. Proc.,* 1975, 34, 153-158.

[96] Andrew, D; Aspinall, R. Age-associatged thymic atrophy is linked to a decline in IL-7 production. *Exp. Gerontol.,* 2001, 37, 455–463.

[97] Ortman, CL; Dittmar, KA; Witte, PL; Le, PT. Molecular characterization of the mouse involuted thymus: aberrations in expression of transcription regulators in thymocyte and epithelial compartments. *Int. Immunol.,* 2002, 14, 813–822.

[98] Klug, DB; Carter, C; Gimenez-Conti, IB; Richie, ER. Thymocyte-independent and thymocyte dependent phases of epithelial patterning in fetal thymus. *J. Immunol.,* 2002, 169, 2842–2845.

[99] Hardy, RR; Hayakawa, K. B cell developmental pathways. *Annu. Rev. Immunol.,* 2001, 19, 595–621.

[100] Rawlings, D; Dorshkind, K. B cell development. In: Benz EJ, Shattil SJ, Furie B, Cohen HJ, Silberstein LE, McGlave P, eds. *Hematology: Basic Principles and Practice,* 4th edn. New York: Churchill Livingston, 2005. 119–133.

[101] Johnson, KM; Owen, K; Witte, PL. Aging and developmental transitions in the B cell lineage. *Int. Immunol.,* 2002, 14, 1313–1323.

[102] Kline, GH; Hayden, TA; Klinman, NR. B cell maintenance in aged mice reflects both increased B cell longevity and decreased B cell generation. *J. Immunol.,* 1999, 162, 3342–3349.

[103] Kirman, I; Zhao, K; Wang, Y; Szabo, P; Telford, W; Weksler, ME. Increased apoptosis of bone marrow pre-B cells in old mice associated with their low number. *Int. Immunol.,* 1998, 10, 1385–1392.

[104] Stephan, RP; Sanders, VM; Witte, PL. Stage-specific alterations in murine B lymphopoiesis with age. *Int. Immunol.,* 1996, 8, 509–518.

[105] Labrie, JE; Sah, AP; Allman, DM; Cancro, MP; Gerstein, RM. Bone marrow microenvironmental changes underlie reduced RAG-mediated recombination and B cell generation in aged mice. *J. Exp. Med.,* 2004, 200, 411–423.

[106] Miller, J; Allman, D. The decline in B lymphopoiesis in aged mice reflects loss of very early B-lineage precursors. *J. Immunol.,* 2003, 171, 2326–2330.

[107] Labrie, JE; Sah, AP; Allman, DM; Cancro, MP; Gerstein, RM. Bone marrow microenvironmental changes underlie reduced RAG-mediated recombination and B cell generation in aged mice. *J. Exp. Med.,* 2004, 200, 411–423.

[108] Park, Y; Gerson, SL. DNA repair defects in stem cell function and aging. *Annu. Rev. Med.,* 2005, 56, 495–508.

[109] Dorshkind, K; Horseman, N. The roles of prolactin, growth hormone, insulin-like growth factor-I, and thyroid hormones in lymphocyte development and function: insights from genetic models of hormone and hormone receptor deficiency. *Endocrine Rev.,* 2000, 21, 292–312.

[110] Kincade, PW; Medina, KL; Smithson, G. Sex hormones as negative regulators of lymphopoiesis. *Immunol. Rev.,* 1994, 1376, 119–134.

[111] Savino, W; Dardenne, M. Neuroendocrine control of thymus physiology. *Endocr. Rev.,* 2000, 21, 412–443.

[112] Olsen, NJ; Kovacs, WK. Gonadal steroids and immunity. *Endocrine Rev.,* 1996, 17, 369–384.

[113] Olsen, NJ; Viselli, SM; Fan, J; Kovacs, WJ. Androgens accelerate thymocyte apoptosis. *Endocrinology,* 1998, 139, 748–752.

[114] Guevara Patiño, JA; Marino, MW; Ivanov, VN; Nikolich-Zugich, J. Sex steroids induce apoptosis of CD8+CD4+ double-positive thymocytes via TNF-α. *Eur. J. Immunol.,* 2000, 30, 2586–2592.

[115] Lamberts, SWJ; van den Beld, AW; van der Lely, A-J. The endocrinology of aging. *Science,* 1997, 278, 419–424.

[116] Knyszynski, A; Adler-Kunin, S; Globerson, A. Effects of growth hormone on thymocyte development from progenitor cells in the bone marrow. *Brain, Behavior, Immunity,* 1992, 6, 327–340.

[117] Montecino-Rodriguez, E; Clark, R; Dorshkind, K. Effects of insulin-like growth factor administration and bone marrow transplantation on thymopoiesis in aged mice. *Endocrinology,* 1998, 139, 4120–4126.

[118] Miller, RA; Chrisp, C; Galecki, A. CD4 memory T cell levels predict lifespan in genetically heterogeneous mice. *FASEB J.,* 1997, 11, 775–783.

[119] Miller, RA. Biomarkers of aging: prediction of longevity by using age-sensitive T-cell subset determinations in a middle-aged, genetically heterogeneous mouse population. *J. Gerontol.,* 2001, 56, B180–B186.

[120] Harper, JM; Galecki, AT; Burke, DT; Miller, RA. Body weight, hormones and T-cell subsets as predictors of lifespan in genetically heterogeneous mice. *Mech. Ageing Dev.,* 2004, 125, 381–390.

[121] Miller, RA; Garcia, GG; Kirk, CJ; Witkowski, JM. Early activation defects in T lymphocytes from old mice. *Immunol. Rev.,* 1997, 160, 79–90.

[122] Kirk, CJ; Miller, RA. Age-sensitive and insensitive pathways leading to JNK activation in mouse CD4 T cells. *Cell. Immunol.,* 1999, 197, 83–90.

[123] Tamir, A; Eisenbraun, MD; Garcia, GG; Miller, RA. Age-dependent alterations in the assembly of signal transduction complexes at the site of T cell/APC interaction. *J. Immunol.,* 2000, 165, 1243–1251.

[124] Garcia, GG; Miller, RA. Age-dependent defects in TCR-triggered cytoskeletal rearrangement in CD4$^+$ T cells. *J. Immunol.,* 2002, 169, 5021–5027.

[125] Cullinan, P; Sperling, AI; Burkhardt, JK. The distal pole complex: a novel membrane domain distal to the immunological synapse. *Immunol. Rev.,* 2002, 189, 111-122.

[126] Tong, J; et al. CD43 regulation of T cell activation is not through steric inhibition of T cell–APC interactions but through an intracellular mechanism. *J. Exp. Med.,* 2004, 199, 1277–1283.

[127] Garcia, GG; Berger, SB; Sadighi Akha, AA; Miller, RA. Age-associated changes in glycosylation of CD43 and CD45 on mouse CD4 T cells. *Eur. J. Immunol.,* 2005, 35, 622–631.

[128] Gupta, S; Su, H; Bi, R; Agrawal, S; Gollapudi, S. Life and death of lymphocytes: a role in immunesenescence. *Immunity and Ageing,* 2005, 2, 12.

[129] Green, DR; Droin, N; Pinkoski, N. Activation-induced cell death in T cells. *Immunol. Rev.,* 2003, 193, 70-81.

[130] Ashkanazi, A; Dixit, VM. Death receptors: signaling and modulation. *Science,* 1998, 281, 1305-1308.

[131] Gupta, S. Molecular steps of death receptor and mitochondrial pathways of apoptosis. *Life Sci.,* 2000, 69, 2957-2964.

[132] Fagnoni, FF; Vescovini, R; Paserri, G; Bologna, G; Pedrazzoni, M; Lavagetto, G; Casti, A; Franceschi, C; Passeri, M; Sansoni, Shortage of circulating naïve CD8+ T cells provides new insights on immunodeficiency in aging. *Blood,* 2002, 95, 2860-2868.

[133] Gupta, S. Tumor necrosis factor-α-induced apoptosis in T cells from aged humans: a role of TNFR-I and downstream signaling molecules. *Exp. Gerontol.,* 2002, 37, 293-299.

[134] Gupta, S. Molecular mechanisms of apoptosis in the cells of the immune system in human aging. *Immuno.l Rev.,* 2005, 205, 114-129.

[135] Aggarwal, S; Gupta, S. Increased activity of caspase-3 and caspase-8 during Fas-mediated apoptosis in lymphocytes from aging humans. *Clin. Exp. Immunol.,* 1999, 117, 285-290.

[136] Gupta, S. Tumor necrosis factor-α-induced apoptosis in T cell subsets from aged humans. Receptor expression and downstream signaling events. *Exp. Gerontology,* 2002, 37, 293-299.

[137] Gupta, S; Bi, R; Kim, C; Yel, L; Chiplunkar, S; Gollapudi, S. A role of NF-κB signaling pathway in increased tumor necrosis factor-α-induced apoptosis of lymphocytes in aged humans. *Cell Death Diff.,* 2005, 12, 177-183.

[138] Brzezinska, A; Magalska, A; Szybinska, A; Sikora, E. Proliferation and apoptosis of human CD8+CD28+ and CD8+CD28- lymphocytes during aging. *Exp. Gerontol.,* 2004, 39, 539-544.

[139] Herndon, FJ; Hsu, HC; Mountz, JD. Increased apoptosis of CD45RO- T cells with aging. *Mech. Ageing. Dev.,* 1997, 94, 123-134.

[140] Miyawaki, T; Uehara, T; Nabu, R; Tsuji, T; Yachie, A; Yonehara, Y; Taniguchi, N. Differential expression of apoptosis-related Fas antigen on lymphocyte subpopulations in human peripheral blood. *J. Immunol.,* 1992, 149, 3753-3758.

[141] Shinohara, S; Sawada, T; Nishioka, Y; Tohma, S; Kisaki, T; Inou, T; Ando, K; Ikeda, M; Fuji, H; Ito, K. Differential expression of Fas and Bcl-2 protein on CD+ T cells, CD8+ T cells and monocytes. *Cell. Immunol.,* 163, 303-308.

[142] Ghia, P; Melchers, F; Rolink, AG. Age-dependent changes in B lymphocyte development in man and mouse. *Exp. Gerontol.,* 2000, 35, 159-65.

[143] Boyd, RL; et al. The thymic microenvironment. *Immunol. Today,* 1993, 14, 445-459.

[144] Petrie, HT. Role of thymic organ structure and stromal composition in steady-state postnatal T-cell production. *Immunol. Rev., 2002,* 189, 8-19.

[145] Fridkis-Hareli, M; Zúñiga J; Yunis EJ. Hemopoietic Stem Cells and Autoimmunity: Impaired Mechanisms of Thymic Selection or Genetic Predisposition? *J. Stem Cells,* 2006, in press.

[146] Takeoka, Y; et al. The murine thymic microenvironment: changes with age. *Int. Arch. Allergy Immunol,* 1996, 111, 5-12.

[147] Haynes, BF; Hale, LP. The human thymus. A chimeric organ comprised of central and peripheral lymphoid components. *Immunol. Res.,* 1998, 18, 175-192.

[148] Germain, RN. T-cell development and the CD4-CD8 lineage decision. *Nat. Rev. Immunol.,* 2002, 2, 309-322.

[149] Starr, TK; Jameson, SC; Hogquist, KA. Positive and negative selection of T cells. *Annu. Rev. Immunol.*, 2003, 21, 139-176.

[150] Jamieson, BD; et al. Generation of functional thymocytes in the human adult. *Immunity*, 1999, 10, 569–575.

[151] Poulin, JF; et al. Direct evidence for thymic function in adult humans. *J. Exp. Med.*, 1999, 190, 479–486.

[152] Kong, F-K; Chen, CH; Six, A; Hockett, RD; Cooper, MD. T cell receptor gene deletion circles identify recent thymic emigrants in the peripheral T cell pool. *Proc. Natl. Acad. Sci. USA*, 1999, 96, 1536–1540.

[153] Sempowski, GD; Gooding, ME; Liao, HX; Le, PT; Haynes, BF. T cell receptor excision circle assessment of thymopoiesis in aging mice. *Mol. Immunol.*, 2002, 38, 841–848.

[154] Thoman, ML; et al. The pattern of T lymphocyte differentiation is altered during thymic involution. *Mech. Ageing Dev.*, 1995, 82, 155–170.

[155] Phillips, JA; Brondstetter, TI; English, CA; Lee, HE; Virts, EL; Thoman, ML. IL-7 gene therapy in aging restores early thymopoiesis without reversing involution. *J. Immunol.*, 2004, 173, 4867–4874.

[156] Hirokawa, K; Utsuyama, M. Animal models and possible human application of immunological restoration in the elderly. *Mech. Ageing Dev.*, 2002, 123, 1055–1063.

[157] Kuro-o, M; et al. Mutation of the mouse klotho gene leads to a syndrome resembling ageing. *Nature*, 1997, 390, 45–51.

[158] Hsu, HC; et al. Age-related thymic involution in C57BL/6J x DBA/2J recombinant-inbred mice maps to mouse chromosomes 9 and 10. *Genes Immun.*, 2003, 4, 402–410.

[159] Globerson, A. Thymocyte progenitors in ageing. *Immunol. Lett.*, 1994, 40, 219–224.

[160] Tyan, ML. Impaired thymic regeneration in lethally irradiated mice given bone marrow from aged donors. *Proc. Soc. Exp. Biol. Med.*, 1976, 152, 33–35.

[161] Hirokawa, K; Kubo, S; Utsuyma, M; Krashima, C; Sado, T. Age-related change in the potential of bone marrow cells to repopulate the thymus and splenic T cells in mice. *Cell. Immunol.* 1986, 100, 443–451.

[162] Doria, G; Mancini, C; Utsuyama, M; Frasca, D; Hirokawa, K. Ageing of the recipients but not of the bone marrow donors enhances autoimmunity in syngeneic radiation chimeras. *Mech. Ageing Dev.*, 1997, 95, 131–142.

[163] Brelinska, R. Thymic epithelial cells in age-dependent involution. *Microsc. Res. Tech.*, 2003, 62, 488–500.

[164] von Freeden-Jeffry, U; Vieira, P; Lucian, LA; McNeil, T; Burdach, S; Murry, R. Lymphopenia in interleukin (IL)-7 gene-depleted mice identifies IL-7 as a nonredundant cytokine. *J. Exp. Med.*, 1995, 181, 1519–1526.

[165] Peschon, JJ; et al. Early lymphocyte expansion is severely impaired in interleukin 7 receptor-deficient mice. *J. Exp. Med.*, 1994, 180, 1955–1960.

[166] Sempowski, GD; et al. Leukemia inhibitory factor, oncostatin M, IL-6, and stem cell factor mRNA expression in human thymus increases with age and is associated with thymic atrophy. *J. Immunol.*, 2000, 164, 2180–2187.

[167] Burgess, W; et al. The immune-endocrine loop during aging: role of growth hormone and insulin-like growth factor-I. *Neuroimmunomodulation*, 1999, 6, 56–68.

[168] Davila, DR; Brief, S; Simon, J; Hammer, RE; Brinster, RL; Kelley, KW. Role of growth hormone in regulating T-dependent immune events in aged, nude, and transgenic rodents. .*J Neurosci. Res.*, 1987, 18, 108–116.

[169] Napolitano, LA; et al. Increased thymic mass and circulating naive CD4 T cells in HIV-1-infected adults treated with growth hormone. *AIDS,* 2002, 16, 1103–1111.

[170] Montecino-Rodriguez, E; Clark, R; Dorshkind, K. Effects of insulin-like growth factor administration and bone marrow transplantation on thymopoiesis in aged mice. *Endocrinology,* 1998, 139, 4120–4126.

[171] Turrini, P; Zaccaria, ML; Aloe, L. Presence and possible functional role of nerve growth factor in the thymus. *Cell. Mol. Biol.,* 2001, 47, 55–64.

[172] Dardenne, M. Role of thymic peptides as transmitters between the neuroendocrine and immune systems. *Ann. Med.,* 1999, 31, 34–39.

[173] Pond, C. Paracrine relationships between adipose and lymphoid tissues. implications for the mechanism of HIV–associated adipose redistribution syndrome. *Trends Immunol.,* 2003, 24, 13–18.

[174] Diamond, F. The endocrine function of adipose tissue. *Growth Genet. Horm.,* 2002, 18, 17–23.

[175] Fantuzzi, G;Faggioni, R. Leptin in the regulation of immunity, inflammation, and hematopoiesis. *J. Leukoc. Biol.,* 2000, 68, 437–446.

[176] Mandrup, S; Lane, MD. Regulating adipogenesis. *J. Biol. Chem.,* 1997, 272, 5367–5370.

[177] Masoro, EJ. Possible mechanisms underlying the anti aging actions of caloric restriction. *Toxicol. Pathol.,* 1996, 24, 738–741.

[178] Sell, C. Caloric restriction and insulin-like growth factors in aging and cancer. *Horm. Metab. Res.,* 2003, 35, 705–711.

[179] Pahlavani, MA. Influence of caloric restriction on aging immune system. *J. Nutr. Health Aging,* 2004, 8, 38–47.

[180] Graham, DB; Bell, MP; Huntoon, CJ; Weaver, JG; Hawley, N; Badley, AD; McKean, DJ. Increased thymic output in HIV-negative patients after antiretroviral therapy. *AIDS,* 2005, 19(14), 1467-1472.

[181] Hale, LP; Haynes, BF. Overview of development and function of lymphocytes. *In* Inflammation: Basic Principles and Clinical Correlates, Gallin, JI; Snyderman, R (Eds). Lippincott Williams and Wilkins, Philadelphia, 1999.

[182] Haynes, BF; Hale, LP. The human thymus: A chimeric organ comprised of central and peripheral lymphoid components. *Immunol. Res.,* 1988, 18, 61-78.

[183] Douek, DC et al: Changes in thymic output with age and during the treatment of HIV infection. *Nature,* 1988, 396, 690-692.

[184] Haynes, BF; Hale, LP; Weinhold, KJ; Patel, DD; Liao, HX; Bressler, PB; Jones, DM; Demarest, JF; Gebhard-Mitchell, K; Haase, AT; Bartlett, JA. Analysis of the adult thymus in reconstitution of T lymphocytes in HIV-1 infection. *J. Clin. Invest.,* 1999, 103(4), 453-460.

[185] Livak, F; Schatz, DG. T-cell receptor alpha-locus V(D)J recombination by-products are abundant in thymocytes and mature T cells. *Mol. Cell. Biol.,* 1996, 16, 609-618.

[186] Walker, RE; et al: Peripheral expansion of pre-existing mature T cells is an important means of CD4 T-cell regeneration in HIV-infected adults. *Nature Med.,* 1988, 4, 852-856.

[187] Symmons, D. In: Rheumatology, third ed., Mosby, Philadelpiha, 2003.

[188] Mamula, MJ; Gee, RJ; Elliott, JI; Sette, A; Southwood, S; Jones, PJ; Blier, PR. Isoaspartyl post-translational modification triggers autoimmune responses to self-proteins. *J. Biol. Chem.*, 1999, 274, 22321–22327.

[189] Allison, ME; Fearon, DT. Enhanced immunogenicity of aldehyde-bearing antigens: a possible link between innate and adaptive immunity. *Eur. J. Immunol.*, 2000, 30, 2881–2887.

[190] Wucherpfennig, KW; Strominger, JL. Molecular mimicry in T cell-mediated autoimmunity: viral peptides activate human T cell clones specific for myelin basic protein. *Cell*, 1995, 80(5), 695-705.

[191] Ebringer, A; Wilson, C. HLA molecules, bacteria and autoimmunity. *J. Med. Microbiol.*, 2000, 49, 305–311.

[192] Hasler, P; Zouali, M. Subversion of immune receptor signaling by infectious agents. *Genes Immunity*, 2003, 4, 95–103.

[193] Bruunsgaard, H; Pedersen, BK. Age-related inflammatory cytokines and disease. Immunol. *Allergy Clin. North Am.*, 2003, 23, 15–39.

[194] Renshaw, M; Rockwell, J; Engleman, C; Gewirtz, A; Katz, J; Sambhara, S. Cutting edge: impaired Toll-like receptor expression and function in aging. *J. Immunol.*, 2002, 169, 4697–4701.

[195] Hammond, KJ; Kronenberg, M. Natural killer T cells: natural or unnatural regulators of autoimmunity? *Curr. Opin. Immunol.*, 2003, 15, 683–689.

[196] Ghia, P; Melchers, F; Rolink, AG. Age-dependent changes in B lymphocyte development in man and mouse. *Exp. Gerontol.*, 2000, 35, 159–165.

[197] Huppert, FA; Solomou, W; O'connor, S; Morgan, K; Sussams, P; Brayne, C. Aging and lymphocyte subpopulations: whole-blood analysis of immune markers in a large population sample of healthy elderly individuals. *Exp. Gerontol.*, 1988, 33, 593–600.

[198] Viau, M; Zouali, M. B lymphocytes, innate immunity and autoimmunity. *Clin. Immunol.*, 2005, 114, 17–26.

[199] Shoenfeld, Y; Isenberg, D. The Mosaic of Autoimmunity (the Factors Associated with Autoimmune Disease). Elsevier, Amsterdam (1989).

[200] Bhowmick, NA; et al. Stromal fibroblasts in cancer initiation and progression. *Nature*, 2004, 432, 332-337.

[201] Suda, T; Arai F; Hirao A. hematopoietic stem cells and their niche. *Trends in Immunology*, 2005, 26, 426-433.

[202] Fuchs, E; et al. Socializing with the neighborgs: stem cells and their niche. *Cell*, 2004, 116, 769-778.

[203] Reya, T; Morrison, SJ; Clarke, MF; Weissman, IL. Stem cells, cancer, and cancer stem cells. *Nature*, 2001, 414, 105-111.

[204] Loeffler, M; Birke, A; Winton, D; Potten, C. Somatic mutation, monoclonality and stochastic models of stem cell organization in the intestinal crypt. *J. Theor. Biol.*, 1993, 160, 471-491.

[205] Doetsch, F; Caille, I; Lim, DA; Garcia-Verdugo, JM; Alvarez-Buylla, A. Subventricular zone astrocytes are neural stem cells in the adult mammalian brain. *Cell.*, 1999, 97, 703-716.

[206] Welle, S; Brooks, AI; Delehanty, JM; Needler, N; Thornton, CA. Gene expression profile of aging in human muscle. *Physiol Genomics.*, 2003, 14, 149-159.

[207] Hamatani, T; Falco, G; Carter, MG; Akutsu, H; Stagg, CA; Sharov, AA; Dudekula, DB; VanBuren, V; Ko, MS. Age-associated alteration of gene expression patterns in mouse oocytes. *Hum. Mol. Genet.,* 2004, 13, 2263-2278.

[208] Pansarasa, O; Bertorelli, L; Vecchiet, J; Felzani, G; Marzatico, F. Age-dependent changes of antioxidant activities and markers of free radical damage in human skeletal muscle. *Free Radic. Biol. Med.,* 1999, 27, 617-622.

[209] Huang, H; Patel, DD; Manton, KG. The immune system in aging: roles of cytokines, T cells and NK cells. *Frontiers Bioscience,* 2005, 10, 192-215.

[210] LeMaoult, P; Szabo, P; Weksler, ME. Effect of age on humoral immunity, selection of B cell repertoire and B cell development. *Immunol Rev.,* 1997, 160, 103-114.

[211] Szabo, P; Shen, S; Telford, W; Weksler, ME. Impaired rearrangement of IgH V to DJ segments in bone marrow Pro-B cells from old mice. *Cell. Immunol.,* 2003, 222, 78-87.

[212] Kirman, I; Zhao, K; Wang, Y; Szabo, P; Telford, W; Weksler, ME. Increased apoptosis of bone marrow pre-B cells in old mice associated with their low number. *Int. Immunol.,* 1998, 10, 1385-1392.

[213] Johnson, KM; Owen, K; Witte, PL. Aging and developmental transitions in the B cell lineage. *Int. Immunol.,* 2002, 14, 1313-1323.

[214] Naylo, K; Li, G; Vallejo, AN; Lee, WW; Koetz, K; Bryl, E; Witkowski, J; Filbright, J; Weyand, CM; Goronzy, JJ. The influence of age on T cell generation and TCR diversity. *J. Immunol.,* 2005, 174, 7446-7452.

[215] Lutz, CT; Moore, MB; Bradley, S; Shelton, BJ; Lutgendorf, SK. Reciprocal age related change in natural killer cell receptors for MHC class I. *Mech. Ageing. Dev.,* 2005, 126, 722-731.

[216] Fernandez, G; Good, RA; Yunis EJ. Attempts to correct age-related immuodeficiency and autoimmunity by cellular and dietary manipulation in inbred mice. *Immunology and Aging,* Eds. Makinodan,T; Yunis, EJ. New York Plenum Press, 1977, 111-133.

[217] Tulunay O, Good RA, Yunis EJ. Protection of lethally irradiated mice with allogeneic fetal liver cells: influence of irradiation dose on immunologic reconstitution. *Proc. Natl. Acad. Sci. U S A,* 1975, 72, 4100-4104.

[218] Yunis, EJ; Fernandes, G; Smith, J; Good, RA. Long survival and immunologic reconstitution following transplantation with syngeneic or allogeneic fetal liver and neonatal spleen cells. *Transplant. Proc.,* 1976, 8, 521-525.

INDEX

B

D

E

F

I

Q

R

T

U